Clyde

Knick teammates first blessed Walt Frazier with this handle. Like the notorious Clyde of crime, Walt is cool. His off-court dress is the height of fashion. His on-court ball hawking is famous. His direction of the Knicks' scoring machine is known for its deadly efficiency. But unlike the other Clyde, Walt Frazier talks honestly. Here he tells about his childhood, his troubled years at Southern Illinois, the early days with the Knicks, and New York's great drive to the championship. This was pro basketball's finest moment that year and it's told by one of pro basketball's finest players—as he saw it.

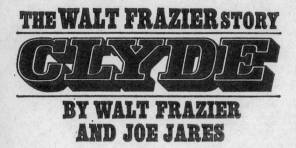

THE WALT FRAZIER STORY
CLYDE

BY WALT FRAZIER
AND JOE JARES

BOOKS

GROSSET & DUNLAP
A NATIONAL GENERAL COMPANY
Publishers   *New York*

Tempo Books is registered in the U.S. Patent Office
Published simultaneously in Canada
ISBN: 0-448-05420-5
Tempo Books Edition 1971
Reprinted by arrangement with
Holt, Rinehart and Winston, Inc.

First Printing, December 1971

Printed in the United States of America

For
Eddie Wynn
Jack Hartmen
and
Norman Blass

Contents

Chapter One

Nobody Calls Me Walt Anymore

RED HOLZMAN came in and said, "Well, it's a big game tonight."

Normally that typical understatement would have gotten a big laugh, but nobody in the Knick locker room even smiled. The guys were uptight. Nothing was funny.

It was less than 30 minutes to game time—the seventh and final game against the Los Angeles Lakers to decide the world championship of basketball. And our most valuable player, Willis Reed, the captain, was lying in pain on the training table, waiting until the last possible moment to receive injections of carbocaine and cortisone. Two games previous, Willis had been injured, forced to leave the game. Somehow we won that one, but the sixth game, which we played with Willis in street clothes, was a Laker rout. Chamberlain just ate up Hosket, DeBusschere and Bowman.

We knew Willis would start the seventh game. But there was no way he would finish it. He could hardly walk. Wilt would work on him. It was just a matter of time before the captain would be forced to the bench.

1

Reed stayed behind in the locker room when we went out to warm up. There was a buzz in the stands, a murmur. We knew what was being said: "Where's Willis? Is he going to play? He'd better get out there pretty soon or he won't have time to warm up enough." Then Cazzie, who was late out of the locker room for some reason, ran out from the tunnel and the fans for a second or two thought he was Willis. They stood up to start clapping but saw it was Cazzie and quieted down. False alarm. The Lakers at the other end of the floor were looking around for him. You could feel the tension.

Finally, at 7:34, after we'd been out there about 15 minutes, the captain came out and the hollering and cheering that greeted him practically shook the building down. The wave of noise was bouncing off the curved walls and deafening us. Cazzie clapped with glee. Dave the Rave raised his right fist. I slapped Willis' hands.

It was the beginning of the end of the greatest season a basketball team could hope to have. It predicted a climax that would be the envy of anybody who ever played the game. And for me, up to that point in my life, basketball had truly been the name of the game.

If I'm sitting around an airport or a hotel lobby, it's inevitable that some fan of the New York Knickerbockers will walk up and say, "Hi, Clyde."

"How are you doing?" I'll say.

"I could tell you by your psychedelic suit," he'll say, or, "I could tell by your Clyde lid."

I think it was Nate Bowman who first called me Clyde. It was right after the release of the movie about a group of Depression-era gangsters who traveled around Texas, Oklahoma and Louisiana holding up banks and shooting people. It was called "Bonnie and Clyde."

Before the film ever hit the theaters, Nate and my other teammates on the Knicks would get on me about my mod clothes. Then, in Baltimore on a road trip, I bought this $40 cocoa-brown hat, made of Italian velour with a wide brim. The first time Bowman laid eyes on it he pinned the nickname on me. The guys even spread the rumor that I carried a machine gun around in my big suitcase.

That's my name now—Clyde. The fans like it and I dig it, too.

Nobody calls me Walt anymore.

The nickname fits my style on the court: stealing and gambling and dribbling behind my back to escape pursuers. When the game is tight and the fans in Madison Square Garden are roaring, I love to flick the ball away from the dribbler. In an instant, if my gamble pays off, we've flipped over from defense to offense without the other team getting a shot. The crowd roars all the louder when I pass the ball to Dick Barnett or Bill Bradley racing up the court for an easy lay-up. The thefts seem to come in bunches, exciting the crowd and demoralizing the opposition.

It's all anticipation and quickness. I've good reflex actions. If there's a fly buzzing around in my room, I'll snatch him out of the air. The flies are learning to avoid me. So are other guards in the National Basketball Association.

I very seldom break anything. If I drop an object I usually can catch it before it hits the floor. I was in a cocktail lounge once with a friend and he set his glass down on a piece of ice. It slipped off the bar and I grabbed it in midair without spilling a drop.

My job on the Knicks is to keep my teammates happy (by feeding them passes), play good defense and score a few points to keep the opposition's defense honest. I want to be in double figures in rebounds, assists and scoring—while holding my man down. That's the kind of all-around game I strive for.

I'm proud of what an ex-coach, Charlie Eckman, said about me after a 1969 play-off game against the Baltimore Bullets:

"You might have seen the best guard in the league tonight. What didn't he do? He saw, he passed, he shot, he stole the ball, he played defense and he refereed. He did everything but serve lunch. He's the best guard I've seen since Oscar [Robertson] and I've been in this league since it started."

Fashion plays its role even on the court. The Knicks gave me jersey number ten, which is fine because I think guards should have smaller numbers, like quarterbacks. I got tired of conventional white sneakers and white laces, so I put some orange laces on my shoes— Knick colors. When I ran out of orange laces, I put on blue, which worried me a little because we had been winning with orange. So that night I scored 43 points and we won.

I like to dress the way I feel. When we're losing, I dress conservatively. When it's raining and gloomy outside, I wear somber things. When we're winning, I splash on the colors. My clothes are flashy because I feel good most of the time.

One day after practice I got into one of my wildest suits and went over to my bank, Irving Trust. This is the place with the friendly ad saying, "You can call us Irving." I carried a little brown bag and was wearing sunglasses and the big Clyde hat. The whole bit. I walked in and right away I could feel all the suspicious eyes on me: the customers and the bank dicks and the clerks. I was afraid all those people had seen the movie and were getting uptight. I took the hat and shades off and just cooled it. Even as I left, after transacting some perfectly respectable business, I got the fisheye from a guard.

I guess I inherited my fondness for clothes from my father. He was a sharp dresser. When I was a little boy, sometimes I'd try on his shoes and coats after he had gone to work. Naturally his clothes were too big for me and I couldn't wait until I got big enough to borrow his stuff.

When I was in college I wore collegiate clothes— loafers, button-down collars. I couldn't afford too much and it never bothered me. When I went to New York and was making good money with the Knicks, I started buying the kinds of things I'd always wanted. I've spent a lot on clothes my first three years as a pro, but I don't figure I blew it. I don't spend a lot on drinking, I don't smoke, I don't gamble, I don't spend a lot on women. So I figure a guy has to spend it somewhere.

I have more than 30 tailor-made suits, 7 hats and about 12 pairs of shoes—4 pairs are alligator skin in various colors. Then there are the vests, the ties and the $2,000 sealskin coat. I've heard that pro football player Leroy Kelly has 119 suits, so I don't feel extravagant. But the closet in my hotel room is much too small and I had to get a long showroom-type coat rack that stands out in the open.

I've got a Clydemobile, too, a canary-yellow Cadillac Eldorado with a white top and white pseudo-sports car interior. It matches one of my best outfits: yellow suit, bright-yellow scarf and brown shoes. In college I didn't even know what an Eldorado was.

I'm lucky to be reaching the top in pro basketball right now because I think the sport is destined to rival the popularity of baseball and football in the '70s. In July 1969 the research department of Batten, Barton, Durstine & Osborn conducted a survey of more than 4,000 people in 60 cities. It found out that pro basketball was the fourth most popular spectator sport after major-league baseball, pro football and college football. But you should remember that the NBA is only 24 years old! A mere infant, especially on the west coast.

I was on the cover of *Sports Illustrated* last December 8 and the issue sold 91,000 copies on the newsstands. The *SI* circulation department says pro basketball covers sell better than anything but pro and college football.

Our sport didn't have a national TV contract for the '62–'63 and the '63–'64 seasons, but the ABC network picked it up in '64–'65, kept it for six seasons and last February signed a new three-year contract calling for a minimum of 28 games a year. More than 20 million people watched the Boston-Phoenix game on TV last Christmas day.

Pro basketball is the best game for television. Baseball is too slow and football comes to a stop after every play. In pro basketball the action is continuous, the weather is never a problem, there are only five men per side to keep track of, the court is small and the ball is big (which is more than you can say for a hockey puck). I don't see how it can miss, especially with easily identifiable superstars like Jerry West, Wilt Chamberlain, Willis Reed, John Havlicek, Oscar Robertson and now Lew Alcindor.

Probably the best indication of how popular NBA players are getting is our acceptance in the vital field of bubble gum. Baseball has had a corner on the bubble-gum picture card market for years, with football getting some attention, too. Basketball players have been used, but not nearly as much. Last season Topps Chewing Gum, Inc. came out with Topps Pro Basketball Bubble Gum.

The kids must have been buying it up as fast as it hit the candy counters because seemingly every other scrap of paper thrust under my nose for an autograph was a Walt Frazier card. I wonder how many Walt Fraziers it took to trade for a Willis Reed?

I can remember as a boy getting a big kick out of collecting pictures of baseball players. With each stack of picture cards we got four or five pink slabs of gum, most of which we threw away. The manufacturers apparently got wise. In each package of this Topps offering there were ten cards and a bonus drawing ("Extra! Super-star pin-up in every pack"), but only one small piece of gum. Sort of like buying a package of Raleigh coupons with one cigarette tucked in.

I was one of the guys chosen to be a superstar pin-up, but the color cartoon didn't look at all like me. Some of the information on those cards wasn't too accurate, either. Bob Weiss of Chicago, only 6 foot 3, was listed as a center. A note on the back of Cazzie Russell's card said he was noted for his exceptional defense.

Topps didn't get to use photos of NBA players for free, of course. I think their original offer came through the league office. Then the Players Association voted that we accept the deal and have the photographs taken at the training camps. The players were for it because the revenue would go into our pension fund, but some of the owners didn't approve. Perhaps they wanted to control it or get cut in. Bill Bradley, our player representative, kept us informed on what was going on.

We went ahead and had the photos taken anyway. For a quick rundown on which NBA owners were our foes in the Great Bubble-Gum Controversy, all you have to do is shuffle through a stack of the cards. Players from Detroit, Milwaukee, Philadelphia and San Diego were allowed to show the names of their cities on their jerseys. The rest of us were not. We had to wear sweat shirts or, as the Knick players did, put our jerseys on backward. It was too bad because, backwards, the jerseys had an unfashionably high neckline.

If I'm lucky to be coming along in the NBA right now, I'm doubly lucky to be playing in New York City. New York is a great place for an unattached guy, especially the unattached athlete. It's the best place by far for business opportunities. And I love the New York fans.

They appreciate defense. It wasn't so popular for awhile, but it's made a comeback. The fans at the Garden don't urge us to run up the score. They scream and yell for us to keep the other team from reaching 100. If Dave DeBusschere puts the clamps on the other team's hotshot forward, or if I frustrate a rival guard, we're almost as heroic as Willis Reed, who scores the most points. At tense moments during the play-offs last season they'd chant, "Defense, defense, defense!"

People tell me the kids out on the playgrounds are dribbling behind their backs and doing their damndest to stop the other guys from scoring. They call out, "I'm Clyde now."

The fans in New York are very knowledgeable, from Adam Clayton Powell, who appointed himself the Knicks' official chaplain, right down to 13-year-old Ricky Evans of the Borough of Queens, president of the Walt Frazier Fan Club and editor-in-chief of the *Walt Frazier Bulletin*. The bulletin has a drawing of me with mustache and Clyde hat labeled, "Wanted by the NBA for stealing the ball, public Knick No. 1."

Ricky runs my latest satistics in every issue, stages contests, has guest columnists and generally tells the fans all about it, including what I like for dinner and how I threw left- and right-handed passes in highschool football. All this for 15-cents-a-month dues. The members wear orange-and-blue buttons that say, "I am a Frazier Fanatic."

I date any one of a number of girls—nobody special. I usually have a date after night games, when I like to go out and relax. There's no better area than Manhattan for nightlife. If I feel like dancing, I might go over to Nepenthe's at 48th and Lexington, a swinging little place. Or I might go down to Harry M's in the Garden-Penn Station complex. Most of the players, with or without girls, go in there once in a while to stand at the bar and have a few beers.

The thing I have to be careful about is giving out player tickets. Each guy on the Knicks gets three comps for Garden games and if I have two or three girls coming, I mustn't sit them side by side. I have to swap with other players and hope their seats are far enough away to avoid trouble.

Keeping the girls straight is my problem, but I have a Manhattan attorney, Norman Blass, to keep my business affairs in order. There wasn't too much to worry about until last season, when the popularity of the Knicks caused the offers to cascade in. Now I'm a regular tycoon. It wouldn't have happened in Detroit or Seattle.

I endorse a basketball for the Gabriel company. I make personal appearances for an air-freight outfit. I did some radio commercials for Supp-Hose socks and posed for some sweater ads in *Ebony*. Norman had me sign up with the American Felt Slipper Co. to endorse a Clyde sneaker (in Knick colors). Incidentally, the American Felt Slipper Co. doesn't make felt slippers anymore, nor does it use felt on anything. Then the Gotham Pressed Steel Corp. has come up with a Willis Reed-Walt Frazier boxed game called "Double Dynamite," with "fingertip snap-action shooters" and "all steel see-thru styrene backboards."

The deal I'll enjoy the most is my basketball camp at Camp Seneca in the Berkshires, near Pawling, New York. Norman asked me if I'd be interested in running a camp. I had had three years of experience working at Reed's camp and others, so I said, "Sure, why not?" The Van Arsdale twins, Dick Barnett, Dave Stallworth and others will be there to help me. I hope to teach thievery.

I don't think all this side action interferes with my basketball because it's not my money at stake. That's the way I want it. If Gotham Pressed Steel or American

Felt Slipper were partly or totally mine, business problems and profit-and-loss statements could affect my concentration. It would be distracting. I don't want to invest a great deal of dough until maybe my last couple of years in the NBA.

All my side deals are geared to whatever time I have available, so I don't have to steal any time that should be devoted to the Knicks. Norman makes sure this is stated in the contracts. I read the contracts, too, and if there's something I question or don't fully understand, I ask him about it and perhaps have him make a change. Even if you have the world's greatest lawyer, you still want to know what's going on.

Last February 9 was probably the biggest day in my career as a tycoon. Not a typical day, mind you, but an example of what can happen to a popular pro athlete in New York City.

We had no practice that day, so I got up about noon. I wanted to wear a conservative outfit that would photograph well. I put together a green suit, yellow shirt, green vest, green tie and green alligator shoes. A Wall Street banker might not call that conservative, but it was my idea of toning down. I crossed to the east side of Eighth Avenue from the hotel and walked up one block to the grand opening of Battle & Clyde's Penthouse, an enterprise I'm in with defensive back Mike Battle of the New York Jets.

Battle & Clyde's is a barbershop, somewhat more elegant than those most people go to. It's on the top floor at 500 Eighth Avenue and has five chairs (which can be curtained off for privacy), a sunroom, showers, an art gallery and a boutique. An ex-actress named Bobbi Donin is in charge. You can get a hair styling for

$7; shave and comb cost $7, sauna $3, hairpiece servicing $10, heat-cap treatment $8, manicure $3 and pedicure $8. If you're ever in the neighborhood and need your toenails trimmed, go on up.

We had food and drinks, so it was like a little party. There were television cameras, photographers and newspapermen all over the place. It was only supposed to last a couple of hours, but at 4:30 people were still taking the guided tours and chitchatting with the lady hair stylists. I finally had to leave. I had a five o'clock appointment over on the East Side at the law offices of Forsythe, McGovern, Pearson & Nash. And I was tired of smiling.

Norman and my teammate, Dave Stallworth, were waiting for me in the firm's offices, along with executives of Beauty Masters, Inc. of Greenwich, Connecticut. Traffic was murder in midtown Manhattan and made me late. With all the attorneys and underwriters and vice presidents looking on and a photographer snapping pictures, I signed a contract to help promote a new line of "cosmetics and personal care products" (Black Heritage Ezee Comb and Black Heritage Natural Hair Sheen) marketed for black men. The contract called for several commercials on TV and radio and some personal appearances. I got cash, royalties and 2,000 shares of stock.

Norman, Stallworth and I then drove out to Queens for dinner and then an appearance at the Forest Hills Jewish Center. Hundreds of shouting, excited kids were there for a sports night. We gave autographs and answered about four questions apiece. Before we left we picked up a generous fee. I drove Norman and Dave home and then went home myself and got in bed.

For awhile I stayed awake reviewing the day. I wasn't quite 25 years old and I wondered what I had been doing in hair styling salons and Park Avenue board rooms. Things were nice and plush for Clyde. But I remembered when he was plain Walt Frazier.

Chapter Two

It's Tricky Dribbling on Dirt

BEING THE firstborn—and a boy—in a family that keeps producing daughters is learning housekeeping the hard way. I can change diapers, run a vacuum, handle a steam iron, cook a meal. Even when I was married, I'd wash my own clothes.

I was born March 29, 1945, to Walter and Eula Frazier, the oldest of nine children. There's me, then Mary, Brenda, Janice, Brezita and Renita (twins), Ethel, Phyllis and Keith (who's just turned 12).

The first house I remember is the one on Fraser Street, near where the Atlanta Stadium is now. The time I remember best is playing ball in the street, sliding for home across a sewer lid and breaking my arm. Two weeks later, at my aunt's home in the projects, I fell off a slide and broke the other arm. Those are the only two broken bones I've ever had (knock on wood). Not long after, we moved into a duplex on East Avenue, a quiet, tree-lined street in northeast Atlanta, with my grandparents living in the next apartment.

Frazier family life in Atlanta was close. Grandma Frazier's Sunday meals were too much. I can remember those sugar-cured hams and hot browned biscuits with butter melting down the sides. Sometimes, now, I'm alone in my New York hotel room. It's Sunday, hours from game time. I'm thinking of East Avenue in Atlanta and baked ham—and the closed-in feeling of my four walls bugs me.

Because there were two Walts in the family, I was called June, short for Junior. Now if somebody calls me Clyde, they know me from New York. If they call me Walt, they knew me in high school or college. Anybody calls me June, we grew up together.

I remember the first day of school. I cried so hard my mother couldn't leave me. She spent about the whole day there. I guess I got used to school fast. About a week later my father was supposed to pick me up after classes were out. I was waiting for him and he didn't come so I took off and walked home by myself.

"What did you leave for, boy?" my mother demanded.

Just then my father came up the steps outside. She decided to tease him. Pushing me into the kitchen, she went to the front door.

"Where is that boy?" she demanded.

"Don't know," my father replied. "I went there but he wasn't anyplace."

Then she trotted me out and eased his mind.

My Uncle Eddie Wynn, my mother's brother, is only a few years older than I am. He's been more like a father than an uncle. Only his mother calls him Eddie. Everybody else in town calls him Chello or Chell. He wouldn't like to think so but it's because he's shaped like a cello. He went to Carver High, a vocational school, and was the trainer when the teams were really great. He was one of those who didn't have athletic ability but liked to hang around the team and go on the game trips. He'd invite me over to watch Carver's football team work out and meet the players. He would brag about me and tell the boys how good I was going to be.

"My nephew is going to be great," he'd say. "He's going to be everything!"

"That one?" the guys would kid him. "He won't be nothin'!"

"You'll see, we're going to fool the world."

He used to bring me things from the Carver equipment room—girls' tennis shoes (the only ones that would fit me) and oversized jerseys. I'd roll up the sleeves of the jerseys and flop around in them night and day.

Chell could be a disciplinarian, like his teaching me how to drive a car when I got to be 16. It was a horrible experience. I'd roll through a stop sign and he'd say, "What did that sign say?"

"It said, 'Stop.' "

"All right, then!" He wasn't gentle about it.

One Christmas, when I was seven, I asked my mother for a trumpet so I could learn music and she came through for me. I was learning pretty good, training myself when everybody else was out of the house and couldn't complain about the racket. But when Chello found out about it (maybe he heard me across town) he informed me I was going to lay that trumpet down. I wasn't going to be in any band. He had dreams for me and they didn't include any visions of a new Louis Armstrong. Anyway, the trumpet disappeared and I have a good idea who was responsible.

I still talk to Chell on the phone. He works at a laundry in Atlanta and keeps watch on some property I own down there. He has some of my trophies and doodads on his mantel and some magazine clippings and photos of mine framed on the wall. He couldn't be prouder.

I was a kid who loved to play sports from sunup to sundown. When I couldn't play, I watched. First thing up, eight o'clock in the morning, I'd read the sports page. I can remember sitting on the porch many a Georgia summer morning reading the Atlanta *Constitution,* checking out all the baseball players, their batting averages, runs scored, errors, ERAs—all that.

There was a playground nearby behind Nathan B. Forrest Elementary School, like three blocks away, and most of my time was spent there. It was open from 10 A.M. to 6 P.M. during the summers, and after classes at other times, and you could play basketball, softball or football—I played all three depending on the season. The supervisor was a lady and in the playroom she had most of the equipment a kid could need, including Scrabble, pool and Ping-Pong. We always had a lot of kids hanging around there; this was our life. If that playground teacher didn't show up, we were lost. Grant Park, with a zoo and a cyclorama, wasn't too far away, but when I was growing up, it wasn't integrated. Blacks had to go in the back of a bus to a park across town.

We didn't have asphalt basketball courts at our playground; we played on dirt. It's pretty tricky dribbling on dirt. It wasn't too bad when it was dry, but if it had rained, there was a mess. You had to dribble over a hole here, a gully there, uphill and downhill. We had nets on the baskets, though, which is more than I can say for the parks in New York City.

Mostly I played with older kids, like when I was in the fourth grade, I was playing against seventh graders. I really wasn't that big. I looked even smaller hidden in those floppy jerseys, but they said I had the talent. Since I was quiet, I never argued one way or the other in those typical no-referee half-court games, so they could put up with me. I was considered a team man. We used to have these shooting contests where there would be a line and you had to outshoot another guy from behind it. We shot for nickles and dimes and older guys would put me in the game because I shot pretty good. I never felt any pressure because it wasn't my money. Who knows, maybe it was the start of learning how to play under stress, sort of a Madison Square Kinder-Garden—if you'll pardon the pun.

We had a Little League baseball team, too, sponsored by Eagle's Barbershop and coached by Mr. Hill. We worked out every morning in the summers. He was a great coach and taught us a lot of baseball, the proper way to warm up, run the bases, bat and field. I started out as a center fielder, moved to shortstop and one day when our catcher was out of town I played at catcher, liked it and stayed. I was in the fourth grade when I began playing organized six-man tackle football for the elementary school. I was the quarterback.

Leadership's a funny thing. You don't say to yourself, okay, I'm taking charge. You just find yourself running the show. No one appoints you, there's no nominating committee, it just happens. In baseball I was the catcher, in basketball the ball handler, in football the quarterback.

It's the same all over now with my kid brother Keith. He's like me—quiet (you never know he's around) and a sharp dresser, the best-dressed guy in his class. If his pants aren't pressed and neat, if they don't fit up over his shoes just right, he won't wear them. When I was his age, I had to wear sneakers, but he wears shoes and stays up at night shining them. He's smart in school, too—A's and B's. But sports is the main thing, like I was home recently and played baseball with him, just hitting him fungoes. I mean I hit the ball as high as I could. That cat would just go and get it, man! One time it was on a basketball court and it was a real high fly; it took a minute to come down. He waited by the pole holding up the backboard, and as soon as the ball came down he stepped around the pole and caught it.

Keith lives with my other grandmother in the Bowen Homes projects. I played basketball against four other guys in the projects one time. Keith stood around and I could tell he was proud I was his brother. Then when I came around him, it was, "Uh, you know, he ain't nobody."

This is the way the whole family acts when I go home, and if I called today and said I'm coming home tomorrow, my sisters would tell everybody in the whole town but when I got there, it would be like I was nobody. All the Fraziers, they like to play it cool.

One member of the family didn't always appreciate my interest in athletics. My dad's brother, Willie Frazier, lived with us. He didn't enjoy sports and was always telling me I shouldn't play this or I shouldn't do that because I was going to get killed.

We had a TV set at home and it got full use when

sports events were on. We got the Washington Redskins' games in Georgia. I can remember Sundays in the winter, quietly going into the living room on my grandparents' side to watch the game, or whatever was on leading up to the game. I rooted for Georgia and Georgia Tech—I knew all the fight songs—and Notre Dame, too; I guess, because the Fighting Irish were the most publicized and you could always get their games on television or radio. My grandmother worked for these white people and they gave her a Paul Hornung helmet. She passed it on to me and did I love that helmet! I played football in it, wore it in the house, went to bed with it on.

In the summers the kids in my neighborhood would always go to Ponce de Leon Park to see the Atlanta Crackers of the Southern Association. (They tore the park down when the Braves moved down from Milwaukee to play in the new stadium.) In those days we could mingle with the players. After all, the Memphis Chicks weren't exactly the St. Louis Cardinals. We knew the trainers and we could go into the clubhouse sometimes and help shine the shoes, look at the uniforms, play with the bats and gloves. We worked at the ball park, too, cleaning it up. That was my first job. Was I proud! I could tell my mother I had to go to work and that was a good feeling. We made a little money and we got into the games free, which is what we were really after.

We spent more time having fun than watching the games. We'd sit in the bleachers and carry on. We'd race behind the billboards for home runs and if a ball came in the stands, we'd grab it before an usher could. Old guys dozing in the sun in the bleachers, we'd give them hotfoots. My folks would go fishing and want me to go along, but I wouldn't if the Crackers were in town.

It was an okay boyhood. Sports kept me out of most trouble (except at Ponce de Leon Park) and the Baptist church had an influence, too. My parents weren't strict in making me go but I felt a need. I really went to hear the sermons; I dug what the preacher had to say. I remember once in high school our football coach took us to Martin Luther King, Jr.'s church, although he wasn't there that particular Sunday and his father gave the sermon. I was surprised it was so small and crowded and that it had white people in it. I hadn't seen too many white people in Atlanta going to black churches.

I don't go to services very often anymore, but I still consider myself religious.

Chapter Three

The Clock Is Bleeding

DAVID T. HOWARD High School, where I spent five years, grades 8 through 12, is on Randolph Street in Atlanta's fourth ward. It's a big brick building on the fringe of the downtown area, named for David Tobias Howard, who had nothing to do with the Howard University in Washington, D.C. David Howard had been a prominent undertaker in Atlanta's black community when the school was built in 1924. White funeral parlors wouldn't handle black bodies and black people placed a lot of value on being buried with a little class. (If you weren't allowed to live in style, at least you could be planted in style). So I guess Mr. Howard of Atlanta did all right for himself.

Howard High was big on sports. Maybe the teams should have been called the Undertakers or the Diggers, but they weren't. They were the Rams.

The football field was a small, very rough area of gravel, more or less okay for practice, but real games had to be played elsewhere. The school gym at least had a hardwood floor and the seating wasn't bad. But the lighting—forget it!

Howard, an all-black school, was a member of the GIA (Georgia Interscholastic Association). We never played any white teams (GHSA—Georgia High School Association). I don't remember any talk about the two playing each other and it never occurred to me as something that might happen. (The schools are mostly integrated now, but Howard is still all black, I believe. No whites live near enough.) The faculty, from black colleges in the South like Morehouse, Clark and Spelman, did a pretty good job.

Howard wasn't considered the best high school or the rowdiest either. It was in between. There were clubs and gangs, like in any school, but I wasn't in them. I was a loner, pretty much like I am now. I had one good buddy, Marvin Cato. We were at the playground one day when a guy who was working at a Zesto soft ice cream store told us he was quitting.

"How about if we try to get that job?" Marvin asked me.

We went down and talked to the guy. We'd never done curb service, but we said we had.

The first day was miserable. We'd go out to the cars with trays loaded down with hamburgers and French fries and ice cream. We didn't even know how to hang them on the windows. The customers had to show us what to do. We made something like $10 in sympathy tips that day, but the boss was so mad he was going to fire us. Then his brother said, "Oh, let's keep 'em awhile."

We worked there more than two years. In the winter when not too many people wanted ice cream, we'd set up a basket in one corner of the storeroom and toss a crumpled-up paper cup at it. In the summer, we'd bring a stick and play baseball against the side of the store. Over the roof of the building was a home run. I was on the small side when I started at Zesto but those hamburgers, hot dogs and malteds really helped.

With our Zesto tips, Marvin and I bought at '49 Ford coupe together. That car *never* ran. It stayed in the shop more than it did on the street. We had to park around the corner on a hill so we could roll it down to get it started. It was funny. '49 Fords were mostly used to run moonshine—Georgia corn liquor or "white lightning." Every night I'd be coming home in that car, after dropping Cato off, and every night there was the police to stop me to check out the trunk. What money we wasted on that junk heap! I vowed I'd never buy another raggedy car.

I had one girl I liked some in the tenth grade, but generally the female sex made me nervous. I guess I've learned better since. Instead of dates, there were dances on Monday nights and if I went, I'd just stand around. I went for nice clothes but I couldn't afford more than a suit at a time. Hats were in at Howard. I favored caps, like Ben Hogan wore, you know, thrust forward low over the eyes. I was a pretty dapper fellow in my Hogan. No Clyde, you understand, but fairly sharp.

I didn't step right in at Howard and dazzle the school with my athletic ability. I didn't like eighth-grade football, the way they were playing, so I didn't go out for the team. My friends had told the coach that I would be a good player, so he was always telling me, "Come out, come on out." I got tired of telling him no, so I wouldn't even go to see practice.

The basketball coach asked me to come out for the eighth-grade team and I told him I had to be at work at five. He said there'd be no problem, that after practice or a game he'd make sure I got to work on time. My boss at the Zesto place said okay. I tried out in the middle of the season. I can't remember what position I played. I was maybe six feet tall and I was good. I played the same way as today—I could pass, I could rebound, I could dribble with either hand. I always had these things. The eighth-grade team had to practice on the stage of the gym because the girls' team had first call on the floor; we always had a great girls' team.

In my sophomore year, the coach, T. Herman Graves, started me at center. I scored pretty good—I was about 6 foot 2 by this time—but we didn't have the talent and couldn't get going.

The game I remember best that year was the first. You're naturally excited that you made the team and when we dressed in the locker room, I forgot to put on my shorts. I warmed up like everybody else in my sweat suit. A little later the coach told me to get in the game. I started to take the sweat pants down but I didn't get them down too far because I saw I didn't have anything on underneath but a jock. I pulled the pants up quickly and told Coach Graves I had to go to the locker room. He was mad, I guess, but when I got back he put me into the game. The people down front were still laughing at half time. Every time I think about that game, it gets a little drafty in the room.

I played some baseball in the tenth grade. I was a catcher, a good glove man, but not that tough a hitter. I decided it took up too much time and I didn't go out again.

My last two years of basketball, George Coffey was the coach. That really changed things around for me. We had a 6 foot 9 kid then, Ed Johnson (now with the New York Nets), so it was a cinch I wasn't going to be the center. Mr. Coffey moved me to the backcourt. I've been playing there most of the time since. Even when I go home now, guys say, "Hey, you're playing just like you did at Howard."

Those last two years, Howard never lost a basketball game to another city team, even the Price Wildcats, who had been the power. Most of the contests came down to a last deciding free throw or a long desperation shot. We were pretty good at those last-second heaves.

In the last three minutes our scoreboard would turn red, so we'd say, "The clock is bleeding!" The guys loved to take those shots from three-quarters down the court and we actually made quite a few. I remember once against Smith High there were only seconds left and I got fouled. Most of the teams I've played on, the other guys looked to me for leadership, so this was no time to blow my cool. I didn't. I made both free throws.

We had a fine team with Johnson at center and two good forwards, Robert Butler and David Edwards, and a good guard who was a year behind me in school. He was a typical Howard High product—he never, as far as I know, went to college. Too many ex-athletes in Atlanta are hanging around the bars on Auburn Avenue, guys who could have made it if they'd been willing to work at it. Even if you hate going to class and figure college is a waste of four years, it's worth it, believe me. You live better ever after.

Even though we were the powerhouse team in Atlanta, we always seemed to blow it in the state. My junior year we lost by one point. When I was a senior, the tournament was in Savannah, where Merv Jackson, later a star at Utah and a pro in the ABA, was the big gun. We were the team to beat. We knocked off a team from Savannah first and the next night we met a team we'd already beaten once. If we got past them we'd be in the finals. As soon as the game started, we began throwing the ball away, then I fouled out, and zap! Howard had blown it again.

I took it hard. I can remember coming home and sitting outside, crying.

When I was in the tenth grade, I approached Graves—he was football coach, too—and told him I was ready, that I was coming out for football, but he didn't believe me because I had told him the same thing in the ninth grade. I showed up, though, and he put me at quarterback, third string. I was pretty shaky and I wasn't that good a runner. We would have wind sprints and all the backs would leave me. I was so slow, in fact, I couldn't outrace some of the linemen. But I could pass and Graves taught me how to mix up plays and run a team. During practices he would call the plays so I could get to know what to do in certain situations.

We had a bad year. The regular quarterback got hurt. I had moved up to second team, so for the last four games I was the quarterback and we lost all four. The whole school was blaming me.

The next year I was the first-string quarterback right from the start. We won eight straight and were undefeated going into the big Milk Bowl game for underprivileged children. We played Washington High, always our biggest rival and always our last regular-season game. Washington had been tied once, so this battle had a big buildup. About 11,000 people came out to Herndon Stadium at Morris Brown College.

(Mr. Herndon is a big insurance man, one of Atlanta's many black millionaires, I'm told.)

I remember we were running good, really sweeping them off the field, but we couldn't seem to score. Whenever we were at their goal, we fumbled. We got to their five-yard line about four times straight and lost the ball. We had a great sweep we called the 47. I'd call that and then the 28, which was the same play around the opposite end. We were moving down the field sensationally until I called for a reverse that really broke our backs.

I carried out my fake and I could hear the crowd hollering. I thought we had a touchdown but our runner had fumbled. Washington picked up the ball and their guy ran about 90 yards for a touchdown. That took a lot out of us. In plain fact, the guys gave up. We lost 21 to 14 and along with it the city championship and the right to play for the state title. Washington finally lost to a high school from Augusta that had Emerson Boozer, now a star on the New York Jets.

I'll always remember what the coach told us after we'd come off the field: "We might be small now, but next year we'll be mighty!"

The next year, with a small number of experienced players, we *were* mighty. As a senior I was the Johnny Unitas of Atlanta. I could pass with either hand. Guys might be hanging all over my right arm, so I'd switch and pass with my left, ten yards or so out to the flat.

I used to watch pro ball on television a lot, so I knew that when you had a lead near the end of the game, you ground out the yards. I'd run a dive play to this side, then a dive play the other way. When it was third and two, I'd fall forward myself. I could read the defenses.

Like if they were in a six-two, I'd call a trap up the middle. If they were in a tight line, I'd call a sweep. We even had audibles I could call at the line of scrimmage.

Chello used to take a bunch of us to semipro games and I'd sit off by myself, not saying a word, studying the game, concentrating, analyzing the quarterback's moves.

My mother made all our games, partly to see me play and partly to watch my sister Mary, who was a majorette. She would scream and holler, "Don't kill my son!" And the guys would say, "Hey, man, I think your mother gets tireder than you do out there."

Ours was no one-man team. We had a lot of good players, including a little halfback with guts, Willie Harris, who would run into anybody. But we weren't the favorites. We were rated only so-so. Price High had the great team.

We started off losing. We had a center who was pretty big, but Coach Graves had to demote him because he fumbled so much. Coach replaced him with a more sure-handed guy who weighed 185 but who could block. Finally Coach got rid of all his big guys and started using linemen who had ability.

We promptly won seven games in a row, including the one against Price that meant the championship. "You can beat Price," Chello told me before the game and I believed it.

Price was leading 14 to 13 with a minute and 30 seconds to go and we had the ball on our 20-yard line, third down. I thought at the time that it would take the slickest moonshine runner with the fastest '49 Ford to get 80 yards through Price for a score. They rushed hard and made me switch hands for a left-handed pass.

As I threw it a guy hit me right in the back, so the ball went directly to one of Price's defensive backs. Instead of running it out of bounds, downing it or trying to return it, he just stayed where he was, jumping up and down with glee. One of our guys came over and grabbed the ball away from him and ran downfield until he was knocked out of bounds.

The official said it was our ball, first and 10 to go, which didn't really bother Price because there was less than a minute left. I called a down-and-out pass to a halfback. Our first-string man was injured so this guy was a sub. But he was fast. As I threw the ball, their defensive man fell and my receiver ran from about midfield to their 10, where he was knocked out of bounds. Thirty seconds on the clock. Players were babbling in the huddle.

"Shut up, I'm running the team," I said.

Some of them wanted to run a 23, which would have been into the line, but I knew from watching the pros that you should run the ball near the sideline so you could step out and stop the clock. I called a 44 bootleg and everybody went for the fake. They chased after the other guy and, hiding the ball, I had a clear path to the goal line. But our fullback, instead of blocking, was standing in the way on the 1-yard line. A Price lineman knocked me out of bounds.

It was fourth and goal to go, the last play, four seconds left. The fullback came back into the huddle crying over his foul-up. I slapped him on the helmet and told him to shut up.

"Run a quarterback sneak, Walt," the linemen said. (They never did learn to be quiet in the huddle.) "We'll get it, we'll get it, we won't let you down."

I really couldn't come up with a better idea. I was supposed to be running the team and I couldn't let anyone feel I was cracking up inside. The ball was snapped and I just lowered my head and went in.

The coaches were crying, the players on both sides were crying (for obviously different reasons), everybody had tears in their eyes. Even when we took off, guys on their team were still on the field sobbing. We, the victors, paraded through the Howard campus. There were mobs of people, cars with horns honking, the whole big scene.

I like looking back on those days. I was a hell of a passer, if I do say so myself. I could throw long or short and I could run a team. But I knew, too, that there were no black quarterbacks in major college or pro ball. I said, "Forget football, Walt, concentrate on basketball."

Chapter Four

Think You Can Play Forward?

I WASN'T exactly an academic whiz in high school. C's suited me fine. With those marks, I wasn't thinking college. Like so many other black kids, I didn't know anybody who had higher education except some of my teachers.

When I was in eleventh grade and doing okay in sports, a couple of the coaches began working on me a little about trying to get a college education.

"How about Tennessee State or Grambling?" they'd ask. "Maybe you could get an athletic scholarship from one of those schools."

That meant getting my grades up. State and Grambling were all-black colleges with great sports traditions, but you still had to have a few smarts.

Some of my pals thought I should at least go to Clark, which was right in Atlanta, but I never considered that. You'd have to average 50 points a game at Clark before someone would come and watch.

I guess I could have gone to Morehouse or Morris Brown if I'd really wanted to. The trouble was, I didn't. I was reminded that State really might take me.

33

A guy named Harold Hunter was the coach and our center, Ed Johnson, went to visit and he really liked it. I was wondering, too, whether it might be better if I could get into an integrated school. It seemed to me that I could get a better education competing in classes with whites.

The trouble was that recruiters from white colleges and integrated colleges weren't scouting the black high schools of the deep South too much. A recruiter from Kansas got in touch once and said they'd like me to come visit. But the day they suggested, I was receiving an award, so my coach said I couldn't come. I never heard from them again. Then West Texas State got in touch. I was glad they wanted me, but it was for football, and I said no.

Then, the end of my last year in Howard High, a man named Samuel Johnson came to see me. He was as big around the belt as Chello, and almost as concerned about my future. He was working for some Christian organization and had been following me, it turned out, all through high school. He told me that he'd been in Indianapolis and had seen Oscar Robertson and all those guys at Crispus Attucks High School who were making schoolboy headlines.

He explained to me that there was nothing in it for him, he just wanted to see me placed somewhere so I could continue my education and get a chance to play basketball. He knew Branch McCracken, coach at Indiana, and he tried to get me in there. I talked to Mr. McCracken on the phone and I was excited because at that time Indiana had the Van Arsdales. I knew Indiana and the Big Ten had real basketball tradition. It didn't work; I failed the exam.

Mr. Johnson also knew somebody who knew Jack Hartman, the coach at Southern Illinois. "Why don't you go up to Southern and look around?" he suggested another time. By now, I'd graduated from Howard. In fact it was late August, just weeks before fall classes began. But I wasn't too worried because I knew that Tennessee State was waiting for me.

Southern Illinois flew me. It was my first airplane ride and, just like the Clyde of today, I fell sound asleep. The stewardess woke me up when we were about to land in St. Louis. Coach Hartman was away on a trip and his assistant, George Iubelt, picked me up at the airport.

One of the first things I was shown was the SIU gym. It looked to me like it would hold about a thousand people. I just took it for granted that it was the practice gym. Our old gym back at Howard High was better than this. I could see the lighting wasn't so hot and there didn't seem to be much ventilation. (It wasn't until I'd signed in and was part of the SIU scene that I found out it was the regular college gymnasium.)

Iubelt really sold me on his school. He was easygoing, friendly, the kind of guy you could communicate with. I liked him a lot. And the campus was beautiful, with woods right in the middle, modern buildings mixed in with some older ones and, alongside, a manmade lake.

After we'd looked all around and talked some more, I told Iubelt that I'd like to come to SIU but that I'd have to talk first to Mr. Johnson. When I got back home, my mother was all excited. I guess she'd thought it was unreal—her son a college man.

Mr. Johnson asked me how I liked the school and I

said it was pretty nice. He said he figured it would be a good idea to go there. He'd been told Hartman was one hell of a good coach. That's when I really decided it would be SIU. It felt good to have my mind made up. (I never did check out Tennessee State.)

Johnson continued to keep in touch with me all that first year I was at SIU. Like he'd send me $20 here and $20 there. He had a sixth sense about knowing when I was really short. I'd be flat busted and along would come a letter and a check. He really babied me along my freshman year. He'd keep telling me I was doing good—stuff like that. (I haven't heard from him since my sophomore year. He was always doing a lot of moving around, going to Europe, things like that. Maybe he's abroad now. All in all, he's about the finest man I've ever known.)

I entered Southern Illinois in the fall of 1963 on what was called a "work-program scholarship." I was supposed to work at some job two hours a day out of the season and one hour a day in season. It wasn't until school had officially started that I met Coach Hartman. He watched me play a couple of games with the freshman squad and put me on an NCAA scholarship. This got me $15 a month for laundry and incidentals.

I was never supposed to see it, but when I brought my high school transcript on to SIU, I happened to read on it that, in the opinion of the college counselor at Howard, it was unlikely I'd ever finish college. The counselor had written "doubtful" in estimating my chances of making good at the college level. That kind of motivated me. I think I always do best when people expect the least of me. (Like coming to the Knicks, it was always Bradley getting the notices, Bradley who was going to save the Knicks. Bill was going to do this, Bill was going to do that. I was never mentioned, but I knew that I could do it if I had the chance. I probably tried harder than if Bradley had never been there.)

Freshman classes were tough for me. I found out I was behind, way behind. For other students it was more like a review of things they'd had in high school. I'd come into a math class and the professor would take it for granted that I'd had certain fundamentals. I hadn't. I found that whenever I could get anything out of a textbook I did all right. Stuff like history I could handle. Lectures, too, were new to me. I wasn't used to taking notes and it took me two quarters to get the general hang of it.

I made 2.8 the first quarter and again the second. Third quarter, I decided I was going to take more difficult subjects and if I couldn't manage them, I'd leave, pack it in and go to a smaller school. I signed for history, more math, philosophy, and it was fun. I even studied on weekends. I found out the kind of questions instructors were likely to ask. I'd talk to other students, see what kind of preparation they were doing for exams. I did all right, better than 3. It was really good for my morale.

SIU required two years of ROTC. That was another new scene for me. Everybody hated it. I only went during the winter when I could wangle it because in the spring you really had to get out there and drill. In cold weather, chances are you just went to meetings and saw old war pictures. The few times I had to be out on the drill pad in hot weather were terrible, but funny, too. Sometimes you stood so long in formation when it was really hot, guys would keel over. You'd be standing beside a guy and pa-LONK! The guy next to him would go and you'd start feeling dizzy yourself. The commander would be screaming by this time and more guys would fall. It was straight out of Gomer Pyle.

I'd never known many whites, but at SIU I always had white roommates and we got along great. There were a couple of bad times, of course, but nothing really serious. Once I registered late for a quarter and I was put in a four-man suite instead of a two-man room. There was space for two in the front room and for two in the back. This guy was asleep in a bed in the front when I came in, so I just quietly went to bed without waking him. When I woke up in the morning, he'd gathered up his things and moved into the back room.

Freshman basketball was great. It was all local talent except for me. We had Ed Zastrow from Morton Grove, Illinois, Roger Bechtold from Belleville, Clarence Smith from Zion and Ralph Johnson from Trenton (Illinois, not New Jersey). We played 14 games and ran up some really fantastic scores. We played teams like Kentucky Wesleyan, Evansville and Paducah Junior College and whenever we played the varsity, we gave them a tussle. They never beat us by more than three or four points.

The fans in Carbondale were all excited, saying we were the best freshman team they'd ever had. They were calling me the Georgia Peach. I got some nice write-ups in the local press. Some writers were beginning to compare me to Chico Vaughan, the greatest SIU player in history. For 14 games, I averaged 22.7 points, hit close to 60 percent of my field goal attempts and averaged just under 10 rebounds a game. My weakness was free throws I made 52 of 85 for .612. That's bad.

The old gym was all right for freshman games since we didn't have that many fans anyway. The court was regulation and the basket setup was good. Besides, I knew that by the time I would be playing varsity, we'd be in the new gym that was being built. While it was going up, Coach Hartman took me over and we looked around. (For my money, the SIU arena still is one of the better gyms. It seats over 10,000 and has a fully equipped training room and a concourse around the top where the gymnastics team works out. I didn't like the floor all that much. I thought it was hard on the legs.)

My sophomore year, I didn't start because I was behind George McNeil, who was a better guard. It wasn't until the fourth game that I even got in. We were on our way to meet Kansas State when Hartman approached me on the train.

"Do you think you can play forward?" he wanted to know.

I told him yes.

"All right," he said, "you might start."

I thought he was just jiving because, after all, this was K-State we were going to play, big college stuff. I was excited anyway. When Hartman read the starting lineup in the locker room before the game and said "Frazier," I couldn't even get my sweat pants off, I was so nervous.

I not only played forward for Hartman, I scored 18 points. The guards were McNeil and David Lee, a little guy who did a lot of moving. I had nothing to do with running the team. All I was supposed to do was shoot and rebound, defend against forwards. But that didn't give me too much trouble because I'd always been pretty good on defense and I knew how to block out. Now that I was in college, my weight was up to 190, so I had enough heft to let people know I was there.

I played against Dave Stallworth of Wichita State that season. He was an All-American, I was a sophomore and it was a hell of an experience. Wichita State was number three in the nation at the time and Dave the Rave did whatever he wanted to on that team. Anytime he wanted the ball, he got it. The time we played against Dave, I held him to 12 points for the first half, which was pretty good. Somebody else had him the second half. (We kid about it now. I tell him how I really held him down.)

As a sophomore, I was SIU's leading rebounder and, behind McNeil, the leading scorer. Mac and I were battling it out, like he was averaging 20 points a game and I was averaging 19. I admit I wanted to be the leading scorer at the end of the year. Any forward wants to be tops in the scoring department. But I wasn't show-boating, taking bad shots, refusing to pass when a teammate was open.

Evidently some of my teammates weren't so sure. All of a sudden, the guys weren't feeding me the ball the way they had been. A player would start around this way, see me and go the other way. It began to be a struggle even to score 15 points. I don't know, maybe it was because I was a sophomore, maybe some of the guys thought I should wait my turn.

Then at the end of the year we were playing Evansville. The game was real tight. It could go either way. Hartman had decided not to start me. It dawned on me that I wasn't just getting a rest, I was getting benched!

Benched for nothing, at least nothing I knew about. He wasn't about to give me any reason, either. I don't now why, to this day. I sat there in a state of shock, not thinking, just feeling. Then I made up my mind I wasn't going to play. I'd really psyched myself.

We'd begun to sag out on the floor against Evansville. The game was getting away from us and Hartman finally called me to get in. I told him I couldn't, I was sick. He got all upset. It was the end of the half then and we went into the dressing room. When it was time to start again, Hartman told me, "Since you're sick, don't go out on the bench." The fans started yelling, "We want Frazier, we want Frazier."

After the game—we won by one point—Dr. Donald Boydston, the school's athletic director, came to me and asked me what was wrong. I told him the same thing—I was sick.

I've had low points in my life, but nothing like that. I guess it usually happens that way. I mean, you get up one morning and everything seems okay. But everything isn't. It's gone wrong for some reason and you don't dig why. You're just not with it anymore. With me, it was like I wasn't part of the team. No one says anything, but it's clear enough. Here I was, about to finish my best year of basketball and zap! I'm on the bench, I'm telling the coach I can't play, that I'm sick.

It seemed obvious the only thing I could do was leave school, check out of SIU and head for home.

Chapter Five

In Love with Defense

WHAT HAPPENED wasn't all sound and fury, after all. Not right then, at least. Coach Hartman sent for me. We talked it out. I told him I wanted to finish out the season if I could. Everyone at SIU had given me a great opportunity and I fully appreciated it.

Hartman said, "All right." I was back on the team and playing again. We went to Evansville for the NCAA small college tournament and just missed winning the championship. During the tournament, I averaged 17.1 points and 9.2 rebounds a game and made second-team Little All-America.

But I wasn't happy. I was back on the team and playing, but it wasn't right. The team freeze was still on. I couldn't make contact. I stopped going to classes. I just didn't show. I'd sleep late and mess around playing pool or watching TV. My roommate had a set and I'd stay up watching the late, late, late show. I knew I was letting a lot of people down, most of all myself, but that didn't stop me. In more affluent segments of societies, they have a nice term for it when their collegians get into trouble, something about a "sophomore slump." Maybe it applies to blacks from Atlanta on athletic scholarships, too.

At any rate, it was too late when Coach Hartman found out. He was on a recruiting trip when the grade slips came into the basketball office at the end of the quarter. His assistant called him and told him that I'd lost my scholastic eligibility. I never liked to lie, but I'd told the coach that I was going to class. That was the main hurt, telling him that lie.

He hurried back to school and called me to his office. "What do you think you're doing?" he yelled at me. "You had a great opportunity to do something, to be somebody and now you go screw it up."

Which was true. I didn't knock what he was saying.

He didn't even try to convince me to stay in school. You could tell that he had given up on me. Maybe because I'd lied to him about going to class. I couldn't blame him. I was mad enough at myself and I sure enough was embarrassed. I quietly went back to my room, packed my gear and took off for home.

It was really Doc Boydston, I guess, who kept it from getting worse. He phoned me when I got back to Atlanta. He tried to set me straight. He told me all the things I already knew—like how I was just hurting myself. My parents influenced me, too. So I called Doc back and told him if he really meant what he'd said I wanted to come back. I said that I'd do better, I was through with goofing off.

"Okay," he said, "the school is willing to give you another chance."

I hadn't flunked out, I was just ineligible to play ball. Southern Illinois was going by Missouri Valley Conference rules, which stated that an athlete had to have so many cumulative hours toward his degree. I didn't have enough at that point. My scholastic average was high enough for me to stay in school, but now I had to pay my own money. That's when things really changed around for me.

I saw how hard people worked for their dough. Here I had been going to school for free and getting spending money on top of that. I'd really had it great.

All that summer I worked at this cotton mill, pushing bales because I wanted to get stronger. I could have gone back to one of my old jobs, but they were easy work—no muscles. At the mill I wore weights on my legs all day and sometimes I'd put in 12 hours dragging those extra pounds around. Any hard work I could do that was available, I did it. After they found out I went to college, they wanted to get me an easy job, like walking around finding lost bales. I told them, "No, I don't want it," The foreman couldn't believe it, he really couldn't. He looked at me like I was crazy.

I went back for my third year at Southern Illinois and I think this is when I fell in love with defense. I had to practice it day in and day out, me and four other scrub-guys, never playing any offense at all for a whole year. We just played half-court defense against the varsity and I looked so good Hartman would get ticked off and take me out of the scrimmages. I always rallied the scrubs. Like every day we would come to practice and just demoralize the varsity. Hartman treated me hard. He didn't cut any corners for me, didn't do me any favors, and I didn't want him to. I never went below a 3.0 after that.

George McNeil and David Lee averaged 31 points a game between them that season and the varsity finished with a 22–7 record (McNeil got drafted by the Detroit Pistons, about the eighth round, but he didn't stick because they had Dave Bing coming in and a few more guys). SIU lost to Kentucky Wesleyan in the final of the NCAA small-college tournament after beating Wesleyan twice during the regular season. I didn't make any of the tourney games. I couldn't stand it to go over there and watch them play.

That 22–7 record, when you consider he had lost a second-team Little All-America forward (me), was a tribute to Coach Hartman's ability. He's a real master at getting the most out of his players. A lot of guys didn't have all that much talent, like Ralph Johsnon, but whatever talent was there Hartman could find and dig out. Ralph was a big, gawky, clumsy kid wearing glasses when Hartman first scouted him in a small-town game in Illinois. At one point, just running down the court, Johnson fell, broke his glasses and cut his head. He came back into the game a little later, ran into the stands chasing a ball and injured himself again! Most coaches would have walked out right then, but Hartman saw extra motivation or something, took him anyway and stuck by him. In one game at Southern, Ralph made a bunch of errors and the fans started to get on him, boo him. The coach stood up and shook his fist at the crowd.

His practices were well organized. He went carefully from one phase to the next phase, starting out with lay-ups, then a passing drill, then maybe he'd divide the squad up into offensive and defensive teams— very little wasted time. Even now with the Knicks, we don't practice like he had us practice. He knew when to slack off and when to pour it on. Some days you'd be saving yourself for the after-practice run and he'd tell you, "That's enough. Showers!" So the next day you might go all out and then he'd tell you to run. You could never figure him out. He'd tell us, "Never save, never hold back, always go full force. Don't anticipate me running you after practice." I loved his coaching, the way he ran the team, the way he taught the game.

We always played a lot of defense. The years I played, the offense was all right, but the defense was really strong. Hartman had strict rules. Never let a man drive base line, that's a sin. You can't get help that way, so always run your man into the middle and think team defense and always help out. You begin to take great pride in your defense. Hartman understated his basketball philosophy when he said, "We believe defense to be as important as offense." Defense was his religion!

He talked sometimes about his coach at Oklahoma A&M (now Oklahoma State), Hank Iba. Just like all the other ex-players from that school, he always called him *Mr.* Iba. There's a story about two Oklahoma State grads meeting and one tells the other, "Say, I named my son after Mr. Iba."

"Henry, eh?"

"No, we named him Mister."

Hartman is from Shidler, Oklahoma, right near the Oklahoma-Kansas line, and he actually played more football than basketball at Oklahoma State. He was an All-Missouri Valley quarterback (the school wasn't in the Big Eight then) and played pro football in Canada before he went into high school coaching and then moved to Coffeyville Junior College in Kansas, not far from Shidler. He was at Coffeyville seven years and had a 32–0 record his last season there.

Besides defense and the slow break, he must have

learned his ideas of discipline from Iba—too much from the old school, I think. You had to be very discreet around Hartman—he didn't want you to say certain things. He didn't want you to say anything really. He was strict about hair, like he didn't want us to wear sideburns or long hair or anything, black or white. He'd make all the guys trim down. We were scrimmaging some team in St. Louis and we had this 6 foot 8 Andy Kukic who liked to wear his hair long. We were losing bad, so Hartman called a time out and said, "Andy, either get a haircut or start singing!" Just out of the clear blue! As if Kukic's hair had something to do with our playing bad.

Hartman has asked me from time to time to talk to high-school stars for him and I have gladly, but I let them know he's strict. I can usually tell the kind of ball-player who can play for Hartman. He's going to be like me, a little shy. He'd have to be kind of a quiet, conservative guy, not real outgoing, not a real swinger. That's the only kind of kid who can play for Hartman because you've got to follow orders. I don't tell Hartman this, but I'm sure he can sense it, too. I'm sure he can tell right away if a guy will be able to make it for him, because *he's* not going to change.

"If you want to be a great all-around player, Hartman's the guy," I tell the recruits, "but it won't be easy. He's hard."

I recommended Chuck Benson of Atlanta to Hartman. He was a nice guy and I figured he could play under Hartman because, although he went to Washington High, he wasn't cocky. He was a Jim Thorpe in track; he could get 30 points in a meet because he did so many things well. I told the coach about him and the kid came up to visit, and I guess he really liked it. I left it up to him if he wanted to come. I told him how Hartman was, real strict, and he said okay. Later I saw in the Carbondale paper that he had signed a letter of intent.

It seemed like I was always getting in trouble with Hartman. If it wasn't grades, it was something else I was doing. I wasn't a thief or a thug or anything, but things happened. My marriage for instance.

I was maturing by now and getting more socially hip. One night I was with a girl I kind of liked. I'd been waiting all night for a slow record to come on so I could ask her to dance. One finally did. Well, the music started out slow and then five seconds later it was a fast number and I was stuck out there on the floor. I just had to improvise. She couldn't tell whether I knew what I was doing or not. I started dancing from then on.

I met my wife, Marsha, an SIU student, the year I sat out from competition. Hartman never liked his players to be married. I don't know if he thought he would lose control or what. He didn't know about my marriage until after it happened, then he called me into his office. It had gotten to the point where I couldn't face him without having problems. He didn't seem too upset and asked if there was anything he could do to help us along. I told him I thought I'd be all right. We were closer together after I got married because he was always telling me I didn't take care of my responsibilities, which was true, but after I got married, I did.

Two things I never wanted to do were going into the Army and getting married, but after I was in it— marriage, not the Army—I accepted it. We lived in a trailer on the edge of campus, close to all our classes. Mostly, we had fun. Marsha became pregnant during the basketball season and I was all excited, like I wanted a boy, but I doubted we'd have one because I traced my family history and all I could see were girls. Ed Zastrow was a pretty good friend of mine and in the late stages of Marsha's pregnancy I kept his car close in case I had to rush Marsha to the hospital. So, around five o'clock in the morning she said, "I think it's coming." I went out to the car and it was freezing cold. The car wouldn't start.

We were a little panicky, but I finally got the car going and rushed her to the hospital. She had a long labor period. I sat through most of it until she fell asleep and I went back to school. I told Hartman that Marsha was in the hospital. When I got back she was coming out of the delivery room. I knocked on the window and said, "What is it, what is it?" The nurse said, "It's a boy." I think that was my proudest moment.

We had already decided he was going to be Walt III. I had said, "We'll name him Walt. I can't think of a better name than that." She said okay. He had his mouth wide open when I first saw him, a big baby, eight pounds, nine ounces and no hair at all. I wanted him to be born in Chicago, not Carbondale, but Marsha, who was from Chicago, wouldn't go for it. I think people take pride in where they're born, like whoever heard of Carbondale? Even coming from Atlanta and going north, people look at me strange. He'll probably say he was born in Chicago anyway, since he's being raised there.

Later, Marsha and I would have problems, bad enough for us to separate. She's living now at her parents' home in Chicago, where Walt III is doing fine. When he was a baby he was real fat, but now he's slimming off and he's getting tall and he's kind of handsome. I won't pressure him into doing something he doesn't like. I'll just try to save as much money as I can for him so he can get an education or do whatever he wants.

When I go home to Atlanta first thing my family says is, "When are you bringing the Third home?"

I can't see marriage for me again anytime soon. I had never pictured myself being married, just like I had never pictured myself going to college. Once I was married, it was all right, but I don't think I'll try it again for awhile.

I like the way my life is now. I like to go when I get ready and come back when I get ready. So, until I'm through with basketball, I'm staying single.

Chapter Six

What the Hell Is a Saluki?

NOBODY WAS ever better prepared for a basketball season than I was in the fall of 1966.

The Southern Illinois Salukis were about to step out of the small-school category and shock everybody by fighting their way to the championship of the National Invitation Tournament in Madison Square Garden. Even red-hot basketball fans didn't know what a Saluki was or how fine a coach Jack Hartman was. They were going to find out soon.

I had spent the whole previous season playing defense with the scrubs. Then I had to stay in Carbondale and go to summer school, so I played every day in the gym with anyone who was around. More important, I got on a weight-lifting and isometrics kick. I was never satisfied with my jumping. A lot of guys have natural leaping ability, but I never did. Opponents could often jump over my back and take away rebounds.

I went to see a physical education professor, Robert Spackman, an authority on isometrics. He had written books and I knew some football players he had put on programs—Jim Hart of the St. Louis Cardinals, for one. He prescribed exercises for me. At first they were kind of rough, but I like training. I got to the point where I'd almost rather lift weights than play ball.

I had a whole little routine I'd do, just like the Mr. Americas at Muscle Beach. We had a waist-high table and I could step up on it with 25 to 50 pounds of weights in my hands. I really got that strong. Then I did isometrics, sitting down and pushing against this steel contraption that could be set at a 60-, 90- or 180-degree angle. It wouldn't budge and you had to strain against it for 16-seconds periods. There was a leaded jacket I'd wear, and ankle weights. I had a heavy golf club that I'd hold at the end and let go down to the floor and then pull up, to strengthen my forearms.

I didn't like going down to the training room where the football players worked out. They'd be picking up 300 pounds like it was nothing. I always waited until they cleared out, then I'd put a lot of weight—up to 300 pounds—on my shoulders and do toe raises.

I still do a lot of the same exercises in my hotel room in New York, trying to build my biceps, forearms and legs. To keep the people on the floor below from complaining, I bought these quiet, rubber-coated weights that don't clank. I set them down carefully. Sometimes an urge hits me to work out—it might be 12 o'clock at night. I don't talk to any of the other Knicks about it and I've never tried to persuade a guy to do it, because the urge has to be in you. I don't know anyone on the team who lifts; the coach and the trainer don't say anything about it. That's the thing about the pros, you're on your own.

I was spending about four hours over in the gym

every day that summer at SIU and I could see and feel the results. My body was shaping, losing fat. I was still the same weight but solid. When I went to play ball I could feel the difference. Very few guys could jump over my back and if they did I was strong enough to pull the ball out of their hands. After I played a game or two and saw all this progress, I made up my mind to stick to the weights.

People were telling Hartman about my weight training. They saw me there every day, all my spare time, like if I had a class at 11 o'clock or 10 o'clock, I'd be over there early and do isometrics for an hour. Hartman came in one day when I was working out.

"You're going to get too strong," he said.

"No," I said, "I know how to handle it."

The thing is, you don't bulk up your muscles, you stretch them. Like I'd hold a broomstick over my head and rotate my shoulders back and forth, side to side. Weight lifters who lift for bulk just lift, they don't stretch, and their muscles tighten up. These guys can lift 300 pounds, but they can't shoot a basketball ten feet.

When I started playing with the other varsity members that fall, Hartman saw the improvement. "Those weights really helped you," he told me and he said to others, "Frazier's strong as a damn bull!" He had always had his players on some kind of weight program, but now he set me up as an example. Usually the other guys just went in the training room and jived around. I told them, "Hey, you're wasting your time."

When I wasn't lifting weights or pushing against immovable objects that summer I was working at the Illinois State Fair in Du Quoin (a few miles north of

Carbondale) as a bouncer in a discotheque. One member of the SIU physical-education staff was the manager and another was the ticket taker, so we sort of had control. Coach Iubelt got me the job to earn a little extra money and it was fun. I didn't have to bounce anybody because there never were any fights or troublemakers when I was there. If there had been, the weight lifting would have come in handy. I fell in love with the horses at the fair—Clydesdales, naturally—and when I wasn't busy at the discotheque or the gymnasium I was enjoying the town of Carbondale. It's a small town, but there's always a crowd at the few gathering spots.

When practice started in the fall we were pretty optimistic. Our top three scorers, including George McNeil and David Lee, were gone, but we had a real good sophomore from Centralia, Illinois, Dickie Garrett, plus all those guys who had played frosh ball with me: Smith, Zastrow, Bechtold and Johnson, our 6 foot 7 center who seemed to be recovered from a bad ankle and a ruptured kidney. Hartman had turned down a job offer from Memphis State to stay at SIU.

Then the whole thing almost went down the drain. The day before official practice started I went to push off with my left foot and I overextended and sprained my left big toe. The shoe split when I pushed off and my toe went all the way over. I thought it was gone. I couldn't even feel it. I took off my shoe to see if the toe was still there. It actually felt like I had only four toes.

We didn't think it was that serious, but the next day I couldn't walk at all. A month later I still hadn't played, but I kept up my strength, lifting the weights and doing isometrics to stay ready. Hartman got to the point where he thought I was acting.

"Why should I be acting?" I said. "I've been working hard all summer to play ball."

I couldn't even bend down enough to shoot free throws. Things looked pretty grim until a guy came in to talk to Doc Spackman. He knew someone who had had a similar toe injury. This man devised a pad which fit snug under the arch of the foot and somehow relieved the pressure. He put this foam rubber thing in my shoe and said "Try that."

I went out and I could run! Was I happy! I played the rest of the season with that thing in my shoe. (Even now there is arthritis in my left big toe. I can't play without rubbing liniment on it.) My teammates used to call me Clubfoot. The shoe with the extra padding was a size 13 and the other one was a 12.

The first indication of what kind of season it was going to be came in the second game, at St. Louis U's Kiel Auditorium, after we had murdered State College of Iowa by 35 points. St. Louis had a 7-footer, Rich Niemann, and 6 foot 7 Eugene Moore, but we outrebounded them and beat them 69 to 59. I had 21 rebounds, which showed the truth in what Hartman had said before the season started: "We're awfully small for a college team, but, of course, it's not how tall you stand, it's how tall you play, and we have some pretty good jumpers." A statement after the game by their coach, Joe Brehmer, kind of made me sore.

"This was our worst game," he said. "If we play this way against a [Missouri] Valley team, we'll lose by 40 points, not 10."

It was just this kind of attitude that made it hard for

Hartman to find games against major, or so-called major, schools. If they beat us, it meant nothing, but if we beat them, they were embarrassed. What do you tell your alumni if you lose to some nobodies from Southern Illinois?

Then we traveled to another Missouri Valley stronghold, Louisville—Westley Unseld, Butch Beard and the whole gang. By this time I was used to the padded shoe and used to playing forward for Garrett on defense (Dickie had to play guard on defense because at forward he couldn't box out well enough and he'd get shoved around in the rebounding battles). Louisville beat us in a double overtime and I had 26 points, including three straight shots to tie the score with three seconds left in regulation time.

That got us some notice, but the real recognition came in the Sun Bowl Tournament against Texas Western, the defending national champions. Hartman and the Texas Western coach, Don Haskins, had both played under Hank Iba, a strong believer in a man-to-man defense. Hartman had a mind of his own, though, and to offset the quickness of the Miners' guards, Bobby Joe Hill and Willie Worsley, he put us into a 1-3-1 zone. In the NCAA finals the previous March, Hill had twice stolen the ball at mid-court from Kentucky. We beat them 59 to 54 and then were ranked number four at the time. The next night we lost to Southern Methodist by two points after I fouled out with 1:55 to go (thanks to a Southwest Conference official working the game). We didn't lose again the rest of the season.

The most thrilling game was the return match with Louisville, this time at our campus arena. We had followed their progress through the Quaker City Tour-

nament over the Christmas holidays and we hoped
nobody would knock them off because we wanted them
to come into Carbondale undefeated. Sure enough they
were unbeaten in 14 straight games and ranked number
two in the polls. The whole week leading up to the
game we never doubted we could beat them. We had a
sellout crowd and enough television announcers and
reporters to cover a Presidential Convention. We beat
them 53 to 50. I scored 16 points, 7 the last two
minutes.

There were other teams on our schedule, small-
college teams that were just as tough for us as Louisville, or almost. We had to play Kentucky Wesleyan
in the Panthers' field house in Owensboro. They not
only were undefeated but had beaten us out for the
NCAA college-division championship the season before. We couldn't help but notice the championship
patches they all wore on their sweat suits. A writer
from *Sports Illustrated* was there, planning to do a
story on whichever team won. The little gym was loaded with pro scouts, including Red Holzman from the
Knicks.

Here's where all that weight training and condition-
ing I had done came in handy. I'm not claiming that the
whole Saluki team was just Walt Frazier. Dickie Garrett
was shooting real good, we had that tough team defense
instilled in us by Hartman, and Clarence Smith usually
did an excellent defensive job. It was just that I always
felt I could take charge from the top of the key, where
I usually found myself, and make things happen when
it counted. I tied the Wesleyan game on a long jump
shot with a minute or so left, stole the ball at half-court
and went in for a lay-up and grabbed a key rebound.

(And Ralph Johnson, not nearly as clumsy as he had been in high school, did a great job on Wesleyan's Little All-America center, Sam Smith.)

In three consecutive games that SIU won by a total of five points, I scored the last seven versus Louisville, the last six against Southwest Missouri and four of the last five against Kentucky Wesleyan. I attribute it to the weights.

After that loss in El Paso to SMU, we zipped through 15 straight opponents—Kentucky Wesleyan twice, Evansville twice, Southwest Missouri twice, Wichita State, Indiana State, Abilene Christian. Zipped maybe isn't the right word because some of those games were real tight and we needed a lot of poise to pull them out.

I had been picked as a second-team Little All-America as a sophomore and that was a big thrill. I was proud because I could show something to the people back home. I knew that two Evansville players on the first team, Larry Humes and Jerry Sloan, deserved to be there, so I figured the other three guys ahead of me were just as good. I would have been glad to be honorable mention or anything. This season I was picked on both the Associated Press and United Press International first teams with Earl Monroe of Winston-Salem State—Earl the Pearl—and another fellow I was going to get to know later, Phil Jackson of North Dakota.

Near the end of the season we were still thinking about the NCAA small-college tournament. We wanted to host the regional in our arena, but the authorities told us no, that it was going to be at Southwest Missouri, which had a real tough team. Hartman wasn't too hot for playing down there again since we'd only beaten them by one point the last visit and we'd probably get the shaft this time. So we started thinking about the National Invitational Tournament (NIT) in New York.

That might have been a little uppity on our part, but we'd been upstarts and upsetters all season and we saw no need to change right then. We took a vote and everybody said, "Yeah, let's go to the NIT"—the catch being that we hadn't heard any official word from the selection committee and were putting ourselves way out on a limb. Doc Boydston got on the phone right away to the committee and told them we sure would like an invitation.

Well, Hartman called us together one day before practice and announced that we had been accepted by the NIT. There was very little hurrahing. He just said, "Let's go to work," and we went out to practice.

It must have been a big thrill for him, though, because he had played in the NIT years before as a freshman guard at Oklahoma A&M. The great Bob Kurland, supposedly the first of the big men in basketball, was a sophomore on that team, which lost to DePaul University in the semifinals. Hartman said DePaul had George Mikan as its center and Oklahoma A&M had to play the last few minutes with only four men because everybody else had been hurt or had fouled out. Hartman was one of the four.

One of our biggest treats was not having to fly to New York in one of the rickety school airplanes. No sir, we went big, a TWA flight out of St. Louis with the press riding along (the St. Louis papers had adopted us as their team). Usually we flew everywhere in the school-owned DC-3, Air Force surplus. People thought it was such a big deal, the team had its own plane, but that thing was so slow the birds would pass us up laughing. It took us about 12 hours to get to Texas one time. And the air pockets. This one time we hit an air pocket and we lost altitude like going down in an elevator. One guy was stuck up where you put your coat!

In New York we worked out at the High School of Printing on 49th Street near the Garden and the big thing in the newspapers was our nickname, the Salukis. Jerry Izenberg in the Newark *Star-Ledger* wrote a little verse:

Princeton has its Tiger; BC has its Eagle.

Rutgers is the Queensmen, a title truly regal,

But from frigid New York City to Kentucky's old Paduchee,

There's just one burning question—what the hell is a Saluki?

Everybody wanted to know the same thing and our publicity man, Fred Huff, must have explained it a thousand times. The rest of us, too. A Saluki is an Egyptian hunting dog, very fast, maybe the oldest pure breed in the world. There are pictures of them on ancient tombs in the desert—great, swift hounds that pharaohs used on the hunt. The area of Illinois that SIU is in is called Little Egypt, so that's how the whole theme got started. They tell you about it in a brochure when you're an entering freshman. It's unique, it's different.

The NIT had picked 14 pretty good teams; Syracuse, Providence, Rutgers, Villanova and St. Peter's from the East; New Mexico and Utah State from the West; Marshall and the Atlantic Coast Conference runner-up (which turned out to be Duke) from the South, and Nebraska, Tulsa, Memphis State, Marquette and Southern Illinois from the Midwest. Don Kennedy, the coach at St. Peter's in Jersey City, heard unofficially that his team, the Peacocks, were going to open with Tulsa and he almost spent the money to fly out and scout them. Just in time, I guess, he found out he was playing us. St. Peter's was leading the nation in scoring, like 94 points a game, but they had no height and after they got their NIT bid they must have let down a lot because they lost three straight games before the tournament started.

We were really nervous that first night. *Madison Square Garden*—this is all you hear when you're a kid. Everybody in the place, 15,357 fans, was going for the home team. So we were a little jittery but in the two and a half minutes before the half-time buzzer we had a 12 to 4 burst and went into the dressing room with a 41 to 29 lead. We came out after the intermission and ran them off the court. We won 103 to 58, 45-point margin and the most lopsided victory in the 30-year history of the NIT. Garrett had a fabulous shooting night, 13 of 18; I hit 7 of 12 and had 24 points.

The newspapers the next day raved about our defense. People in the East weren't used to that kind of defensive pressure. Winning that first night allowed us to stay in New York another week, so we did a little sight-seeing—very little, like we'd walk down one side of the street and back on the other. We were lost.

The second game was against Duke, which had finished second in the ACC Tournament. Hartman scouted them there and had us all scared with his reports on Bob Verga and their big center from Montana, Mike Lewis, and two big forwards. They had this size advantage and were really pounding us on the boards, but we worked hard and turned that around. Maybe Duke was tired from their league tournament, but for whatever reason they used a 3–2 defense against us. It was 37 to 37 at half time, but again we came on strong in the second half. Roger Bechtold did a good job hounding Verga and we just started boxing out, doing a better job of getting and holding position under the boards—Garrett, Clarence Smith and I had 32 rebounds among us. We went into a stall with 2:43 left and won 72 to 63.

I'm glad Duke was tired. Rested, they might have run us out of the place. They never gave up and stayed in the game until the end. I had 17 points, but skinny little Garrett's 11 rebounds was the most impressive statistic. Afterward the reporters were trying to get the secret of our success out of Hartman.

"It's just team balance and hard work," he said. "Those are simple terms and you'd like me to throw out something fancy and theoretical, but that's it."

Rutgers was almost our downfall. The Garden was packed with 18,499 people that night and by this time we were picked as the betting favorites. Everybody was talking about the Salukis and how beautifully we played together. Rutgers had a terrific shooter, Bob Lloyd, maybe the best free-throw shooter who ever played college basketball, and another good guard to go with him, Jim Valvano. Valvano actually hurt us more than Lloyd. He scored 20 points in the first half and helped them jump off to a 14 to 4 lead, then a 44 to 36 half-time lead. I got my third foul in the first half, so Hartman put us into a 2-3 zone.

We switched into a 3-2 zone in the second half (a

long way again from Hank Iba's teachings) and sliced
the lead to 46 to 44. The score was tied at 66 to 66
with 4:12 left when Johnson missed a lay-up and I
leaped up to tap it in and give us the lead for good.
(Although Johnson was awkward, we worked together
smoothly on the court. He knew when I would pass and
was always ready. Sometimes even Willis Reed isn't
ready for my passes, but Johnson was. He realized
most of his points were coming off me for easy lay-ups,
so he was looking for them.) That game I had 26
points and, more important, 18 rebounds. Garrett had
22 points.

It just seemed to be our team's personality that we'd
be behind at the half, keep our poise and come back to
win. We didn't go into a game meaning to do it that
way, but that's how it seemed to turn out. We met
Marquette in the NIT final, with 18,499 people there
and I don't know how many more watching on national television. I felt so confident I went out and bought
a $3.95 blue-mesh dress shirt the day of the game.

Both teams were cautious and deliberate in the first
half and I guess Marquette was better at that style
because they led us 34 to 23 at half time. Same old
story. In the dressing room Hartman told the team to
step up the defensive pressure and showed us a few
ways to do it. He said I should be getting the ball more
often. We came out and really demoralized them, just
demolished them, outscoring them 25 to 4 in one
stretch. Clarence Smith did a great job of keeping the
ball away from their center, George Thompson, down
low in the key. We won 71 to 56, Marquette's second-
worst beating of the season.

Well, it was pandemonium after the buzzer. We had

about a hundred fans in from Carbondale by that time and they picked me up on their shoulders and paraded me around. I can remember holding up my finger for number one and everybody shouting, "We're number one." It was my greatest thrill. I really had chill bumps.

I was voted the most valuable player (88 points, 52 rebounds, 19 assists in four games) and Hartman and I went on national TV with Frank Gifford. I knew my mother and father and all my people down in Atlanta were watching; it was the first time they had seen me play college ball. My mother said later I was the talk of the town. Some people booed when it was announced I was the MVP. They apparently thought Bobby Lloyd of Rutgers should have won it. Leonard Koppett of *The New York Times* wrote:

"Frazier ... earned the most valuable player award as much for his floor play, feeding and opportunism as for his scoring. He is a junior, although he sat out one year and will be eligible for pro offers this spring. From what the full quota of pro scouts saw of him this week, he'll get some good ones."

When the team got back to Carbondale, after a stop in St. Louis to switch to our old DC-3, there was a big crowd waiting for us at the little university airport and the people carried us around the ramp on their shoulders. There were signs, "Walt Frazier for Mayor" and "Walt Frazier for President," and a motorcade into town, led by fire trucks.

UCLA had a great team that year with Lew Alcindor and it won the NCAA championship. We had a good team, I think almost a great team. After that loss to SMU we won 19 straight games, but we lacked the real big man. That might have hurt us if we'd ever met

Lew, but then, we had great team defense. We would have come up with something to offset his height, probably a zone defense like everybody else was using except that we knew how to apply pressure at the right time. A game between us would have been interesting.

Anyway, I didn't have to explain very often anymore what a Saluki was. And I figured that that victory and MVP trophy were going to be worth thousands of dollars to me.

Chapter Seven

It's the Knicks

UNTIL THE NIT, I'd never really considered myself good enough for the pros. I knew I had one season left at Southern Illinois, but my class had been graduated so I was eligible for the draft.

A few guys from some of the pro teams started calling and Coach Hartman told me I'd be smart to get a lawyer. He recommended James Zimmer of Carbondale. By that time, Baltimore, Chicago and Seattle all had made contact. The Knicks called just once. My lawyer told everybody I hadn't decided whether to stay in school another year or to turn pro.

Actually we were stalling, waiting to see the draft results. If something good happened and the money was right, I'd go pro. If there was nothing exciting, I could always stay another season at Southern Illinois.

We figured I'd be Seattle's pick. I didn't like the idea too much. I don't go for rain and in Seattle, man, it's like they've got a leaky faucet above the whole state of Washington. Off and on, drizzles the whole day.

I was in class when the word on the draft came. Zimmer called me over to his office.

"It's the Knicks," he said.

"What do the Knicks want with me? They've got five guards already!" I yelled at him.

What a surprise! Bad, I mean, not good. I figured they were just going to use me for trade bait. Then I found out you can't trade a number one draft choice until a year later. I felt better. It's interesting to look back and see who went ahead of me in that draft: Detroit took Jimmy Walker of Providence; Baltimore took Earl Monroe of Winston-Salem State; Chicago took Clem Haskins of Western Kentucky; Detroit, which had two first-round picks because of an earlier trade, took Sonny Dove of St. John's. New York had fifth pick—me. Seattle had its turn next. They took Al Tucker of Oklahoma Baptist.

The Knicks' general manager, Eddie Donovan, said later that they would have taken me even if Walker or Earl the Pearl had still been up for grabs because the club was more impressed with my "overall game" and because I was "way ahead of the other two on defense." Flattery doesn't get a general manager anywhere at contract time, so maybe it's the truth.

Not everybody agreed with Eddie, that's for sure. A sports writer for a national magazine said this in a wire to his editors:

"From our observation, Frazier is not quite as good as Duke's Bob Verga and a light-year away from Providence's Jimmy Walker."

Hartman, despite the trouble I had caused him at times, wanted me to stay at Southern Illinois. Without exaggerating them, he talked to me about the advantages of another year in school. He never really pressured me. He just put the facts on the table. If I stayed at SIU, I would get my degree and probably have a good whack at making the Olympic team. If I had the kind of senior year Hartman thought I was capable of, I could command more money from the pros. Plus I had status in college ball.

On the other hand, I wasn't a single guy. I had to think of my family first. I could get injured or we might not win the NIT again or we might have a losing team.

It was the first time Zimmer had handled anything like this and he did a hell of a good job. Eddie Donovan flew out to talk to us. It was back and forth, nip and tuck, wait and see.

I got worried, thinking maybe they wouldn't want me if I held out too long. Then I told myself, "Forget it, I can still go back to school." I guess inside I knew I really wanted to go to the Knicks. New York, that's the town everybody wants to play in.

The Denver Rockets in the American Basketball Association had drafted me, too. They talked to my lawyer and made a fantastic offer, but they wouldn't put any dough in escrow. We asked around and discovered Denver had very little money. Out of all the pro teams, they had the least capital.

With the Knicks, I knew I'd be getting my paychecks on schedule. Madison Square Garden, which owns the Knicks, is on the stock exchange. It's sure. The Knicks knew what bad shape Denver was in, but maybe it got me an extra $5,000 or $10,000 to have the ABA sniffing around.

We finally got together on a figure and Zimmer told Hartman I was going to take the offer. We had kept him informed all along. Doc Boydston, the athletic director, wished me well. I told my mother I could always go to school in the summers and finish but I couldn't always come into so much money. She said okay, go ahead.

I was very excited when I went to New York to sign. They staged a big press conference. I had never had that much publicity before. I was being interviewed and taken around to radio and television stations. The coach, Dick McGuire, talked to me. Nothing concrete, just something to this effect: "We're glad to have you, but it's going to be tough to make the team." Donovan was telling me about guys who hadn't made it because they were out of shape or they hadn't worked on this or that aspect of the game. But nothing just then could deflate me.

I dropped out of school as soon as I'd signed. I was too excited to concentrate on studies. Marriage was becoming a pressure, too, and wondering about my chances of making the pros took all my thinking time. The Howard High counselor who put "doubtful" on my transcript was right, although he never guessed why I didn't finish. I plan to get that degree in physical education nevertheless. I've already gone back one summer to pick up credits.

(Even though I'm picking up phys ed credits, I don't think I'd like to be a coach. I found that out during my first pro play-offs. I wouldn't be able to take it. While I'm playing, I'm not nervous, but sitting on the bench I'm shaking and sweating. I'd have a breakdown, I'd want to be out there playing so bad.)

That summer before my first season I came up to New York to take care of some business. It just so happened that the basketball floor was down in the Garden. Howie Komives, Dick and Tom Van Arsdale and Bill Bradley were having a little workout. Bill had come back from his Rhodes scholar stay at Oxford in June and he had a nice, fat contract estimated in the papers at $500,000 for four years. Irving Mitchell Felt, chairman of the Knicks' board of directors, had said it was "one of the largest amounts ever paid to a professional athlete in a team sport."

I watched awhile. Bradley was a hell of a passer, like they said, and he could shoot. I thought he was really tough. I said to myself, "These guys are too good for me."

In August I was back in New York again for a series of appearances called "A Day with the Knicks." We'd travel around upstate going from one kids' camp to another, a different camp every day, putting on a sort of clinic. The kids enjoyed it and I did, too. The Knicks paid us a few hundred a week and you could get in shape early. Our group included Willis Reed, Mike Riordan, Neil Johnson and Howie Komives. I noticed that Willis was all they said he was.

Before and after working with the campers, the players would go one-on-one against each other. Komives knew he'd be up against me for a guard spot, so he really tried to chew me up. I never showed him any of my real stuff. Usually I let him beat me. I was simply finding out his best moves. Me, I just shot whenever I was open. It paid off.

I didn't beat many of the guys but mostly I was holding back against all of them—all of them except Riordan. I tried like hell to beat Mike. The way he'd beat me was by driving to the basket (he's a great driver). It didn't really bother me. I was satisfied. I was scoring all my points from outside, which I'd be doing anyway in real games. Mike and the others, when the one-on-one match got tight, they'd start driving. I figure it's not worth getting butted in the mouth, trying to stop a drive in practice.

Cazzie Russell and Bradley like to play one-on-one as practice during the season, but I feel it's only good for staying in shape in the off-season. I'll find a guy then who can really give me some competition, but during the season you can get hurt jiving around. You can really overdo it.

A lot of guys, especially guys from out of town like Emmette Bryant and Archie Clark, keep in shape over the summer and get a little relaxation playing at a playground at 155th Street and Eighth Avenue in Harlem. It's a big program founded by a guy named Holcombe Rucker—he died in 1965—and it has a pro division called the Rucker Pro Tournament. It's supposed to be sort of an "in" place for the basketball underground, a place where some unknown guy like Herman the Helicopter sometimes embarrasses a big-reputation NBA player.

I don't play in it. During the summer I like staying out late at night too much. The Ruckers play around three o'clock. I don't like to get up until maybe two or two-thirty and I don't feel like rushing to a game right then. Also, I don't like the outside court. There are no nets and they play with an ordinary playground ball. I guess I've gotten spoiled since my dirt-court days. Most of the guys are just standing around because, like me, they've been out all night and it's hard to run in the 90-degree heat. I played two games my rookie year and figured it was a waste of time.

They do have good competition there and I don't mean to knock the ballplayers. Some people say there are guys there who should be in the pros, but there's a difference between the playground and the real thing. Most of the players have had a shot at the pros. They give some excuse or another, so who knows?

When I wasn't in New York that first summer, especially in the three weeks between the upstate clinics and the opening of the Knicks' training camp, I worked out in Atlanta. I'd play a little one-on-one, run up and down stadium steps and maybe jog ten laps around the Howard High field.

My parents were upset that I was driving up to New York by myself, so my grandfather gave me this old pearl-handled .22 caliber pistol he had. All my life I had been afraid of guns. My parents never wanted me to touch them because when I was a kid a lot of dumbbells got killed fooling around with weapons. But now my family was afraid for my safety and armed me with this pistol.

On the drive north I didn't sleep in motels. I'd only sleep for two or three hours at a time in my car and start driving again. I kept my hand on the pistol when I was sleeping, just in case. I kept that gun a whole year.

One day the following summer I was home, visiting at an uncle's house with some friends. My uncle was showing off a .22 pistol. So I had to show off with him. "I've got one, too," I said and reached into my glove compartment. I pointed my pistol in the air and pulled the trigger. It went phfffft and smoke drifted out. That gun had been in my grandfather's attic so long the bullets had practically disintegrated. Nothing like that ever happened to the original Clyde.

On a Sunday the Knicks gathered at the Garden. We had physical exams and I met all the guys I had seen on television, like Dick Barnett. I had once tried to pattern my free-throw shooting after him (I was sort of lackadaisical on the line until I saw how he was so intent). Then we all went to McGuire Air Force Base in New Jersey. We slept at a motel about a mile away, two to a room. It was nice going by the guards in the morning, being saluted. We had good facilities, including steam baths, saunas, weights—everything we needed to get in shape. We spent four hours a day on the court, two hours each session, from ten to twelve in the morning and from five to seven in the evening. At night after those workouts we were so beat that all we wanted to do was sleep. On weekends we were allowed to go into New York City.

During the morning it was more of an orientation drill, wind sprints and brushing up on defense, passing and dribbling. In the evening sessions we scrimmaged and it was tiring. Still, it was easier than in college. We did a lot more running at Southern Illinois than we do in the pros, and the drills were more demanding.

There were no initiations like I've heard there are in pro football and I was glad about that. A guy has enough to worry about without any clowning around. It's a dog-eat-dog situation during training camp. I was a rookie trying to take away somebody's job and the veterans were trying to protect themselves. That was to be expected. It's still that way until the season starts. Then you're supposed to do anything you can to help each other. Komives was a guy who stayed overly aggressive, but he's the only one, I think. Even now, since he's been traded, whenever we play Detroit he gets a little rough.

I've always been a loner, so I didn't run around with

anybody except my roommate, Phil Jackson. I had played against him and his team, North Dakota, over at Evansville. I kidded him about how I had beaten him to death. We had a beautiful relationship and we're still tight.

There were lots of guards, Komives and Barnett (the starters), Freddy Crawford, Emmette Bryant, Riordan (who didn't make it that year) and me, plus Bradley who was due to get out of the Air Force soon. That's pretty stiff competition. Willis had even told me during the clinics that he was surprised that I had signed.

There were times at camp I was depressed because I didn't think I was playing up to my ability—I *knew* I wasn't. I was nervous, too. I knew I could be playing better, but somehow I couldn't shake loose. I was handling the fast break all right but I wasn't shooting at all, so naturally I wasn't scoring. And if I did get a setup I couldn't make an accurate shot.

Our first exhibition game was against Chicago at McGuire AFB. I was so shaky I was missing lay-ups. I played fair defense and I passed the ball okay but as far as shooting went, nothing! It got so bad I made up my mind I'd be strictly a defensive player, that I'd just pass the ball off and not think about scoring. You can figure for yourself what that did to team effectiveness.

On September 26 we were playing Chicago in the third exhibition game on Long Island. I was at the free-throw line, we were one point behind, two seconds to play and I had three chances to make two. I missed all three—the inglorious "hat trick." The last shot bounced off. I went for it in a scramble with McCoy McLemore of Chicago and my right ankle got twisted between his legs. I mean twisted. It was so painful it just had to be broken. I could see myself being out the whole year. Not many guys can claim three missed free throws and a broken ankle in two seconds of elapsed time. If my pearl-handled pistol had been handy I'd have shot myself—phffffft.

"What's wrong?" the trainer asked me as I hobbled around.

"It's broken," I said.

I went into the locker room and he put ice on it. That's all he could do. I was to see a doctor the next day. By this time I had moved into the Paramount Hotel near the old Garden. Nate Bowman lived there, too. He helped me put some more ice on my ankle. I tossed and turned most of the night. Finally I got to sleep. When I woke up the next morning, I had forgotten all about the ankle and I got out of bed like always. I had to go to the bathroom so I casually jumped out of bed. I like to have died!

I borrowed a walking stick and went to the doctor who told me I hadn't broken a bone after all but had severely strained ligaments. He told me it wouldn't help to stay off it and it wouldn't hurt to stay on it.

I was out a whole month, even put on the inactive list, a fine way to start my professional career. I don't think I would have started anyway but I would have been playing because the Knicks were going bad. I was a good ball handler and they were losing by throwing the ball away. Near the end of games they just blew. Teams would start pressuring and the Knicks would fall apart. Like against St. Louis, they almost threw away a 20-point lead in five minutes.

I was getting impatient and so were the Knicks. The ankle didn't seem to be getting any better even though I was getting whirlpool treatments and everything else anybody could think of. They wanted me to try it out and I would tell them I didn't think it was ready. I finally started working out slowly.

I sat mostly on the sidelines and watched and, even though I knew my ball handling would be valuable, every game drained a little confidence out of me. By the time I was ready to play again my offense was completely gone.

My first official pro start was on October 28, 1967. It was at home in the Garden against Detroit and I started out great with some beautiful passes. The nervousness wore off a little, but my shooting still wasn't there; my timing was terrible. I was actually afraid to shoot and I kept hoping nobody would give me the ball. It was hopeless. We needed points, so McGuire took me out. It wasn't until after the January All-Star game that I began to feel right.

Another rookie made his debut in 1967. It was quite a bit bigger than mine, especially in publicity. "Dollar Bill" Bradley was back from the service in December. A lot of people considered him the greatest college player of all time while he was at Princeton and, of course, he was smart enough to win a Rhodes scholarship to boot, a real Frank Merriwell in the flesh. He played 20 minutes in his first game, a three-point loss to Detroit, and scored eight points, had two assists, five rebounds and committed three fouls. Not bad, considering all the ink he was getting and the fans who expected maybe a magician.

There were 17,524 fans who came to see Dollar Bill play against St. Louis on December 12. He played a hell of a game, scored 23 points and looked real good;

but there was one catch. He made a key mistake that blew the game. There were about 12 seconds left, we had a two-point lead and possession of the ball. Naturally, with no necessity to shoot, we should have fiddled around for the 12 seconds. Instead, Bill tried to drive in for a basket, the shot got blocked, the Hawks drove down court, made a basket with a second to go to tie the game and won in double overtime.

Bill felt terrible, yet nobody really blamed him. The guys accepted it because he was a rookie and had all that pressure on him.

He was great in that St. Louis game, but then the guards on other teams started to use him because he was slow for backcourt. It started to work on his mind when he'd come in the game. Opponents would clear out one side and his man would go one-on-one on him. The same thing had happened to Cazzie the year before when the Knicks were playing him at guard. If you're getting embarrassed in front of 19,000 people, what can you think? You can't think offense. You're just thinking what a fool you must look like. Later, the Knick management realized Bill was out of position and put him at forward where he was more comfortable. There he was going up against bigger men but maybe he had a little quickness on them.

There's no doubt that a lot of pressure was taken off me because of Bradley. It probably helped me get acclimated easier without too much being expected of me. Plus I like Bill, all the guys do. I can understand that the guy came along at the right time from the right school, so he got a lot of money. He's not the kind of guy you could hate for it. He's not a braggart, he's just a nice guy and money doesn't seem to mean anything to him. He just wanted to play ball and become part of the team, and he did.

One columnist in New York wrote, "Walt Frazier . . . wanted Bill so badly his nostrils were quivering and his hands were moving so they left their mark on Bradley's skin every time Bill made a feint or pass or cut or took a shot."

Not true. I wasn't jealous of Bill. How could I be? I was from Southern Illinois, some small school out in the boondocks, and I had gotten a break and been the number one draft choice of the Knicks. In a way I admired Bill for what he had. When I guarded him after he joined the team, I never had any malice or anything like that. I was anxious to play my best against a player with his reputation. It wasn't like the sports writer implied, that I was all psyched up to guard the guy.

Anyway, despite the publicity and the crowds, we kept losing. The defeatist attitude of the club was depressing. It rubbed off on all of us. I thought, "If they don't want to win, what can I do? I'm just a rookie. I can't change them." It's very easy to lose your confidence when you aren't playing. You start to downgrade yourself and it's difficult to stay mentally ready. For awhile, when we were losing under McGuire, I never wanted to play. I would sit on the bench and think, "I hope he doesn't call on me. I don't want to go in."

It was just that bad.

Chapter Eight

Red

THE BIG turnaround for the Knicks—and for me—came just after Christmas, 1967. The brass replaced Dick McGuire with Red Holzman. It happened after a game in the Garden.

We had just lost—we were *always* losing to somebody—and were struggling along with Baltimore at the bottom of the eastern division. We were all getting dressed when Eddie Donovan came in and said, "Players, don't leave. We're going to have a meeting." Then Ned Irish, president of the Knicks, came in.

"Coach McGuire," he told us, "is being replaced by Holzman." He added that Dick was moving into Red's job as scout.

Holzman and McGuire were both there and it seemed clear to me that McGuire was really hurt. You don't often see a pro coach with tears in his eyes. I hope you can understand when I say I was glad for Dick. I always thought he was too nice a guy. He let the ballplayers run over him.

The first day with Red was amusing. As a scout, he'd jived around with the players, but now we didn't know what to expect. He'd called a meeting in the Garden at ten o'clock. Everybody was there except

83

Bradley, Dick Van Arsdale and Howie Komives and Van Arsdale came in laughing. Red looked at them, looked at the clock and said:

"You're fined ten dollars each."

The guys looked at each other. You could just about read their lips as they said to themselves, "Hey, what's he think he's doing?"

Bradley came in five minutes later than Dick and Howie.

"You're fined fifteen dollars," Red said.

From then on the guys knew he meant business. I think he gained instant respect. I know he got mine.

Whenever McGuire had fined anybody, he hadn't made it stick. The guy would come up with some jive excuse and Dick would let him go. Not Red. He fined the first eight players $100 apiece not long after he took over. It was kept quiet but he hit us for that much and he took it out of our next checks.

"You guys that are playing are fined a hundred dollars for not hustling," Red said, short and simple.

Some guy piped up, "Hey, I haven't been playing but about ten minutes!"

"It doesn't matter. You're part of the team."

Little things like that I liked. Even when the team was going bad, Red still had control. McGuire would take a guy out and he'd come over to the bench and start talking back. "Why'd you take me out?" Anybody yakked at Red, he told them he was the captain of the ship until it went down. To tell you the truth, I don't think he really wanted the job.

When the team started going right, he gave us the $100 cash back. We were never too sure he'd do it another time.

Anyway, at that first meeting we talked about things we were doing wrong, things that we were going to do and things we weren't. No more guys going for themselves, no one worrying about his scoring average paying more. More points, we'd figured, meant better paychecks. It hadn't generated team happiness, that's for sure. This may sound childish of a group of professionals, but in a lot of ways pros are as bad as highschool players. Maybe worse, because bigger egos and bigger stakes are involved.

Red insisted he was not going to tolerate a man shooting a jumper from 40 feet out when a teammate was open under the basket. And none of this being taken out of the game and storming down to the end of the bench to sulk.

Red came in as though he was really going to work the hell out of us. Like he said, "Don't plan anything social because we might practice any day." We were going to start reviewing game films, which some of the guys didn't dig. Under McGuire we'd never practiced weekends and Red was talking about doing that, too. He came in with a full-court, man-to-man press. I mean from the time the opponents threw the ball inbounds he wanted you down there on them, harassing them all the way up court, like Indians attacking a wagon train. We had been used to picking them up at the half-court line. Switching to the new way was really tiring.

The guys were teed off. They didn't really want to work. Neither did I.

But as time went on, we started to win games. We were reviewing more movies than *The New York Times* film critics and we could see what we were doing wrong. We became more of a team, a defensive team. Instead of one or two guys doing all the gunning, everyone was looking out for the other, hitting the open man. Red was pulling us together.

Red was *coaching;* this is why the Knicks came on. It might sound silly, but a lot of coaches don't coach. They take for granted that because a guy is a pro he knows what he's doing. Trouble is, sometimes he doesn't. Coaching makes a big difference in the NBA.

Red would always tell you what you were doing right and what you were doing wrong. In practice, he didn't just toss the ball out and have us run up and down the court. He'd go over things. Like you'd have a ball over here with the defensive man over there, so what should you do? It was similar to what Hartman did at Southern Illinois. Guys get to know their positions—if the ball is here, then you should adjust over there.

We had so many inbounds plays that Red threw some of them out. He would discuss things with the players. He would ask Dick Barnett, "What do you think of this play?" Or, "Willis, what do you think we should do in this situation?"

I remember once, just after he took over, he pulled me aside on the bus from Philly for a little man-to-man discussion.

"You're a much better ballplayer than you're showing. You can really be great, you've just got to get your confidence. I want you to lose a little weight, about five pounds, and start thinking basketball. I saw you at SIU. You were a hell of a player."

Red was emphasizing defense, which was right down my line, so I said to myself, "Maybe this is my chance." I started to have good games. My jumper came back and I'd score 10 or 12 points. It seemed, bang, just like that I was penetrating, I was hitting, I was running—just overnight. I can't explain it fully. I wasn't practicing differently, I wasn't spending any more time after practice, but it just seemed to snap in place. It was the guys having confidence that made me produce.

Before I didn't have their confidence. Now, when the games got tight, they were looking for me, looking to give me the ball so I could set up the offense and get something happening.

At certain times Red would say, "Get in, Walt, I want you to play good defense on this guy and get the team running. Don't worry about scoring." To another guy he'd say, "Just get in and play defense," or "Pass the ball," or, "We need some points."

Komives would always start. "You're playing great ball," Red told me, "but I don't want to start you."

He didn't want to because he thought it would be pressure on me. Since I was playing well, why change anything? Besides, if I started I had a tendency to get in foul trouble early. The whole team had a more idealistic attitude once we were winning. It didn't make any difference if a guy played 20 minutes or 30 minutes, scored 20 points or 10 points, as long as we won the game.

All in all, Red is some coach. He had played for the famous Nat Holman at City College of New York—he was in the NIT twice—and then spent ten years in the pros with the Rochester Royals (now Cincinnati) and Milwaukee Hawks (now Atlanta after a stop in St. Louis). He also coached the Hawks for three years before returning to New York, where he was one of the NBA's best scouts, if not *the* best. Many present Knicks were drafted on his recommendations.

Red doesn't have red hair now. I guess when he did, he got the nickname. He dresses okay for a coach, not sloppy, you know, with baggy pants and ties and shirts cousins give you for birthdays. Red looks pretty sharp even if he is a conservative dresser. A cigar is his favorite accessory.

We get along good, Red and I, for the most part. Whenever he tells a joke, he usually tells it on me or makes me the goat. He might be ready to give the team a lecture on something and he'll say, "All right, Frazier, sit down. Most of this is about you anyway." I used to be his "key man." Every time we'd leave a hotel he'd sneak all the room keys in my pocket. I'd come home and have maybe eight keys weighing me down. Like he'd get all the reporters' keys, too, and dump them in my coat. I'd have them falling out of every pocket. I guess he's superstitious in that way: he always takes his hotel key with him. I used to have to mail them all back.

At the All-Star game in Philadelphia last season he introduced the eastern division players at a banquet and when he got to me he said, "Walt Frazier, he's my man. How ya doin', Clyde?"

Red has a dry sense of humor. He has all these corny little sayings that made up a philosophy of life, like, "Never get your hair cut by a bald barber."

For a long while Red could never catch me for being late, but he always told me, "I'm going to get you, Clyde."

"Never," I'd say. "You'll never get me, Red."

So one time in Vancouver I was on the bus early. That's one of my hangups, always on time. In this business, everybody seems to be straggling in late. So I'm sitting on the bus and when everybody was on, Red said, "Let's go."

"Wait a minute," I said.

"What's wrong?" he asked.

"I forgot something."

"Well, if you go back, it's going to cost you ten dollars for being late."

"That's all right," I said. "I'm saving ninety dollars. I left my hundred-dollar alligator shoes up there."

I'd just bought those 'gators in Seattle, not to mention the suit I'd left behind. That's the first fine I ever got and everybody laughed, especially Red. He had been waiting a long time.

Last season we had arrived at Chicago Stadium and were walking in the door when I looked at my hand and saw my ring wasn't there. It's white-gold, with a cluster of diamonds. It had cost me exactly one grand. I asked Willis to take my bag. Luckily Dave Stallworth was just pulling up to the arena in a taxi, so I jumped in his cab. The driver was a basketball fan. He didn't mind taking me back downtown. He even waited for me while I dashed into the hotel lobby, up the elevator and into my room. I had left the ring under some papers on the dresser. I only lost maybe 15 minutes, but I would have been in real trouble if we had been out by the airport where we normally stay.

"You idiot," Red said when I came in the dressing room, but he was smiling.

I had plenty of time to get dressed.

Of course, Red and I have had differences. I get

annoyed with him hollering out on the practice floor. Like one time he was on me for a defensive goof.

"What the hell is this, Red?" I said. "Other guys, you never say anything to them. Can't I make any mistakes?"

"No," Red answered. It was that simple.

He can get on your nerves, harping on one point. Like another guy lets somebody go backdoor and nothing is said, but if I do it, he says, "What are you doin', Clyde?" Once I really flared back and he just talked me down quiet.

My roommate that first year was Phil Jackson. We call him Head and Shoulders. He looks like he puts on his coats with the hangers still in them. He's also known as the Absentminded Professor. There was an article in the Knick program about us, calling us "The Odd Couple." He's white, I'm black. He's a forward, I'm a guard. He's from the North, I'm from the South. He's from Deer Lodge, Montana. That must be totally unlike anything I knew in Atlanta.

Phil was picked by New York the same year I was drafted. He loves to tell about how much I sleep and watch television. Actually, I only became a big sleeper when I got to the pros. Maybe that's because there's so much idle time. I really don't want to sleep all that much but sometimes I get into bed and find it hard to get up. For awhile it was affecting my play. It took me too long to warm up at the beginning of a game. I experimented and found out that whenever I went out at night and didn't sleep as much, I played better.

I still sleep more than most people. Red can always find me—in the sack. Whenever the Knicks need somebody, they always know where I am. Phil insists I turn on the television, then fall asleep and snore while he's up all hours hooked on the show.

Phil and I play a lot of pool for fun, not money. Eight ball. He's better than I am, really a good pool player. He kills me. And he's a preacher's son. Pool, cards, he plays everything. Where did he ever learn that in Deer Lodge, Montana? He was a philosophy major in college. He's always reading. Once we were in Seattle and he was wearing a Ben Hogan cap. We went into a restaurant and he put it on the rack. We ate and left. The next day we went back to this restaurant and he noticed it on the rack.

"Say, that looks like my cap," he said.

A whole day and he'd never missed his lid.

Phil would always go out after every game and maybe at one or two in the morning he'd bust in, slam the doors, turn on all the lights, read for a while, then go to sleep. After all that commotion, I'd be wide awake.

So one time in Chicago, I left the closet door ajar. It just happened that it was right next to the room door. True to form, here comes Phil at two o'clock in the morning. He throws open the door and it hits the closet door and comes right back and knocks him back into the hall. I really cracked up. From then on he was a little easier about throwing doors open.

Meanwhile, with Red insisting on a full-court press, we lost two in a row, three in a row and the guys were kind of down. Then all of a sudden we started winning five or six in a row and we were just *killing* teams. Philly, for instance, was really bothered by the press and made turnovers by the dozen. We were picking them up and practically getting inside their jerseys. The weaker teams that used to give us trouble, like Seattle, we were murdering just because we were playing good defense. We forced them into key turnovers, getting easy baskets off hustling and running. It made a difference. After a while the guys thought it was nothing, a picnic, to pick up opponents full-court—we call it five for a half-court press, ten for a full-court press. We were tenning teams right off the floor.

I was playing my same role, coming in off the bench, but maybe in the first period rather than the second or third. I'd known even when Red took over that I wouldn't put in much real floor time until the second half, so I had been psyching myself up, making myself believe that I would work my show when the time came. I'd think, "I'm really going to turn it on. It's my time to show what I can do."

I guess I showed it best in the last game the Knicks played in the old Madison Square Garden on 50th Street (that was actually the *third* Garden the city's had; the one we're in now is number four). It was against Philly and I had a pretty fantastic night—23 points, 15 assists, 15 rebounds. I just seemed to get in the swing of things and couldn't do anything wrong. I was driving Wilt Chamberlain and getting the ball past him somehow. I was making nice passes, I was stealing the ball, I was all over the place, which is the way I like to play. I set my goal at figures like that every game.

I really liked the old Garden better than the new one. It had more atmosphere, more of the flavor of the New York fan. Like the people seemed to be in the game. You could hear them calling, "Bum, you stink!"

They would throw stuff at you, too, through the stale cigar smoke. It was fun.

I'll admit that the new floor is quite an improvement. The old floor must have been a relic from the first Garden, made out of planks that were part of the Mayflower's deck. There aren't any more floors around like that. If the old Garden doesn't go down in the Hall of Fame, the floor should.

We came in third in the eastern division that year. Philly was first and Boston second, so in the play-offs we had to play the 76ers while Boston played the fourth-place team, Detroit. The fans in Philly are pretty rough. They have this one loudmouthed group that sits diagonally across from our bench and yells through the whole game.

I remember one close game in the Palestra, which is a dump, with the crowd too close to the court. We had the lead and one of the refs made a call that the fans protested. Some guy took off across the floor after the official. The ref tried to have him thrown out of the game, but I guess he was a season-ticket holder, so they put him in a seat over by Philly's bench. Then a second guy runs out on the court and starts kicking the ref in the leg and the ref looks around and doesn't see anybody because the guy is a midget! They had to drag the midget off the floor, but I don't think he got tossed out, either.

Wilt the Stilt was no midget, though, and neither were his teammates. They beat us in Philly the first game, we beat them in the Garden to even it up and then we really blew a game at Philly, a game we should have won but lost in double overtime, 138 to 132.

The fourth game, at the new Garden, was on March

30, the day after my birthday, and up to this time I had believed in horoscopes. Somebody gave me a book and under my sign it said something like, "This is your day." I got all psyched up. Like I was going to score 40 points and the Knicks were going to win the play-offs. I got all dressed up in a new striped suit with a white tie and black and white shoes. Real Clyde.

So in the game I was dribbling up court and I slipped on some sweat. I didn't fall down, just slid. I heard something pop. I actually thought somebody had hit me on the leg. It wasn't painful, but I called time out, started to walk toward our bench and almost fell down. At first I thought it was the Achilles tendon in my right foot, but we went into the locker room and it turned out to be a small tendon near the Achilles. I couldn't stand up on my toes on that foot. I couldn't play in the next two games and we lost both, each by 16 points.

That's not all. After the game I stayed around talking to reporters. Finally I went back to my hotel room at the Paramount. Somebody had broken in, walked off with watches and rings, a tape recorder, a radio and some cuff links. I was lucky they didn't steal any of my suits. I guess they didn't appreciate my taste.

I opened a window, took the astrology book and threw it out. Some lucky day.

Chapter Nine

Two Lucky Shots

FOR YEARS the Knicks had been a soft touch, a cinch fourth in a four-team division. If anybody wanted to point out a sorry team in professional athletics, he couldn't go wrong picking the basketball franchise in New York City. In the 11-year span from 1956 through 1966, the Knicks made the NBA play-offs just once (1959)—and then promptly lost two straight games to Syracuse and were eliminated. Three of those years the Knicks had the worst record in the league, two other years they had the second-worst record.

In the fall of 1968, though, all that embarrassment was forgotten. The Knicks, under Holzman, had moved from last in the eastern division to third. Long-suffering New York fans, the Garden brass and the players themselves shared an optimism about the new season. Willis Reed, a natural center, was getting more and more familiar with the forward position; Bradley, Phil Jackson and I all had a year of experience behind us and the Boston Celtics were getting old.

Team optimism lasted as long as the first days at training camp. It was like the beginning of my rookie season all over. We were like a bunch of strangers. Don't ask me why. Nothing Red tried seemed to work.

The guys just weren't ready to do the same things that had worked well for us. I was throwing bad passes and getting off bad shots because I was anticipating guys would roll this way or that (or they weren't rolling at all). It was like Red had just gathered 15 guys or so from the YMCA and from scratch was molding them into a team.

Even so I started out the regular season with confidence. My shot was beginning to go in. The year before if I missed a couple, I was finished. Now I was second in shooting percentage, behind Chamberlain, for the first 20 games. I was proud of that. I wasn't starting, but when I played I really came on. I was averaging about 12 points playing part time, and I was getting assists and rebounding. Mostly, the newspapermen wrote about how bad the team was going. Our record was 6–13.

Finally, about the middle of December, the team jelled. We were winning more games than we lost. One day, in Detroit, Phil Jackson called me on the phone. "Have you heard any trade talk?"

"No," I told him.

"Well, my brother called me and said that he had heard on the radio that Komives and Bellamy went for DeBusschere."

"Aw, you're jiving, man!" I said.

"I think it's for real. Turn on the news tonight at six."

So I had the news on and sure enough, Dave De-Busschere, all-time Detroit player and coach, had been traded to New York for Bellamy and Komives!

I couldn't see it. Bellamy had started really playing, running good, scoring 30 points and stuff, and

Komives, who had always been booed by the people, was getting sympathetic articles in the papers and starting to win back the crowd. He was even getting cheered sometimes. Then, too, we had plenty of forwards—Cazzie and Bradley and Willis. Getting the ball into our big men, Bellamy and Reed, that was our whole game. I couldn't see us overpowering teams like we had before. I had thought we were going to make a move up in the standings, but I figured this would really mess up the team.

The brass didn't say much, just that the trade was made for the betterment of the team. The feeling among the guys when I got together with them was wait wait and see. They were glad to have Dave. He was a good guy and a good player (personally, I didn't think he was having too hot a year; he was a good shooter but slow, bothered by an injured ankle). We played the first game after the trade in Detroit, as it happened, and Dave looked real sharp. You expect that. After somebody's been traded, he always plays harder against his old team.

Then, to demonstrate how lousy I am at evaluating trades, we really caught fire. We won 11 in a row. Dave was really producing. He added quickness to the team (despite the ankle), had his good outside jump shot, played tough defense and rebounded about as well as Bellamy, plus he *played* every game, whereas Bells didn't. I think more important than any of these things, though, was his influence on Bradley. It seemed to me that Dollar Bill matured a lot under Dave, who had been head coach of the Pistons when he was only 24. Before, Bill roomed with Komives or Dick Van Arsdale and they would always gibe him, like Komives would call him "Mr. President" and kid him about not taking a drink. I don't think he could really relax. But Dave he could sort of relate to. They had fun, like he started drinking a few beers after the game, going out with the guys, relaxing.

Cazzie broke his ankle not long after and was out the rest of the season. That's when Bradley really came into his own. Again, due to Dave. During practices you could see them working together, learning each other's moves. They would call me in to run certain plays with them that they thought would work against certain opponents.

One guy, for sure, had no second thoughts about Bellamy leaving. The trade means Willis was back in his favorite position, center, where he had been runner-up for NBA rookie of the year four seasons before. He was a lot more relaxed playing in the middle. At forward he was out of position because he was too slow; he had the same problems that Bradley and Cazzie went through trying to play guard. He was getting embarrassed out there. Guys would get the ball and before you knew it they would be around him. He stayed in foul trouble all the time. He was tickled to be back at center and he started scoring 30 points, 40 points with no trouble at all.

Willis and I have a running gag where we deliver phony Western Union messages to each other. He started it before one game when I was going to have to guard Oscar Robertson. The phone rang at eight o'clock one morning and there was a message for me.

"From who?" I said, still three-quarters asleep.

"It's from somebody named Oscar. He says he's going to score fifty points off you tonight."

So right after we traded Bellamy to Detroit and we were playing the Pistons, I went to Reed's room about six o'clock in the afternoon. He was taking a nap. I knocked on the door and this sleepy voice called out, "Who is it?"

"Western Union," I said. "I got a message for you from a Mr. Walter Bellamy. He says he's going to cram you through the basket tonight."

In the game, the same one Dave did so well in, it started out tough. Bellamy was really going after him, but Willis cooled him off. He's cooled a lot of people off since.

So DeBusschere was happy, Bradley was happy and Reed was happy. Was Clyde happy? Not at first. With Komives gone I knew I was a starter and I didn't know how it would work out, how it was going to affect my play. I had been happy playing 30 minutes a game. But then I said to myself, "What the hell, it's what I wanted, to play full time." I knew that, even if I made some mistakes.

Well, my assist and scoring figures doubled and instead of running the team for maybe half a game, I was running things for the whole game and doing a better job of it. I gained confidence; I liked starting. It got so I didn't want to come out of the games more than 30 seconds or a minute at a time. I'd always tell Red I was okay and didn't need a rest.

I didn't build up my hopes too much for making the All-Star game. I thought I was playing well, but the team hadn't been on the winning side for so long and I wasn't in the spotlight that much. I was right. I didn't make it. Some guys said I should have been on the East team, but those are the breaks of the game.

One thing I'll admit I don't like is that they sort of go with seniority in the NBA, like once you're there it's easy for you to make the All-Star team a second time and a third. It's true in baseball, too, and I guess in most sports. Willie Mays will always get a lot of center field votes and it's the same in basketball with Oscar or Elgin Baylor. Every year guys just vote for them.

One real highlight of the season was the scumball award. I think Mike Riordan, back from the Eastern League, started the whole thing. Somebody designated him as the scum coach, sort of the captain of the scumbags, or substitutes, who scrimmaged against the first team all the time. The scumball award was a gag. It went to the guy who made the worst shot of the game, most of the time an "airball," where he shot at the basket and hit nothing. Only after winning a game did we do this. If we lose a game, it's no joking matter.

We'd come into the locker room and Mike would say, "Let's have it quiet. Tonight we're proud to present the game ball to so-and-so because of a great shot, a ball that not only didn't hit the rim but didn't hit the net or the backboard, either!"

If it was a rookie, he had to stand up on a table and get his scumball. I think I got it only once. Surprisingly, the scumball winners, rookies or veterans, usually accepted it. Well, they never just accepted it *outright*. Some of them tried to get out of it. Bowman was always claiming he was fouled. He was hit on the arm, he always said. But Riodan had the say-so, he was the judge.

Mike the scum coach is a typical New Yorker in that he reads ten papers a day—you never see the guy without a paper in his hand—and he's always eating hot dogs, corned beef or roast beef sandwiches. And if a place has tables and chairs in it, Mike doesn't go in. He likes to stand up because he's used to those New York joints where you rush in, get your hot dog and rush out. We call him "Coney Island." We joke Mike all the time, but he was the absolute scumball authority.

Maybe the worst thing that happened that season, longer-lasting than Cazzie's ankle injury, was Phil Jackson's bad back. We were the Odd Couple, right? Well, we were in San Diego and I came down with some sort of virus and Phil was complaining about his back. A few nights earlier he was going in for a lay-up and got pushed from behind. Maybe it was a week or so before he really started feeling it. He had been trying to play, but he was playing badly—he wasn't really mobile. I guess in San Diego it got to the point where he couldn't take it any longer.

I was having chills. I went in to take a hot bath, which I often do before games because it helps me relax, and all of a sudden chill bumps popped out all over me. I thought at first it was from the water being too hot, but it wasn't. And I was helping Phil because his back was aching—the blind leading the blind. I dressed for the game that night. I didn't feel like it, but I thought maybe I'd feel better later. I just got dizzy and was having chills.

I thought I was going to die! We were at the game and Phil was moaning and I was lying on a bench half dead, waiting for the doctor. The guys were ribbing me, "You just don't want to play tonight." The doctor came and found I had a temperature of 103 and he told me to get into bed. Then he checked out Phil. He hit Phil's knee and there was nothing, no reflex at all.

"This guy shouldn't even be standing," he said. "He shouldn't even be on his feet!"

We went back to the hotel in the same cab. I couldn't stay with Phil because what I had was maybe contagious. I had to get another room. I could hold nothing in my stomach. I stayed in bed all night sweating, burning up, the worst feeling I ever had. I didn't think I was going to make it the next day on the plane. Phil was walking humped over, moving slowly, barely making it himself.

Phil missed the rest of the season and all of the next one, too. He started working out with us in October of '69. Dr. Kazuo Yanagisawa, the head physician at the Garden, had operated on his back and apparently that did the trick. Yana had also been successful with a couple of spinal-fusion operations on ice hockey players. When Phil came back he didn't seem to be favoring the back and could bend over and touch his toes and pick up loose balls. Still, he lost more than a season out of his career, a real shame because he's such a fine defensive forward. It's almost impossible to pass the ball around him without him tipping it or intercepting it. You've got to really strain yourself to get it by him. He can stand on the floor—never leave his feet—and block shots.

My stomach problems went away fairly soon. I think it was from sausages I ate. As a matter of fact, I haven't had sausage since.

One of the problems with playing basketball for a living is you have to be so careful what you eat that it's hard to get any variety into your diet. On a game day you can't go out and fill up on gourmet French food with rich sauces or Italian food with all those spices. Guys who do pay for it. I know. Whenever I eat stupidly, it comes back to haunt me as early as the first period. So I stick mostly to steaks or prime rib and if I'm feeling adventurous, maybe a veal cutlet.

Not that it's very exotic, but one eating place I love when we're in San Francisco is a coffee shop-hamburger joint across from the Jack Tar Hotel, where we stay. This place has the best apple pie in the world, with a special kind of sauce on it. It's out of sight! I almost missed the bus once getting myself a second piece of that apple pie.

Even without Phil and Cazzie, we moved right along with win after win, especially at home, where we had a terrific streak going. We won our 19th home game in a row against Phoenix on February 12 and I scored 20 points and had 12 assists and 10 rebounds. Then No. 20 at home, against San Francisco, was, I think, my best game up to that time: 47 minutes, 24 points, 14 rebounds, 13 assists and 8 steals (6 of the steals leading directly to baskets). By this time it was a common thing for people to compare me to Oscar Robertson; flattering to say the least.

"There's no guard in the NBA I'd rather play with than Walt," said Captain Willis, trying to build up my confidence.

After a 30-point game against the San Diego Rockets, their coach, Jack McMahon, said some nice things about me to Lennie Lewin of the *New York Post*. I have a big envelope in my room stuffed with clippings. This is one of my favorites.

"He'll be a superstar," said McMahon. "He's close to

Oscar's class. He can beat you at both ends." And he added:

"He's a great player. He's got the real drive. He's always coming at you at both ends. You got to worry about him offensively and defensively."

It was a close race in the eastern division, with Baltimore leading, Philly and the Knicks not far behind, and Boston trailing in fourth place, the last playoff slot. We had the Celtics' number, it seemed. One night late in February they thought they had us. They were leading 76 to 67, but Dick Barnett and I got hot and scored the Knicks' last 25 points and we won by four. In one stretch I scored 12 of our 18 points and Havlicek was in foul trouble. Bill Russell began trying different guys on me. Finally he tried Satch Sanders.

Satch is regarded as one of the finest defensive forwards in the NBA, but he was a good defensive *guard* the night he was on me. I hate that guy. I think everybody's got somebody's number and if he was a guard, he'd have mine. I find it very difficult to move on him because he has such long arms. He'll let you act, then he'll react. I can get a step on him, but he's right on me anyway, so I need like two or three steps. I was glad he was only on me late in the game.

One illustration of how I had regained confidence in my shooting came against Boston. I missed my first six shots and still scored more than 20 points. That wouldn't have happened when I was a rookie. From all this I earned the respect of the Boston players, including probably the greatest defensive center of all time, Russell. At the end of the season, when I didn't make the first or second All-NBA team (the first string on one selection was Oscar, Elgin, Westley Unseld, Earl

Monroe and Billy Cunningham; the second string was Willis, Debusschere, John Havlicek, Hal Greer and Jerry West), Russ and Sam Jones both spoke up in my behalf, asking how I could be left off.

It didn't bother me so much. I knew I was young and had plenty of seasons to improve my stats: 17.5 scoring average, 7.9 assists (third in the NBA), 50.5 percent shooting from the floor (second among the guards) and 6.2 rebounds (again second among the guards). More important was what was happening to the Knicks. When you help your team to be a winner, the honors take care of themselves.

There was a chance at the end of the regular season that we would have to play Philly in a play-off for second place, but Baltimore threw a game to the 76ers and we finished third in the division. The Bullets thought they could beat us, so they kept Earl Monroe and most of the first-stringers out of that game. The Baltimore coach, Gene Shue, said he played his best available men, which was a whole lot of baloney. Our guys were really upset. The Bullets thought, evidently, that they could knock us off with no trouble. Plus we lost that second-place money. But it was the principle of the thing—you just don't let another team beat you. Willis was really mad, the maddest guy of all. He was *furious*.

There was a big stink in the papers. Willis was teed off and he made some comments about how he thought it wasn't fair, that the commissioner should look into it. Shue was insisting his players needed rest and he was going to run his team the way he saw fit. It went back and forth. There were no comments on the floor, we just played ball. They wanted to play us, so now they had us. We took the battle to them because we felt we had to prove we were the better team.

The New York fans were practically storming the Garden trying to get play-off tickets. The ticket windows opened at 9 A.M. on March 17 and about 2,000 people already were waiting. Some people had been in line all night.

Before the series Red said it like it was, that we wouldn't change anything. Baltimore changed its whole stretegy and I think it helped beat them. They had Unseld bringing the ball up, trying to tire out Willis. They put a forward, Jack Marin, on me. They put Earl the Pearl on Bradley and Dollar Bill burned him up. They had changed their strategy around and it backfired. In the regular season the two teams had been about even.

I didn't think we'd have any easy time with Baltimore. We blew them out in the sense that we won four straight, but we didn't blow them out by the scores. They were the kind of games where the fans pull their hair out—grueling, nip-and-tuck games that went down to the last minutes. We beat them at Baltimore 113 to 101 (I had 26 points, 7 rebounds and 11 assists in 47 minutes), at New York 107 to 91, at Baltimore 119 to 116 and back at the Garden 115 to 108.

We really had a team effort. Everybody on the Knicks was scoring in two figures. In that third game at the Baltimore Civic Center we were 16 points ahead, then 10 points behind. We caught up. They were dejected because they couldn't shake us. Willis was outstanding in a couple of games where he really ate up Unseld. He had 40-some points in one game in the

Garden, I remember—he went wild. I think he was the man. He dominated the series. It doesn't pay to get Willis angry.

Gene Shue came into our locker room after the last game. He said it had been a great play-off series and he hoped we'd go all the way, which was a nice thing to say. He didn't have to do that, especially since I'm sure he was teed off that they lost four straight. Unseld said, "It's no shock to be beaten four in row when you're beaten by a team as good as New York."

They wanted us to beat Boston, like you root for the underdog because you get tired of one team dominating. I would have wanted Boston to lose, too, if I had been on the Bullets. Out of college I wouldn't have wanted to play for Boston. It's great to be on the Knicks, a team that in the past was a loser but now is a winner. You can appreciate it more. Boston took winning for granted. I was always against them.

Boston beating Philadelphia didn't surprise us. We figured the jinx the Celtics had over the 76ers would work again. It was only surprising they beat Philly so easily.

We lost the first game to the Celtics in the Garden 108 to 100, when nobody on the Knicks was up to par. I scored 34 points, but a lot of times when I score a lot we lose. That's because we're not moving real well, so I take the initiative and try to score myself. The guys weren't too upset by the opening loss. We figured we could still take them. Then we lost real bad in Boston, 112 to 97. I've never seen anything like it—five guys who couldn't make a basket. Five pros! People said it was Russell. I don't think it was Russell. It was just one of those things. We needed that embarrassing loss because we hadn't been really charged up to play Boston. We were overconfident because we had killed them during the season.

We woke up and were keyed up for the third game. I know myself I didn't need any sleep, I didn't need anything to eat. I couldn't wait for that game. I knew we'd beat them and we did, 101 to 91. Our confidence was back.

They beat us in Boston in a very close game 97 to 96 and led the series 3 to 1. We were on the brink of defeat by a team we had thought was over the hill. The fifth game in the Garden we beat them 112 to 104. I didn't say anything about it in the post-game excitement, but in the last minute I had felt pain in my groin muscle. I figured it was just a cramp, but overnight it got worse. By the next morning it was a painful thing. I shouldn't have played the sixth game, but I wanted to try it out and Red let me.

I was only running on pride. I felt I was letting the team down, although I couldn't do anything about it and injuries can happen to anybody. I played it straight at first, but the wise old Celtics soon caught on that I couldn't go left on defense, I couldn't penetrate and then hit the open man (which is my main value on offense), I couldn't get back on defense quickly enough, I couldn't steal or pick up a loose ball. Red finally had to take me out.

I felt terrible sitting on the bench. I was thinking, "I hope it's not a jinx for me being in the play-offs." That was the second play-off in which I'd gotten hurt.

I think without that strained groin muscle we would

have won because they beat us only 106 to 105 with me a cripple, and they needed two lucky shots even to do that.

John Havlicek's shot at the end of the game I remember perfectly. I was watching the clock and watching him. I was sure he'd never get the shot off. He was dribbling to his left, parallel to the free-throw line and toward the sideline. He was off-balance and shooting across his body and just trying to bang it off the backboard so they'd have a chance for the rebound. He was even on the wrong foot—an awful shot, so awful it went in.

Sanders made a lucky shot near the end, too. On Satch's beauty, DeBusschere was all over the guy. It was on a beeline—no arch—and it went right in. I think it was his only basket. Only shot! Hell of a time to make a shot.

But you have to hand it to the Celtics. They hadn't even played .500 ball the last half of the regular season, yet they beat Philly, they beat us for their 12th eastern division play-off championship in 13 years and they went on to beat L. A. four games to three for the NBA title. The final game was in the Forum in Inglewood and the Lakers were stuck with thousands of balloons up by the ceiling, waiting to be released. Naturally. Red Auerbach had to gloat about that.

I'm positive if I had been 100 percent okay we could have taken them in the sixth game. Then the seventh game would have been a great battle. I tossed and turned most of the night after we lost, not from the pain of the injury but from the pain of the loss and my not being able to help more.

After the last game, Red spoke to us in the locker room. He said we'd had a hell of a season and had nothing to be ashamed of because we had really battled them. With a few breaks, we would have won. That was it. All the guys felt the same way. They were downhearted, but they figured there was always next year.

Chapter Ten

B. D. Bailey Howell and Barry

SOMETIME DURING the first half of the Detroit Piston game of October 24, 1969, the seventh game of the season, I went over the 1,000-assist mark. That's a lot of assists, but I hadn't even realized I was coming close to any kind of milestone. I was proud when I was told about it because it was accomplished in slightly more than two seasons, most of the time as a substitute, and only six other Knicks—Carl Braun, Sweetwater Clifton, Harry Gallatin, Richie Guerin, Howard Komives and Dick McGuire—had gone over 1,000 in their *careers* with the club. I want to go down in the record book as one of the greatest assist men the game has ever seen. It's the same thing as being one of the great playmakers.

I'd rather lead the team in assists than scoring because I know good passing is as imporant as good shooting, plus my being a big scorer would put pressure on Willis. He feels it's his reponsibility to carry the bulk of New York's scoring load. If he was second or third he might try to shoot more, take bad shots. I'd rather just lead in assists and chip in with some points.

When I look at the box score, the first thing my eyes go to is the assist column. I honestly get a bigger kick out of a good pass that results in a score than I do in scoring myself. It's a beautiful feeling to hit a free man in range of an easy jump shot or lay-up.

Whoever first thought of giving passers some statistical glory by having an assist column in box scores was a genius. It has probably done more to promote unselfishness and team play than all the coaches' locker-room speeches combined. Partway through last season, when the Knicks were rampaging through the league, *The New York Times* started running more complete box scores of our games. The *Post* had ben doing it all along. Somebody apparently convinced the *Times* sports editor that assists and rebounds were part of "all the news that's fit to print."

In case anybody is vague about it, an "assist" is simply a pass leading directly to a basket. If I pass to DeBusschere in the left corner and he drives around his man for a lay-up, that is not an assist. If DeBusschere breaks around his man and then I flip the ball to him for a lay-up, that *is* an assist. Only it's not always that simple. There are plenty of times when there's some doubt as to whether the feed led directly to the basket. The decision is up to the official scorer.

In the third game of the '68—'69 play-offs at Baltimore, I scored 26 points and, more important, was credited with 17 assists, breaking McGuire's Knick play-off record of 13, which he accomplished twice. I didn't think I had that many. I was pleased, not only because I replaced Tricky (a fine playmaker with New York for seven seasons) in the yearbook, but also because on the road I often get robbed.

In lots of games away from home I think I've fed off for 10 or 12 field goals and I look at the stat sheet and I only have four or five. Last season it got a little better because I was well-known as a passer and got the benefit of the doubt more often. It really used to make me angry when the big names, like Oscar or Guy Rodgers, sometimes automatically were given assists when they passed. They'd get one if they threw it out of bounds to a spectator. In Chicago I could play a whole game and get maybe three assists. The Knicks have a guy at the scorer's table, but the home team's man keeps the official score book.

It's just the opposite in the Garden, of course. I get credit for every one and maybe for some I don't deserve, so I guess it balances out.

I'm told the situation in baseball is similar, except that the official scorer is a newspaperman sitting up in the press box. Batters complain that on the road their hits are called errors, fielders complain that their errors were really hits and pitchers get in the act more than anybody. It's a good thing, I suppose, that athletes don't keep their own statistics.

Naturally, to be the quarterback, I have to have the ball more than the other guys, like Lennie Wilkens at Seattle and Oscar. It wouldn't work to have Wilkens and me in the same backcourt. It would create the same problem Dave Bing and Jimmy Walker had at Detroit, where they both needed the ball to produce. The Pistons also had Eddie Miles, who needed the ball, and Komives, who needed the ball. They should have had two or three balls out there! One man's abilities could not offset another's liabilities. They didn't blend, they didn't mesh. From what I heard Detroit was turmoil.

On the Knicks we're fortunate because the two guards complement each other. Dick Barnett is a great shooter who doesn't like to handle the ball. I like to handle it and don't care too much for shooting. It works out well.

I don't think my teammates resent my having the ball all the time because they see that it works, and besides, I always give it to them when they're in shooting range. It's not like I bring it down and shoot all the time. I'm doing what's best for the team: I bring it down and make the moves, but one of them ends up with the basket. Reed's wisecrack about Clyde the quarterback has been quoted enough.

"On this team the ball belongs to Frazier. He just lets us play with it once in a while."

Nobody, I hope, is going to argue with him. If they do, I'll take my ball and go home.

I jive Willis a little because he usually has only one or two assists. If he gets as many as four he starts doing a little struttin'.

"Hey, Clyde," he'll say in the dressing room, "I'm going to move you out of the assist column!"

(There are always smart remarks when the score sheets are passed out in the dressing room after each game. If a guy shoots 4 for 15, he can expect some hoots. Barnett and Cazzie have a free-throw contest every game. If one of them misses a free throw, he has to pay the other a dollar. If Barnett misses three and Cazzie misses four, Cazzie owes a buck. I guess they've been doing that since they came to the team.)

In college we played a Hank Iba-style offense where I brought the ball down real slow and we worked it around patiently and carefully until we got a good percentage shot. In the pros practically every club fast breaks whenever it gets the chance, but, as in anything else, some teams do it much better than others. The Boston Celtics were noted for years as a run-run-run team because they were better conditioned and they had Bill Russell. With Russ dominating the defensive board against most people, the other Celtics knew they could cheat a little bit toward the offensive end of the court after the other team shot.

The old fast-break basics hold true for the pros, too. The man with the ball must bring it down the middle of the court so that he has three options: pass to the left, pass to the right or keep charging into the key with it himself (maybe "charging" isn't the best word). And there must be teammates filling the two side lanes. It stands to reason that if a guy knows he's likely to get a good pass from the man in the middle, he's going to hustle to fill one of the lanes. A few times down the court without getting at least a look and next time he's going to loaf a little.

A lot of the fans don't realize that one of the main ingredients of a successful fast break is the outlet pass. It's invaluable to have a center or a forward who can get the defensive rebound *á la* Russell and make a fast, accurate pass to a teammate running down the floor. Westley Unseld of Baltimore is probably the best in the NBA at this now. Sometimes he grabs a rebound, twirls in the air and guns it out before he comes down. Bill Bridges of Atlanta and Nate Thurmond of San Francisco do it well, too. Lew Alcindor and Wilt Chamberlain don't.

Some guys can even throw the outlet pass baseball style. One of the great Boston guards, Bill Sharman, tried a court-length baseball pass one day, but he overthrew his man and the ball went in the basket for probably the longest, most spectacular two-pointer in history. According to the story, he turned to the man guarding him and said:

"You never could play defense."

The fast break is most easily run after an opponent has shot from the side because the shooter is likely to be completely out of the play and there will be at least a five-on-four situation at the other end. If the shooter thinks about getting back, he's going to blow the shot.

The Knicks don't burn a lot of teams with the fast break because our two principal rebounders, Reed and DeBusschere, can't get the ball out in a hurry. We even play teams that send everybody but the coach to the offensive board—no rear guard at all—and we *still* can't break back.

When we do get a fast break it's an unusual one because we seldom go all the way in to the basket. We've got great open shooters—Barnett, Cazzie, Bradley, DeBusschere. We often wind up taking a corner or side jump shot because these guys are more comfortable shooting from 15 feet out than making a lay-up.

On the break I know I can find them, a lot of times without looking. I'll be racing down the court and I'll hear one of our guys yell, "Clyde!" and I'll bounce it to his voice. I think my peripheral vision helps, like I can see someone coming other guys can't see until too late. On a fast break I can see the whole court (except behind me). Most of the time it's me in the middle because Barnett is not a real good dribbler and feels more comfortable filling one of the side lanes. And we have forwards who can handle the ball. A lot of times when either Bradley or DeBussschere gets the rebound he brings it down the middle himself.

Fast breaks or not, no NBA team can take its sweet time out there. The 24-second clock dictates that either you take a shot 24 seconds after getting control of the ball or you give it up. When I first came into the league the clock was always on my mind. That hurt. There were already enough things to worry about: the guy trying to steal the ball from me, the pick I should have been setting, keeping the team moving, how long I would be left in the game and a million other things. Now it's old hat.

When I was first with the Knicks, we put the ball up in no time at all. It was like a hot potato. It was a task to hold it for 20 seconds. We have more patience now.

Most players quickly develop a sort of sixth sense that tells them the "alarm" is about to go off. We look at the clock periodically, but if our bench is alert (and Red insists on that) the guys sitting let us know when it gets down to nine or ten seconds left and somebody should fire away. Most of the time a professional team—and a college team, too, for that matter—will get a shot off in way under 24 seconds. I think the only time it's important is late in a game when a team is playing for one shot and working the ball around trying to get the *best* shot. A lot of times, right in the middle of a situation like that the clock goes off.

Most of the time I'm the guy with the ball, so that airfilled piece of leather had better be an old, reliable friend. I should be able to dribble at top speed without looking at it, just like clapping hands in the dark. If it doesn't have enough air pumped into it, I should be able to tell with the first bounce, like a fine shooter can tell if the hoop is too low, too high or too loose after a couple of shots. Bouncing the basketball and at the same time getting around a guy who doesn't have to keep track of a ball himself is not easy, yet that's my main job in the Knicks' offense. I'm supposed to penetrate the enemy's perimeter, force somebody on the other side to double up on me, then not only locate our open man but get the ball to him through the tangle of arms, legs and bodies. If I penetrate and nobody picks me up, or they're too slow in picking me up, then I've got to put the ball up myself. I'd rather pass off, but the threat of my shot has to be there.

My shot is not consistent. I shoot differently every time. If nobody's on me, I might shoot on a beeline, but if somebody's on me, I might arch it enough to get it over him. It should be the same arch every time, but I've never been a consistent guy. I should be like Bradley and shoot precisely the same way every time, but this can be a disadvantage, too, because if a guy's right on him, he shoots the same way out of habit and might have it blocked. Maybe there should be *some* variation. Shooting is like an automatic response for most pros, who have practiced their shots for so many years, and worn out so many balls and nets, that they're not conscious of technique: shoot with the fingertips, put a backspin on the ball, use the left hand for control, arch the ball high to take advantage of the difference in size between ball and hoop, aim for the back of the rim.

Naturally there are exceptions to every one of the fundamentals. Frank Selvy never put any spin on his shots. They floated up to the basket like balloons. You could read the manufacturer's imprint as the ball was in the air. Yet he was considered a fine shooter. On free throws there are a hundred different ways. Hal Greer takes a jump shot. Bob Boozer stands off to the right instead of straight out from the basket, and Ray Scott of Baltimore stands off to the left. Some other guys take free throws from a couple of steps behind the line.

When you shoot in the NBA you have to expect some added weight caused by guys putting their hands on you. At the beginning of each season the refs will start out enforcing the rules strictly, but they always fall back into their old habits. It bothered me at first. I'd get a step on a guy and he'd just hold me with one hand until he caught up. I've had guys like Art Harris of Seattle actually holding me so I couldn't move at all and the refs didn't call a foul.

Besides enforcing the rules against shoving and holding, I think they should have limits on the length of fingernails. Some nights I come home all scarred up. I have consideration for the other guys and keep mine trimmed because I wouldn't do something to somebody that I wouldn't want done to me. The NBA won't allow players to wear rings, watches or bracelets in games, yet long nails can leave some ugly marks and can damage somebody's eye.

One of the weapons that helps me to get by the scratchers and the clutchers is the behind-the-back dribble. I didn't start doing it until I got to high school and then only because it would get me a basket or get me free from an opponent. Otherwise it's a showboat move and my high school coach wouldn't tolerate showboating.

"Whatever you do in practice, do in a game," he

would say. "If you don't do it in practice, don't do it in a game."

I got to be pretty efficient at it, like if a guy unexpectedly ran across in front of me, I'd just put the ball behind my back and go by. When I got to Southern Illinois, Coach Hartman didn't like it. He thought it was strictly a hot dog move, but if it paid off by avoiding a steal, then he wouldn't say anything. I normally use it only when a guy overplays me. If Wally Jones, who is always jumping in and out and giving me a lot of motion, darts toward my left-hand dribble, I'll just go behind my back to my right hand and automatically I'll have a step on him. If he is guarding me "straight up," not overplaying me to one side or the other, there's no sense going behind my back.

I don't really understand myself how I, or any other ball handler, can get it around there without palming. It's practice and instinct, knowing where the ball is and where your man is. A lot of guys go behind their back and have to look for the ball just an instant, but that instant is enough time for a good defensive man to take it away or at least make up the step he's lost.

As for passing behind the back, I very seldom do it unless a guy's wide open and I feel like jazzing up the proceedings a little. I can do it easily with my right hand, but I'm not so good with my left. It isn't often necessary because if you can throw it behind your back, you can probably get it there by safer, normal means (the same is true of the bounce pass, the bounce usually being unnecessary).

A lot of things I notice are helpful, like if the defensive man is standing flat-footed, I can drive by him. If he's in good defensive position, straight up and off me, I know I can't do too much without forcing it. Usually I pass off. I put myself in his position: I know defense and I know how a guy can beat me. I think a lot of catchers should hit better than they do because they know the pitchers, but for some reason that doesn't always work out.

I ad-lib a lot, making up moves as I go along to fit the situation. I've got a lot of spin moves that work all the time, but I never practice them. Whichever way the man guards me, I try to go the opposite way. I never plan anything. I never decide beforehand that I'm going to go this way or that way. It's similar to a batter not anticipating what the pitcher is going to throw, instead using his quick reactions to lash out at whatever is served up.

One of the defensive strategies against me, I've noticed, is to keep me out of the middle, to force me down the sides. It's easier to do, of course, if there's a Chamberlain or an Alcindor clogging up the lane. The Celtics have at times tried to keep me from getting the ball in the backcourt. They want Barnett to handle it because they know I set up 90 percent of the plays. After Boston scores and we have to inbound, one or more of the Celtics will try to screen me from the ball. While I'm cutting every which way, Red is screaming from the bench, "Get the ball, Clyde!" He always wants me to handle it.

We only have six or seven plays (Boston for years had just five basic plays), but each of them has options or alternatives and they're all we need. Of course, we also have special plays for inbounding the ball from certain places and for getting last-second shots. We used to hold up fingers to call the plays, but a lot of times one or more of our men was blocked off and couldn't tell how many fingers were being shown, so we started yelling them out: B, D, Barry, New York. For D I'll call out dog or David and for B I'll say boy or brown. At the end of a game when it's really noisy, I'll try to call them in the backcourt, or we can always switch back to hand signals.

We used to have a play called Bailey Howell, a shot for a forward, but later we changed it to Barry because the Warriors ran it for Rick Barry when he was in the league. We also call it San Francisco. It's such a simple, uncomplicated, obvious play, I never thought it would work. Thinking as a defensive player, I don't see how a *lot* of our stuff works, but it does. On the Barry I dribble into a forward's area, say DeBusschere's, and he pretends he's "going through" (clearing out through the key to the other side), but suddenly he doubles back around me for a jump shot. A lot of times his man is still across court and doesn't know Dave's come back!

D is another play that leads to a shot by a forward. New York is a play where Willis and I are maneuvering on the same side of the key and the guys on the other side are setting up Bradley with screens. He gets a lot of open shots off it.

Plays off the center jump at the beginning of each quarter are fairly simple. If we think we've got a chance for the tip, Reed will nudge it to me and Barnett will break to the basket. The two forwards will "zone up," protect our end of the court.

When we're up against Milwaukee and Alcindor, Red will say, "Think you can get the tip, Willis?"

"Yeah, I'm coming back with it," Willis says, chuckling.

We even have a one-second play. If we're behind and have the ball at the far end of the court, ready to inbound, I'm supposed to throw it the full length to Willis under the basket, who theoretically will leap up with perfect timing, catch it (thus starting the clock) and stuff it through the hoop. We practiced and practiced but never could work it. I'd throw the ball over the backboard or out of bounds.

So one night last season we were in deep trouble in Detroit. One second to go, one point down. Even if we never had made it work, we only had the one play to fit that situation. I took the ball out of bounds and threw it the entire length of the court, Willis leaped up, caught it and put it in. It was right on the money and we won the game. It worked perfectly, as if we knew what we were doing.

We worked an accidental play in San Francisco last season that Red should put in permanently. We could name it the Quarterback Keep or the Bootleg. I was about at the free-throw line with my back to the basket holding the ball out for Dollar Bill, or maybe it was DeBusschere. But his man was too close, so when they came around I just pulled the ball back in. I had already stopped my dribble. Well, they went thataway and so did Jeff Mullins, who had been guarding me. I turned around and was all by myself. Fortunately, I made it. I usually blow those gift shots. It couldn't have worked any better if we had practiced all week.

Red believes that even when a guy is red-hot, as Reed, Cazzie, Barnett and Bradley all can get, we shouldn't start going to him because then the four other players will stand around and turn into spectators. Red stresses constant movement. It's one reason why my job is to keep the guys happy by laying the ball on them. If they know that when they make a good cut to the basket they'll get the ball, they'll do it again and keep doing it.

When Bradley was out with a bad ankle at the end of the last regular season, it really affected the team. Without him we were standing around too much. When he was with us, we were moving this way and that, knowing if we shook loose from the defensive men, he would hit us.

Bill is a great passer. He and I worked some beautiful backdoor plays through the season. As a game goes on, some defensive men get tired and careless. If I notice my man is watching the ball and taking his attention away from me for an instant, he's a pigeon. All of a sudden I just streak to the basket, "going backdoor," and Bill hits me almost every time. Sometimes he has passed the ball before I've taken the first step. It's like telepathy. We look each other in the eye and he knows what mischief I'm thinking about. It means a lot when you learn to play *without* the ball: cut to the hoop at the right moment, keep court balance, get good position for rebounds. Too many players are next to useless when they don't have that ball.

Besides mastering all the intricacies of offense and defense, a successful pro has to show up at the arena mentally and physically prepared. Most of the time we make up our own training rules. Drinking is all right if you can handle it. My philosophy in this game is The Way You Start Out Is the Way You End Up. Like you can start out drinking in training camp and your body becomes adjusted to it. If you do it regularly, it doesn't affect you, but if you drink once a week, you suffer for several days because your body isn't used to it.

I found out there were times I could hang out at parties or night clubs late at night on a steady basis and it didn't affect me and I played great. But if I did it periodically, like maybe once or twice a week, I could really tell the difference.

What I drink depends on what mood I'm in. If I don't really want to drink I take a beer. Scotch I don't buy too much anymore because it gave me headaches. Sometimes I drink Tanqueray gin and orange juice, sometimes Cold Duck, which is similar to champagne.

I tried one cigarette when I was a kid and it was one of the worst things that ever happened to me. Since then I've never had one in my mouth. I can't stand them. The old Garden could be an awful place for non-smokers. I remember once when I was injured I watched a game from up high and I could hardly see through the smoke. I wonder how many regular Garden customers have suffered from smoke inhalation—it can be as bad as a three-alarm fire.

I used to smoke cigars, those dapper little ones, when I really felt like frontin'. After a while, though, they upset my stomach and I could feel it the next morning, so I cut them loose.

On the day of a game I don't like to get keyed up too soon. I've noticed that if I sit in my room and say, "I'm going to go out and kill them tonight!", well, by game time I've lost interest. I'll get out of bed anytime between noon and two o'clock and maybe go shopping, take some stuff to the laundry, see if my pants are ready at the tailor's—errands like this. Then I go back to the hotel and eat something kind of plain. I walk around a little to settle the food down, then I go back to bed and read the papers, watch television or call some of my friends. I try to keep the game out of my mind.

Before leaving for the Garden, across the street from my hotel, I stay in my room for about an hour and listen to rock and roll (The Temptations, the greatest) just to get pepped up. Nate Bowman always had a jazz box—he's a jazz fanatic. I don't like to listen to it before a game because it's so *down*. I like fast music to pep me up.

I leave between 6 and 6:15 and there are always autograph hounds in the lobby of the New Yorker. Most of the time I say I'm running late and I don't have time to stop and sign. I tell them I'll see them after the game—the same old line, and they say, "You said that the last time!" Sometimes I'll sign as I'm walking.

The kids are always bugging me. They come up and knock on my door at nine o'clock in the morning, the middle of the night for me (*Sport* very kindly printed my room number). I say, "I'm sleeping." They say, "We'll wait in the lobby." So I wander down at three o'clock and they're still there, saying, "Gee, Clyde, we thought we'd missed you!" Kids are that dedicated, just to get an autograph!

The players enter the Garden at the service entrance on 33rd Street and take an elevator up to the fifth floor. (I've got a secret exit for leaving the Garden after a game. There are too many people and I'd be there all night signing autographs. What do kids *do* with those signatures anyway?)

I stroll in and if I've received any fan mail, it's been brought in from the office and placed on the shelf of my cubicle (we don't have lockers in the sense of metal closets with locks.) I go through the letters while I'm still in my civvies. Almost every evening there's a good-sized stack there; I guess winning makes people want to write. I've never got any nasty mail, but some of it is really funny, especially the letters from kids who can barely scrawl the words. One said, "Dear Joe Frazier, you're the best center the Knicks ever had." And a little girl sent me her picture and was sad that she couldn't go to my summer camp. "I know you won't take me to your camp," she wrote, "but would you please say hi to me?" Here's a typical letter:

"Walt,

"Wow/ it finally happened. My dream came true. A chance to play basketball with you. I watch you on tv and you are fascinating. My friends call me Clyde. Thats the honest truth too. . . . You ought to see their eyes sparkle when I sink a 15 foot jumper. . . ."

That was from a 16-year old in District Heights, Maryland who wanted to come to my summer camp. News of the camp also drew this one from a kid in Hampton, Virginia:

"Dear Clyde,

"I would like some brochures on your basketball camp. I love your style of play and your clothes. If possible could you send me your telephone number so I can call you one day. I don't mind paying if it's worth it. Could you send me some information on Willis Reed's camp so I can check out the prices and other stuff. How could you help a 5'6" person to make his state champion basketball team 'Hampton Grabbers.' I want to meet you because your the best all around guard in the *N.B.A.*"

An officer of Steuben Glass wrote in saying I was a hero to his 12-year-old son and to him, too. Sometimes I wonder if Martin Luther King, Jr. or the President of United States or great authors ever get worship letters like athletes get. What is it about athletes and movie stars that catches people's fancy so? I'm not complaining. It's just a slight worry in the back of my mind.

Most letters are not too entertaining and just say, "Blah, blah, blah, would you please send me an autograph?" If they enclose a stemped return envelope, I'll send them an autograph, but otherwise no. It would cost me a fortune in postage.

We all get mail from girls wanting to go out with us, but usually those girls are so *bad*. Because of a few experiences, I don't like blind dates anymore. I've never gone out with a letter writer, but I have dated a phone caller or two. All of them were losers, so I just gave up on them. They sounded great, but when I saw them it was a bad scene.

Most guys arrive in the dressing room and immediately start changing into their uniforms, but I don't change until late. I strip to my underwear, put my valuables in the footlocker, walk around barefoot on the blue carpet, sit quietly and finally get around to taping my ankles. I've had some ankle problems in the past, but even if I hadn't, the tape would give needed support and protection. And why take the risk of being injured? Cazzie never tapes his ankles, even after he had an injury—a sign of strength, a Superman kind of thing. I think he's foolish.

The trainer does some taping, but if I didn't learn anything else in college I learned how to tape. Hartman insisted that we tape ourselves because it saved a lot of time, you didn't have to wait in line. Even now I like to do it myself. How tight I put it on varies. If I don't have an injury I'll just put it on moderately tight, but if I have a sprain I'll tighten it up. There's none of this business of shaving ankles to avoid the hair-ripping pain when the tape is removed because we wear this stockinette, like cheesecloth almost, and we wind the tape over that.

The uniform is nothing unique: jersey, shorts and jock. Basketball players have to pay special attention to their feet and mine aren't models of perfect form. I have corns on each middle toe, one of which I scraped in a swimming pool when I was a kid and it never healed right. The corns aren't painful. I don't have to bother much with them. But I still have to smear on some Heet, an analgesic liniment for arthritis, on my left big toe, the one I injured at Southern Illinois. (I also put it all over my back, arms and legs. Luckily it doesn't have too much of a smell.) All of us wear two pairs of sweat socks, which give a little cushion and help prevent blisters.

Most of the guys wear low-cut shoes, but I'm afraid to. I got hurt once wearing a pair. Now it's strictly high tops for me. I used to wear out shoes like a double-duty mailman, splitting them open down near the toes. Part of that was from wearing a new pair in a game instead of breaking them in properly at a few practice sessions. A new pair is more likely to split because it's gripping the floor too tightly while you're stopping and starting.

Shoe splitting is a sign of being herky-jerky, too. I

split a lot of them in my first and second years, but not last season because my game smoothed out. I wasn't taking a lot of jagged, quick steps or making screeching stops. My form had improved and I was more fluid in my movements.

Danny Whelan, our trainer, is around to console us about our corns, bruises, groin pulls, sprains and fingernail scratches. He's a great personality, always jiving around, always coming out with a different story about some city where he visited as a baseball trainer. He's from San Francisco and went to St. Mary's College before going in the Navy and working as a trainer for Rochester in the International League.

Before coming to the Knicks in 1968, he was with the Pittsburgh Pirates and started their "green-weenie" hex. He had this rubber frankfurter that he had painted green. He'd point it at the opposing pitcher or batter. TV cameras caught him at it one day and the gimmick became famous that season. He knows his business and deserves his full share of whatever we win. He holds the team together, so to speak. All the guys love Danny. Including Red.

The last thing I do is put on my uniform, maybe 10 or 15 minutes before Red comes in at seven o'clock. We're all supposed to be dressed and ready to go by then. He talks for about ten minutes, goes over the opposing team, tells what he wants us to do. Red is a great coach in that he tells us what he expects from us and then drives us to do it. He never makes a move without telling us why. He's not a rah-rah talker like in college.

Half time isn't very different. We sit on stools in front of our cubicles. Red talks about what we aren't doing and what we should be doing. Like if we're not playing tight defense, he might tell the guards he wants us to pick them up from the time they bring the ball inbounds. Or he wants the forwards to overplay their men. Sometimes, such as one of the Atlanta games last season, he'll really bawl us out. The Hawks were leading by more than 20 points in the Garden. He came down hard on us then.

On occasions like that he might say, "Frazier, you're dribbling the ball too much. Pass it. Riordan and Barnett, too, you're all dribbling the ball too much." He might tell the big guys to go to the boards harder, stop Bridges from making those long passes or get back faster on defense.

If Red isn't too sore at us, half time is a relaxation period. Some guys sip Cokes, but I was trained through high school and college not to drink anything until after a game. Even water. Sometimes I feel kind of lousy, so I'll have an Alka-Seltzer. Sometimes I'll drink sodas after a game, but a beer is better because it will quench my thirst without all the acid.

After Red's pre-game talk we go out on the floor for the warm-ups. I don't have butterflies in my stomach except for the important games like the play-offs. Sometimes they go away at the tip-off, but it varies. A lot of times in the first five minutes the guys are tight and you see a lot of bad passes and badly missed shots before they settle down.

I like to do some stretches and toe touches, similar to what football teams do on the grass before a game. I'll take only 10 or 11 shots until I feel my timing is there, then I'll stop. If I'm having trouble getting my touch, maybe I'll shoot awhile longer, but I get bored if I just shoot the whole time. I'll dribble around fast, run from one corner to the other, shoot a few shots on the move or run behind a buy and shoot. Clowning. This is the way I loosen up. Then I'll shoot a few free throws and go over and sit down.

It's a warm-up all right, but only about half as much as the other guys go through. I'll plop on the bench and think about what I'm going to do, who I'm guarding— that kind of thing.

And I never watch the other team warm up. That would give them a psychological edge, like I'm standing around in awe. As soon as the tip-off comes, I'll see more than enough of them.

Chapter Eleven

Possums and Phantoms

AFTER A '69 play-off game against Baltimore in the Garden, we were waiting for a bus to take us to the airport. It was maybe an hour late and we were getting impatient.

"Clyde," said Willis Reed, "go steal us a bus."

By the end of my second season I had a reputation not only as a good defensive player but as an accomplished thief in the NBA—a pickpocket gone straight, a guy who they said could snatch the hubcaps off a speeding automobile. My specialties, intercepting passes and poking away the ball from opponents as they dribbled, were turning games around. Nothing shatters a team's morale faster than a steal, especially when that team is only a point behind and a basket could give it the lead. That hurts. Stealing a ball and making a pass that leads to a basket are the parts of basketball I love most.

At the end of the '68-'69 season the coaches voted for an All-NBA defensive team and the points went like this: Frazier 25 (out of a possible 28), Bill Russel

20, DeBusschere 17, Nate Thurmond 15, Jerry Sloan 14.

Bill Russell was a star in pro basketball when I was in the sixth grade. Getting more votes than he did was an honor.

"I voted for him," said Russell. "I can't do better than that."

Basically there are three situations where I can steal: (1) when the man I'm guarding is dribbling the ball between him and me; (2) when the other guard throws a pass to my man; and (3) when an opponent dribbles around a pick set by my man.

Anticipation and stance are two keys. I keep my weight evenly distributed on the balls of my feet (I don't want to get caught standing flat-footed) similar to a boxer, a tennis player or a baseball batter. My knees are slightly bent so I can cut quickly in any direction. A defensive man shouldn't cross his legs unless he has to turn and hightail it downcourt after a guy who has breezed past him. If my right leg is crossed in front of my left and Lennie Wilkens suddenly darts to my right, he's going to have a nice free shot at the hoop while I'm still standing there twisted like a pretzel.

I study our opponents, watching to see if they make the long or the short pass, if they pass off the dribble or have to take the ball in both hands before passing, if they dribble the ball fast or slow (I want to learn the cadence so I can flick my hand in there at just the right time). I try to anticipate my opponent's moves, wait for him to be a little careless, then make my move.

It's bad to react too fast. It's usually on a delayed motion that you intercept a guard-to-guard pass, like playing possum on a guy. You don't look like you're on him, but you really are. If I'm guarding, say, Walt Hazzard of Atlanta, and the other guard, Lou Hudson, has the ball, I'll stand back a ways. I won't be all over Walt or standing in the passing lane between him and Hudson. I'll try to suck Hudson in. With my peripheral vision, I can look straight at Hazzard but also see what's going on off to the side with Hudson. So when he passes, all I need is a step or two and I'm in the passing lane where I can grab the ball or deflect it.

Most of the time I can see it in a guy's eyes, like maybe he's cast a quick glance this way. Or he'll dribble down and call a number for a play and maybe I've seen the play before. Anyway I have a feeling the ball is coming in my direction, so I'll drop back, and at the very moment he lets it go I'll step up. Another situation is when the Knicks are double-teaming somebody in a corner and there's a free man not far from me. If the free man doesn't go to *meet* the pass (which the pass receiver should always do), a lot of times I can get in there and nab the ball first.

When my opponent tries to dribble the ball without protecting it with his body, I can often knock it away, without fouling him, with a quick horizontal jab. Sometimes the dribbler will try a quick switch from one hand to the other right in front of you, a cross-dribble. It's dangerous against a man with quick hands. The thing I try to remember is not to lunge for the ball. If I miss it I'll be out of position. The idea is to slap it away, then go for it.

Sometimes I can knock the ball away by reaching around from behind. It's another variation on the possum game. I let a guy go past and if he keeps dribbling with the same hand, it's easy to jab it away. All I'm really letting him get is a slight angle. Sometimes I can use it when a guy beats me, but my chances of fouling are greater because I really have to lunge.

Most of my steals, though, happen when opponents come around picks or screens. Say my man, Hazzard, moves to the top of the key without the ball to set a pick for the dribbler, Hudson. Hudson brings the Knicks' other guard in to Hazzard (if he can), and if I don't leave Hazzard and take him, maybe he's clear for a shot. Well, sometimes I'm just lying in wait. I don't dart straight out from behind Hazzard, I kind of belly around in a semicircle so Hudson and I don't crash into each other, and I hope I can scoop the ball away just as he puts it down on the dribble, the instant it leaves his hand. He can't take the ball back because he's committed himself. He can't turn, he can't stop. If he does, it's carrying the ball.

If it works, the dribbler is left there like a guy whose Yo-Yo string just broke. If it doesn't work, the Knicks are left with four guys to guard five and I have to scramble back. Stealing is a calculated risk. You can look foolish.

Coaches and managers in professional sports are ingenious. When some guy realized that Ted Williams never hit to left field, he had his players go into the Williams Shift, with almost every defensive man on the right side of second base. It frustrated Williams, at least for a while. In the NBA last season they came up with the Frazier Shift.

Most of the teams got hip in that they split up their guards, keeping them wide apart, seldom or never crossing them. They tried to isolate me, keep me a safe distance from the ball. Like the guard I was on might take me all the way under the basket, to the corners, down the sides, up the aisle to the men's room—anywhere away from that ball. L.A. did it, and Atlanta and Milwaukee. Boston didn't do it because I played John Havlicek and he handled the ball a lot. And teams used very few guard-to guard passes. Chances of double-teaming were dim because the guard with the ball either dribbled my way (without coming over a pick) or passed into the forwards or the center.

The most extreme Frazier Shift was put on by Detroit—I guess it was the idea of the Pistons' coach, Bill van Breda Kolff. My man was Howard Komives and he would go stand in a corner, completely out of their offense! And there was this stupid NBA rule that the defensive man had to be within six feet of the offensive man. (The officials should have been carrying tape measures in addition to whistles.) I couldn't leave Komives because he was always yelling to the refs, "Who's Frazier guarding?" He really made a mockery of things, running back and forth across the lane, making me trail him here and trail him there. Not too many guys would be willing to play that way, just staying out of the offense, but I guess since he was traded he figured he owed the Knicks something.

What could the Knicks do about it? For one thing, these tactics were taking away from the other team's offense. Instead of penetrating, they were going around the perimeter. And Red more and more made sure that I picked up their tough man, so they couldn't afford to isolate him. Like when we played Detroit I would play Jimmy Walker rather than Komives. If they wanted to isolate Walker, good, that was taking away from their

offense. But basically teams still stayed spread out
against New York more than against anybody else.

Eventually that six-foot rule was thrown out. It was
put in originally to keep anybody from using a zone
defense, which would slow up the pro game. The way
the zone-defense rule reads now, it's only illegal if the
center sets up housekeeping in the three-second lane.
Lew Alcindor, for instance, has to guard somebody and
can't stand under the hoop batting away shots like King
Kong swatting airplanes. The referees will give him a
warning. The next time it's a tech. I'd like to think it
was the Komives business that forced the rule change,
but it was more likely the Lakers' clever use of Jerry
West. L. A. Coach Joe Mullaney would have all his
guys clear out one side, taking the defensive men with
them, of course, and leaving West all alone, one-on-one
with his defender. A lot of the other coaches started
complaining and the league sent out a notice about the
rule change. Red went over it with us.

Obviously, there is much more to defense than trying
to swipe the ball. I try to make the man I'm guarding
aware that I'm there, make him uncomfortable to the
extent that he isn't just thinking about making a basket.
I don't want him to come down and look at the basket
all the time or casually look over the possibility ties of
where to pass. First of all he has got to think about
protecting the ball from me. When he's dribbling the
ball in front of him, it's easier for him to take the
jumper, it's easier for him to maneuver. I try to make
him protect the dribble by turning his back and keeping
his body between me and the ball. If he turns his back
and is within good shooting range, then I'll move up

tight because he could leap, turn in the air and shoot, but other than that I'll stay a bit away from him.

Here is where my ideas differ. In the pros, players lean on each other, elbow more and play with one hand constantly pushing, pushing the other guys. The offensive man has to get used to shooting with an extra ten pounds on him. When I'm on offense the shoving doesn't really bother me, but I think it takes a lot out of the defensive man. It's what is called moving your hands rather than your feet. I try to keep the dribbler in suspense about where I am. I don't crowd him and this way he has to keep feeling for me, looking to see where I'm lurking. If he knows where I am it's easy for him to make a move one way or the other. If a guy has his back to the basket dribbling out above the top of the key, why get all over him and wear yourself out? I'll stay off him until he's within shooting range and then I'll tighten up.

Some players *need* contact when they're moving with the ball. When I get caught in a switch and have to guard Elgin Baylor, I try to avoid making contact because he needs it, he wants it when he's barreling across the key (almost always with his right hand—he doesn't like to go left). I just stand off him and he never shoots. He'll move in to me and I just keep backing off him. Chet Walker is the same way, and Billy Cunningham of the 76ers. Willis helps these guys out a lot when they come in on a drive. He'll come out on them and jostle and that's all they want. If he would just let them go, they would be suspended in the air waiting for the other shoe to drop, waiting to be whacked, not knowing what to do until they got hit and could react with the appropriate twist. My idea is to be there with my hand up, but don't give them that shove they're waiting for. It's hard for defensive men to think that way.

The result of this phantom defense, if it's done right, is that the offensive man seldom knows for sure where you are. It psychs him. Bill Russell was a master of the psych. I seldom knew where he was. When I could see him out of the corner of my eye, I was all right, but when I didn't see him, that's when he blocked my shot.

One night he really frustrated me. I couldn't get a shot off no matter what I tried, even when I brought back some of my old Sourthern Illinois moves. I'd drive to the basket, throw the ball up nicely and he'd have his big hand smack in the way. He was everywhere and nowhere at the same time. I could see how in his best days he demoralized guys. When I thought I had a clear layup, forget it. He was coming.

I never see the face of the guy I'm guarding except when he stops his dribble and gets ready to pass. Then I might look at him and try to see where he's throwing it. Normally, I just see from his chest down. Some people believe you should watch the guy's belt buckle because where that's going, the rest of him is going. I might be watching a certain spot on him like his belt buckle, but I've been doing it so long I'm not aware. So much of defense is instinct. When he goes to take the shot and I can't possible block it, I get a hand up in his face anyway to give him something to think about, a distraction.

After my man has shot, I'm not through with him. He might follow up a miss and shoot again. I've got to box him out—hold him away with my back, butt and arms while I'm facing the hoop. Theoretically, if each

Knick does a good job of boxing out, there will be five of us in better position to rebound than the five opponents. I try to make sure my man is checked, then I leave him and move to the basket.

John Wooden, the coach at UCLA, is one of the best teachers of rebounding in the country. When his Bruins won the NCAA championship in College Park, Maryland last March (their sixth in seven years), they outrebounded Jacksonville University, the nation's tallest team. One reason was the quickness of UCLA's front line, but a couple of Wooden's basic principles played a part, too. He works and works and works to get his players to assume every shot will be missed and to get their hands up by their shoulders. He'd love it if every man on his bench got their hands up automatically every time a shot went up. He doesn't stress boxing out that much; he teaches his players to check their men and then zip to the board.

I don't go to our offensive boards (they are Reed's property, and DeBusschere's), so I get most of my rebounds on the defensive end. A lot of times, if my teammates are successful at blocking out, I have a clear shot to get the rebound. It's timing and I've got to notice, too, how well my man follows up. If it's Jerry Sloan of the Bulls, I know I can't leave him too early because he follows up tough, but most guards don't. They just shoot and fall back because they have a responsibility to stop our fast break.

Philadelphia Coach Jack Ramsay dreamed up an incentive plan last season for his players: a $10 bonus for every offensive rebound, a $15 fine when a 76er let his man grab an offensive rebound and a $25 fine when a 76er let the shooter get a rebound. One night the Philly players came out $135 behind.

I think it was an unnecessary burden on the 76ers. With pressure like that you aren't thinking about winning, you're just thinking about keeping your guy off the boards. You aren't thinking about every aspect of your job.

Surprisingly, even though I've held a number of high-scoring players down, I've never had a guy get so frustrated he said or did something mean. I think it's how you carry yourself, too. All the guys respect me for being a good defensive player and they know I never do anything dirty. I never hold a guy, although when I'm trying to steal the ball I might hit his hand. That's one reason why I have a lot of respect for Oscar. I was guarding him when I was a rookie and, in violation of my own rules, I was pushing him, frustrating him. He complained to the refs, but didn't say anything to me.

Getting through picks or screens is the most difficult problem that a guy out of college has in the pros. You want to stick with the man you're guarding because if you switch too much, you find yourself matched up with a 6 foot 10 inch center and he takes you inside and stuffs you through the basket. The whole secret is your teammate guarding the guy setting the pick. He should call it out right away, warning you, "Pick right," or "Pick left." Then you know you've got to step up on your man real tight so you can get "over the pick." You just kind of squeeze through the opening with him. You can't try to beat him to the pick too often because then you're overreacting and he'll reverse his dribble and zip off in the other direction.

You'll be going over the pick okay, but he'll be going

elsewhere. It's all timing and helping out. Like some-times if you're beaten, your teammate should step out and stop the man, just show himself until you get there and then get back on his own man. Never should he let a guy dribble around, but most of the time that's what happens because your teammate is saying to himself, "I'm guarding *my* man," which is the wrong attitude. His job is to stop the guy who's a threat to make a basket.

On some college teams the center, who is usually under the hoop and has a clear view of the entire court, calls out warnings or instructions to the guards and forwards. Bob Lanier of St. Bonaventure was able to do this last season. But talking on defense in the pros is basically from the two men where the action is, where the pick is being set. Of course, Red is always yelling things like, "See the ball" and "Get up on your man, Riordan."

All the big mooses are good at setting picks. I think the best at it was Wayne Embry when he was with the Celtics. I could never get around him on a pick. He was so wide it was like getting around a mountain! Lucious Jackson of Philly sets great picks, too. Bailey Howell of the Celtics sets some dangerous ones—a guy could really get hurt. For instance, if I'm pressing Larry Siegfried full court, he might suddenly spurt by me and take off up court. I sprint right with him, and there's Howell standing there like a brick wall—that kind of pick. It's legal, but you could get killed.

When he pulls that stunt I'll fake like I'm going to collide with him, but at the last second I'll go around him. I can almost sense when a pick is there, like a bat in a pitch-black cave knows where the boulders and outcroppings are, and sometimes I can be looking at my man and see the pick shaping up out of the corner of my eye.

Anytime a guard gets stuck on a forward, the forward licks his chops, but I usually don't mind guarding forwards (I did it regularly at Southern Illinois). They get careless and think they can jump right over me. I can play them tight and because of my quickness, they can't get the ball down on the floor.

There are great shooters—Rick Mount at Purdue was an example—who aren't so good at getting themselves loose from a defensive man, so their coaches install a lot of plays where their teammates pick for them. Guarding Jeff Mullins of San Francisco is like running an obstacle course. I can remember times going over at least three screens trying to keep up with Jeff. I could tell the next day—my body was tired from banging into Jerry Lucas and Nate Thurmond. Mullins is a great shooter but doesn't handle the ball that well going left. A lot of guys are like that.

Mullins uses the pick-and-roll well with Nate, one of the basic plays of basketball. Nate sets a pick for him and just a second after I start to claw my way through, Nate whirls and goes straight to the hoop. If my teammate assigned to Nate has tried to help me too much with Mullins, Jeff whips it to Thurmond alone underneath for an easy two.

Picks and switches and fast breaks and substitutions make it hard to pin the blame on any one guy for letting an opponent score a lot of points. I can remember in Chicago I thought I was doing a great job on Bob Weiss, but it happened at the beginning he got a few fast-break lay-ups. There was nothing I could do about that, but at half time Red looked at the stat sheet and said, "Hey, you better get on this guy, he's got ten points!" Mercy.

Sometimes I think Weiss just has my number. He's left-handed and I just can't seem to contain him the way I think I should. There are a lot of tough guards to contain in this league. I try to keep a little mental book on them, not that it always does any good. Here are some sample entries:

Lennie Wilkens, Seattle: Another lefty. Guarding him is a task because he's so quick. Can only go left, I'm well aware of that, but I can't seem to make him go anywhere else. Wish he'd take up coaching full-time.

Jeff Mullins, San Francisco: Remember to have the trainer stock some more liniment because here I go through the obstacle course.

Archie Clark, Philly: Likes to come down the right side, switch the ball to his left hand and zoom down the middle. I know this is his best move. When he comes down that way, drop off and give him all the room to the right he wants, until it looks like he wants to shoot.

Wally Jones, Philly: Erratic. Streak shooter who can pump ten in a row. Drive him to his left because he prefers to go the other way and let go with his jumper. Loves the right corner.

Earl Monroe, Baltimore: Great body control, not so great knees. Can't hand the way he used to when he was an out-of-sight rookie who deserved the nickname "Magic." Hope he's forced to work hard on defense and tires out. Helpful if he has had to play four out of the last five nights.

Emmette Bryant, Boston: Tricky with the ball but no height. I can let him penetrate and not worry.

Walt Hazzard, Atlanta: Ad-lib player. Can't run plays except at a fast-break pace.

Rick Adelman, San Diego: Can handle the ball in tight situations. When he was a rookie he came in when the game was close and I cackled to myself I was going to steal the ball, but he showed me some moves.

Dave Bing, Detroit: Loves the corners. Leaps over every guard in the league. Send him to his left, opposite his strength.

On Jerry West and Oscar Robertson nobody has the answer, at least not one that works consistently. I try to drive West left. He doesn't have any trouble, but he's not quite as effective. He has that quick first step, but if you stay off him a bit to compensate for it, he'll kill you with jump shots. The Big O goes at his own pace. You can't speed him up or get the ball away from him. I think it was Pete Newell, the San Diego general manager (and former great coach at California, USF and Michigan State), who said Oscar has one hand dribbling, one hand directing his teammates and a third holding off the defensive man. Very seldom does he use quickness. If he comes down on the break he might use it by faking here and going down the middle, but getting his shot off, you know what he's going to do and he dares you to stop it. He'll maneuver you around, bag you in, until he gets to where he wants to shoot from.

Which one is best? Certainly Jerry was last season, but over the years it's been Oscar. I don't think West is that great a ball handler. As far as getting the shot off, one-on-one, he's great, but Oscar can control the game. I don't know which one is better on defense; they're both tough. West boxes out well and so does Oscar. Oscar's a lot stronger. West is probably quicker.

It takes a well-coordinated team effort to stop these guys. Red Auerbach has said we're a "scrambling" defensive team, but I think that's wrong. I'm the only guy who gambles and scrambles. The other guys play fairly safe. We aren't helter-skelter, we aren't running all over the court. We're a good, sound defensive team, with a purpose behind most things we do. I would say that Boston had a scrambling defense with Bill Russell, going out and gambling all the time because he was back there as backstop. Willis is adequate, but we'd get killed if we tried to play the way the guys around Russell did.

Holzman wants us to make opposing guards go down the sides because when guys go down our middle our whole defense collapses. I dont' mean collapses on the man—I mean collapses, period. Whenever a guy goes down the middle Willis will come out too far rather than just laying back, letting him make his moves. So we try to keep the guards down the sides. It's hard to do. It's hard to keep them anywhere.

There isn't much chitchat among the players out on the floor, although some guys will give out with some cocky comments during a game. Like Dick Barnett, whose "Fall back, baby!" became famous, will get hot and taunt his defensive man, saying, "Too late," as the ball swishes through the net. Sam Jones of Boston got cocky sometimes, too. I raced over to get him in the corner one time, but he got the shot off and made it and he said, "Too late, too late, baby." Then, of course, I wanted to get all over him because he was trying to show off.

I don't believe in saying anything much. If I'm killing a guy, I want to keep him nice and calm, I don't want him to get upset. Everything should stay quiet so I can keep on making my points.

Archie Clark and I, we play the same way and we admire each other's game. When he makes a good defensive play, I'll say, "Good play." And when I make a good shot, he'll compliment me and I know he really means it. Flynn Robinson of Milwaukee is from Elgin, Illinois and knows people I knew in college, so we'll chitchat once in a while out on the floor, and Clem Haskins of the Bulls might ask me something about somebody in Chicago.

The ones to watch out for are the compliment givers. You might have a tendency to let up on a guy if he gives you a little praise. Sam Jones was trying to psych me one night, saying, "Gee, Walt, you're really running fast tonight," and, "You're really shooting good tonight." Walt Hazzard told some reporter I was the best young guard in the NBA (not that he's so old) and Wilt Chamberlain told somebody he thought I should have been the most valuable player. I don't like guys to give me a lot of credit because I might want to ease up on them. I don't mean that I work up a hatred of anybody, but I don't like to get too friendly with any player.

Since I'm trying to slow up and stop the best guards around the league, I naturally have to be conscious of fouls and the men who call the fouls. I seldom argue with a referee and never knock him. He might make a horrible call, but I let it go because I figure that during the course of the game the calls will balance out. However, an official should not purposely try to balance it. I can remember more than one time when the man guarding me never put a hand on me and got hit with a foul. So I came right back down on the floor and never touched my opponent and I got a whistle. It might be subconsious, but they *do* try to even up bad calls. Instead, they should just call each one as they see it and, if they screw up, they should say to themselves. "I blew that one and it's gone. Forget it."

A lot of guys in the pros are crybabies. I think that takes away from a player's effectiveness. How can he concentrate when he's moaning about a charging foul three plays back? He's talking, he's wasting his breath, he's getting more tired. The ref will never change his decision and just might say to himself, "Who does this guy think he is? The big star and he's going to call the game, too!" I've seen Oscar get mad at a lot of calls and they'll just call it on him again.

It's no secret that the referees let things get a lot rougher in the pros, but in the latter stages of a game they call it closer than in the beginning, and in the last five minutes they sometimes blow the whistle for meaningless little jostlings. And, basically, the home team gets most of the breaks. That's true in Madison Square Garden, Cobo Arena, Vets Memorial Coliseum in Phoenix or your local bowling lanes. I've seen teams I thought got screwed out of a game at our place and I know on the road we definitely have been.

Each ref is different. Some will let you get away with a certain trick or manevuer and some won't. With some officials I can fake up and then jump into a guy and I'll go to the line. With others the foul will be on me. I have to know the officials just like I have to know the ballplayers. And the refs get to know the players and the players' styles, too. The way you come into the league, and the way you play at first, is how they categorize you. It can be hard later to wiggle out of that pigeonhole if you should want to. Some don't want to, like Elgin Baylor; I think he travels every time he gets the ball. He's been walking through the NBA for 12 years! In my case, I can get all over a guy on defense and get away with it because I came into the league playing tough defense.

If it's a rookie versus a superstar, though, the foul is always on the newcomer. I've found that to be true and so, apparently, has Bob Cousy, who was an All-Time great with the Celtics and now coaches Cincinnati. Cooz decided to reactivate himself as a spot player for the Royals and in just six appearances (33 minutes) he got called for 11 personal fouls.

"They're treating me like a rookie," he said.

I committed fewer fouls last season than ever before, but I attribute it to experience, knowing when to press a man and when not to. Like when the tempo of a game is fast, I can't get all over a guy when we're on the road because the crowd's noisy disapproval will dictate that I'm fouling. Sometimes I can sense that the referee is just waiting for me to touch a man so he can call a foul and get the crowd off his back—again a subconscious thing. Most of the time on the road I play good defense, but I don't gamble as much trying to steal the ball.

In the Garden, when the crowd enthusiasm is at its peak, that's the time I try to make a steal. Most of the time the home team gets the advantage of the call, and then, too, I'm emotionally turned on because the crowd is cheering me and maybe I've made one or two steals before.

I can't end a discussion of referees without touching

on that great NBA custom, "giving fouls." A team is allowed four fouls a quarter. On the fifth or beyond, the opposition gets a bonus shot. If it is a one-shot foul, the injured party gets an extra free throw if he makes the first. On a two-shot foul, he gets three chances (if he needs them) to make the two. The idea is to penalize a team that is fouling too much. Well, some coach way back figured out that if his team didn't have many fouls near the end of a quarter, it would pay to "give" some. As soon as the opposition came over the mid-court line, the dribbler would be fouled on purpose and would get just one free throw, which would be better than giving his team the chance to make a basket (NBA teams make baskets a high percentage of the time).

Often a coach will have a foul-giving specialist on the bench so that some starter doesn't have to get a foul which might contribute to his fouling out later in the game. Mike Riordan on our club became locally famous in his rookie year for the conscientious way he took on this chore. When Mike developed into a valuable substitute, John Warren became the man. Mike would come in as if he was on the most important mission in the world, foul somebody and go right out amid standing ovations!

Last season we didn't get to give many because we usually reached our quota too soon—sometimes Willis gets a lot of fouls early. Also, a team that stresses tough defense—and the Knicks do—usually fouls more. When we do have a chance to give fouls, we try to give them and steal the ball, too. If you're going to give an intentional foul, why not go behind the opponent and maybe swipe the ball from him rather than just go up and hug him like a long-lost brother? We make sure we give the foul, though, like if I reach around Hal Greer and can't get the ball, I just continue up and grab his arm. Most of the teams still use the hugging technique. Larry Siegfried of the Celtics practically tackles you.

I can remember one night I really looked stupid. I thought I had come up with a great gimmick to foil the guy who obviously was going to foul me after I came across the line. I was just over the line, dribbling from left to right so that he was coming at my left side and my shooting arm would be free, and he, as usual, grabbed me. Just as he did I heaved the ball toward the basket 40 feet away, figuring I would get two free throws for being fouled in the act of shooting. But the ref didn't rule that I had been fouled in the act of shooting. He didn't rule that I had been fouled at all. He didn't call anything! The crowd was silent and the ball practically went over the backboard. I felt like an idiot.

Anyway, defense, movement, team—that's the name of the Knicks' game. We got it together for the '69-'70 season.

Chapter Twelve

Ice Water in My Veins

I CAN still remember clearly the feeling among the players in September 1969, when I reported for my third training camp with the Knicks. There was a confidence and an eagerness. I could sense that each guy thought we could win the championship, not just of the eastern division but of the whole league. We felt this was the year that the long hours of scouting, trading and coaching put in by Red Holmzan, Eddie Donovan and Dick McGuire would pay off. They had collected 12 players and 9 of us had been first-round draft choices. That included old man Dick Barnett, Syracuse's first pick ten years before, but didn't include Willis Reed, who, believe it or not, was second-round in 1964 (New York took Bad-News Barnes ahead of him).Willis was everything to the team. If the Knicks had lost me, I think they could have adjusted and won some games, maybe a lot of games, but without Willis our chances for any kind of championship would have been very slim. In this league you've got to have the big man, somebody who's going to get you the rebounds. Willis is so tough he squeezes the air out of the ball.

153

The way he shoots he can score big, and he can be intimidating on defense. He does a lot of things for us out there.

He's also one of the greatest guys I've ever met. There's nothing he wouldn't do for you, I mean anything in the way of money or helping you out with a speaking engagement—a real hard worker. I think being captain is really his thing. He seems to like accepting authority.

Willis has a great way with kids. I've seen him get surrounded by a pack of wild autograph hounds in the lobby of the Hotel New Yorker and make them back down and behave like little gentlemen. He won't stand for them interrupting an adult's conversation. The kids listen to him because he's a man's man, handsomely built with a rugged look. Most women I know dig him.

Dick Barnett's job with us was to score. He was underrated. Like the summer before camp people were saying to me, "What are you going to do with Barnett? You going to trade him?" Hell, I'd answer, we're going to play him! How could we trade him? He might look like he's half asleep all the time with those droopy eyelids, but this man averaged 17 points a game in '68-'69 and he figured to be good for as many the next season. He's a great shooter, he's experienced in the NBA and he *does* play tough defense. A lot of my steals I could attribute to Dick because he was helping out. We worked so well together that he knew just what I was going to do in a given situation.

Then we had Dave DeBusschere, whose job was twofold: help Willis on the boards and guard the other team's toughest forward, be it Gus Johnson or Elgin Baylor or Billy Cunningham. He has motivation, plus

he likes to play physical, he likes to bang into the man
he's guarding. Dave contributes to scoring, but he is not
a great shooter. Bradley we did count on for scoring
because he's a fine shooter and passer, but he doesn't go
to the boards that well. He's an in-betweener, meaning
most of the forwards he has to battle are bigger than he
is, which helps him on offense sometimes (he outquicks
them) but handicaps him on defense.

This was the combination that had worked so well at
the end of my second season and there wasn't much
doubt that Red was going to stick with it. And we had
an excellent bench. The guys came into the camp at
Farmingdale State University on Long Island anxious
to get started. I was as anxious as anybody because I
was in good shape, partly from working at Willis' summer camp in upstate New York.

I was also anxious because the club had done something very nice to jack up my spirits . . . they'd con-
tributed to my bank account.

My first contract with the Knicks was for three years
and, while it wasn't as lucrative as the ones Cazzie
Russell and Bill Bradley got, it was okay for a smallcol-
lege All-America. I mean when I was a kid in Atlanta,
flopping around in second-hand jerseys from the Carver
High School equipment room, I never dreamed I'd ever
be making that kind of money. But values, personal
and otherwise, change with age and experience and
after my second pro season, when I had become a
starter and had been voted the best defensive player in
the league, the club still had me for one year more at
the old bargain-basement prices. I wasn't happy about
it.

The Madison Square Garden managers are pretty hard-nosed. They don't miss too many angles, like they have provided no water fountains in the place. Why should free water be supplied when there are sodas and beer for sale? A fan forks over $7 for a loge seat at a Knick game, $7 for the first promenade, $6 for the court or second promenade and $4 for the mezzanine, so high up that to the spectators there Willis and I look like we're the same size. And just think how many sellout houses they've had—19,500 people buying those tickets and gobbling those frankfurters.

The Garden's got it, man, so why shouldn't it share the wealth? I figured the brass could tear up a player's contract and give him a better one if he was deserving. It had been done before.

I let my attorney, Norman Blass, take care of it. He handles a lot of contract negotiations and he's an old pro at the bargaining table. He knows what a lot of guys in the NBA are making because he negotiates for Walt Bellamy, Howard Komives, Dick and Tom Van Arsdale, Dick Barnett and others. Naturally, I had the final say-so, and if I didn't like what they came up with I could have said no. Norman sat down with Eddie Donovan and of course the Knicks wanted something in return, another year of my services, so the old three-year contract was ripped up and I signed a new two-year agreement, financially better than before. I hadn't been talking to the American Basketball Association, so they didn't *have* to give me a new deal, but they knew a happy worker is a productive worker.

If they hadn't given me a raise, I wouldn't have been mad or uncooperative because after all I *did* sign an agreement binding me for three years, but at the next bargaining session I would have tried to sock it to them. I might have been quite a bit more stubborn.

Experienced lawyers like Norman have an advantage knowing various salaries around the league. The players themselves just have to guess. In the pros discussing salaries is taboo (maybe in the amateurs it is, too). Nobody knows for sure what anybody else is making, which is probably a good thing for morale because maybe you consider yourself the star of the team and you'd be upset if somebody else was making more. It would be a bad situation. You can say what you guess a guy should be making, but whether he's making that or not you don't know.

I think any superstar in the league should be making $100,000 a year. John Havlicek of Boston is supposedly making $500,000 for four years. Baylor and West, they've got to making that much, and Alcindor, Oscar and Chamberlain. I'm not sure Billy Cunningham is there yet, but the next time his contract is up, or when he jumps to the ABA, he will be. Willis should be there after last season if he wasn't already. I think New York is the place to jump up fastest in salary. I think we're paid better than anybody else because we've got the market. The interest is there.

If Willis and I and some other don't get there, we're getting robbed. Look at these guys coming out of college, they're talking about a million dollars like it's a hundred dollars. It's fantastic, everybody's getting a million bucks to play ball. I don't know if the newspaper reports are true, but just half of the amounts they mention would be pretty good. I came along too soon.

As training camp started, my prediction was that the race would be between New York, Philadelphia and

Baltimore in the East, with Boston out of it. I thought Frank Deford of *Sports Illustrated* went out on a shaky limb picking Milwaukee first in the East because I couldn't see a team winning with just one man, even if that one man was Lew. In the West I thought the Lakers were the team. Atlanta had lost Zelmo Beaty and Paul Silas, 6 foot 9 and 6 foot 7, respectively, and I couldn't see them being that tough without Zelmo (who signed with the L.A. Stars of the ABA and sat out the season).

The rookies had to report to Farmingdale first and the veterans could come a week later, but most of the guys checked in early, which was another sign of our eagerness. Barnett and I were there, and so were Bill Hosket, Don May and Mike Riordan. Willis came in a few days later because he had his camp to finish up with and he was opening up a restaurant at 31st Street and Eighth Avenue—a Willis Reed coffee shop near the Garden.

Cazzie came in early, two days after the rookies, but I had seen him during the summer, up in the Catskills at the Maurice Stokes benefit game and at the Martin Luther King game in Philly, and I knew he would be running real well. Cazzie is a buff on physical fitness, so I guess nobody really doubted he'd be in shape, recovered from his ankle injury. Cazzie drinks carrot juice, wheat germ, everything (he got Barnett started on wheat germ). We call him "Stillman's," for Stillman's Gym. I don't think his various concoctions help that much because he still gets sick, tired and injured just like everybody else.

One thing that Cazzie exercises more than anything else is his jaw. He'll sometimes start correcting people's

English. The guys will be just talking, trying to explain something, and Cazzie will butt in with a correction. Then there are times, too, when you have to correct him and he really gets mad about that. But he can talk, that's for sure. When it's quiet and peaceful you know Cazzie isn't around. When he has to go to National Guard meetings, the bus is quiet. He yaks about anything and everything. It's amazing how he can do it.

One reason Caz came in early, besides wanting some ears to bend, was the stiff competition for the two forward spots. These guys really went after each other. Eventually, I think they realized it was not who started but who could help the team the most. Like there would be times when Bradley and DeBusschere weren't doing the job and Dave Stallworth and Cazzie would come in. Before, the competition hand been in the backcourt, but last season we were short on guards and heavy on the forwards.

We had a real good training camp even though most of the guys hate the exhibition season. It's so *boring*. You're doing the same thing over and over, playing in Bangor, Maine one night and Salem, Virginia another night, so you find you can't wait until the season starts. Exhibition games do serve a purpose in that they get you in shape and give the coach a chance to look at the rookies, but other than that they are really a drag.

In one workout at Farmingdale there were times we could have run a certain play if Willis would only take three steps and cross the lane, but he wanted us to reverse the ball all around the perimeter to the side where he was standing. I got pretty angry and the two of us got to bickering. It was a minor thing, coming from being bored with camp, doing the same stuff every day, seeing the same guys every day. It really had me down. Everybody knows your game down to the last ear wiggle and you can't fake anybody.

We started the practice schedule at Salem with a 15-point win over Baltimore. I was sharp: 9 of 11 from the floor, 19 points and 10 rebounds. Then we had a wild fourth quarter against Detroit in Grand Rapids and beat them by 10. Their coach, Butch van Breda Kolff, wasn't too impressed. He should have been.

One of the big events of the exhibition season was Alcindor's debut in the Garden (New York City is his hometown and he starred in high school there), but it was just another game to me. The night before we had played in Trenton, New Jersey, an overtime game with Philly. The gym in Trenton was really packed and it was hot. I played 47 minutes and Willis played 46, so Milwaukee the next day caught us flat and dehydrated. Still it meant a lot to beat Philly, to show them we could beat them. It put something on their minds that carried over into the regular season.

We had a rookie named Milt Williams from Lincoln University in Jefferson City, Missouri. He was looking real tough. He had a chance to make the squad. As a matter of fact, he stayed until the last cut. He was looking better than Mike Riordan in the training period and put a lot of pressure on Mike. When we started playing exhibition games, Mike came on more, gained a lot of confidence and played good ball for us.

Williams was about 6 foot 1 or 6 foot 2, a great jumper—he could stuff the ball—and fast, the fastest guy in camp. Quickness and speed, he had both of them, and he's a good shooter and a good team player. I had trouble stopping him. He tried out with the

Knicks the year before, too, and didn't make it. This time I think he went down to Allentown in the Eastern League. You would think the last cut from the Knicks would get picked up by some weaker NBA team, but I guess the other clubs didn't know about him.

Red gave us a mild little pep talk before the season, nothing rah-rah, just sensible and low-key like always.

"We've got a great team, but we've got to go out on the court and prove it," he said. "We've got the press clippings saying we're great, but we have to show the other teams we are."

The guys believed we could do it, too, as I said. We had a meeting without Holzman in which Captain Willis talked, and if anybody else had anything to say, they could. The gist of it was we thought we had a great team and could go all the way, but we had to play together. There were no emotional teary speeches, just low-key stuff.

We started off the season with an easy 25-point victory over Seattle and it seemed like everybody on the team played well. One of the nice things about the whole evening in the Garden was the standing ovation Stallworth got when he was introduced. Then he played 14 minutes and had 8 points and 6 rebounds, pretty good for a guy with a history of heart trouble.

Dave the Rave was an excellent player at Wichita State (he left school at midterm of his senior year and played for an AAU team with Nate Bowman) and was the Knicks' second choice after Bradley. He averaged 12.6 points a game as a rookie, which is very good, and he was the sixth man the next year until he suffered a heart attack in Fresno, California, on March 4, 1967.

The official name for it was a "posterior coronary." He was only 25 years old.

I was still in college when he had to leave the team. The Knicks were my favorites to watch before I was drafted by them. I liked Barnett for being colorful and Rave was coming into his own then—peole had predicted he would be one of the best forwards in the league in a couple of years.

The game in Fresno was against San Francisco and Rave complained about chest pains and dizziness during the warm-ups and played just a few minutes. The team flew to Frisco that night and he was examined the next day and pronounced fit. He actually played against the Warriors and only had to leave the game because of a leg injury! When the Knicks went back to New York, he was put in St. Clare's Hospital on the West Side. They found heart damage. He was in there for 34 days. I can imagine how he felt, feeling that his career in basketball was over.

A thing like that really shocks people into seeing a need for an education or for something else to switch to. One injury—and it doesn't have to be as serious as a posterior coronary—could end a career.

Rave became coach of an amateur team in Wichita and his weight eventually started going up. He did a little scouting for the Knicks, too. Then one game near the end of my second season the Knicks announced he was coming back. He was in to see a doctor about his heart, but I thought he was just having a checkup. There were rumors he was okay through some miracle, but I never believe rumors until they're verified. I was excited.

It was obvious in camp that he had lost some of his

maneuverability, but there were signs that he was get-ting some of his old Dave-the-Rave moves back.

Early in the season we were playing real good team defense and the knowledgeable Knick fans recognized it as the chief reason for our success. They were fully appreciative when we held a team under 100 points. They started yelling at the ends of games for us to be as stingy as possible. We managed to hold the opposition to two figures in 12 of our first 21 games. The players got a kick out of it, too, because we wanted to have the best defensive average in the NBA. Another thing was that it embarrassed the other team, not being able to go over 100 in a professional game. To me it was like pitching a shutout and I'm sure the other teams felt that way, too, because when they saw they only had 99 points they really hustled to get a basket—and we worked much harder to stop them.

Most of the yelling was probably from the gamblers who were worried or happy aboout the point spread, but it kept us keyed up. Even when the first five got to sit down early, it was exciting to watch the second team play. It was a great feeling because we knew we were preserving ourselves for the next game while giving the reserves some needed working time.

Our toughest test early in the season was against L.A. It was a hell of a game. It had everything, including great shooting. Jerry West put on an offensive show (42 points). He made something like 11 points in a row in one stretch. He was driving, he was hitting the open man, he was doing it all. I didn't think he could have too many more nights like that. But we won 99 to 96. Barnett had only one point at the half, but he got 20 in the second half and pulled us out of that game. I think

Riordan was really helping Dick by coming in and playing good ball so Barnett could get a longer rest on the bench. I got 19 points and 12 assists.

Some people knock pro basketball and say it isn't worth going to a game until the last quarter because what goes on in the first three doesn't matter. I think that's baloney. A lot of games are decided in the last five minutes, but isn't that true in a lot of sports? You can't tell me that that Laker game wasn't fun to watch in the first and second quarters. True, in the pro game a 20- or 25-point lead can disappear quickly, but those rallies that a trailing team can make are great for the spectators. Whenever we play Baltimore, Boston, Philadelphia, L.A. or a lot of other teams, there is action right from the start, action that will have a bearing on the final result.

We won our first five games and then lost at home to San Francisco 112 to 109 and, boom, we slipped from first to third! It was just a temporary slip, though, because Milwaukee and Philadelphia had played fewer games. The Warrior game was one of those nights when everybody was off. There were times when we had rallies going, but we could never catch them. Surprisingly, they beat us even though Nate Thurmond got thrown out of the game in the first period. This might have had a psychological effect on both teams. We thought we had the game all locked up and they knew they had to work harder to make up for Thurmond's absence.

After that loss we went on a tear like nothing the NBA had ever seen. We beat Baltimore by 29, Detroit by 24, Atlanta by 24, Sandiego by 13. We were making believers out of scoffers.

We played Atlanta in the Garden on October 28 and it was televised down to Georgia. My family was watching, so I wanted to play well because they don't get that many opportunities to see me play. Like in college they never saw me play until the NIT. All those years they could only read the clippings I sent them. Most all write-ups are the same, but when you see the game in person, it makes a difference. Well, the Knicks put on a great passing exhibition that night (37 assists), but I was in foul trouble early—three in the first period—and played only 17 minutes. I guess I was too keyed up, trying too hard. Bradley went to the backcourt part of the time I was on the bench and it was funny, a different look with him handling the ball. Riordan played well, too.

"Well, Riordan's taking your place," some friends of mine kidded me the next day.

"Yeah, it looks that way," I said.

"You gotta score twenty points tonight," they said, "or maybe thirty to get even for that game."

"I hope I can," I said.

"I never thought I'd score 43!

I never thought I'd do it in *any* game because I didn't think I shot enough. Even that night in the course of the game against San Diego I didn't realize I had that many. The night didn't start off with any good omen—I even had worn a very conservative outfit for me, a blue suit with a red sport shirt. But I kept pumping them in, a basket here and a basket there, and I just kept going to the free-throw line (I had 15 for 19 from there). But at times in the game I coud see them flash up on the scoreboard something like, "Clyde has 35 points."

I didn't really try to turn it on after that. I still tried to play good team ball, passing off and hitting the open man, but that night it seemed I was open more often than the rest of the guys. I'd come over a screen and the shot would be there, so I was taking it, plus I got a lot of backdoor plays with Bradley where if I didn't get the basket I got fouled.

The most I ever scored in college was 33, I think against Kentucky Wesleyan when I was a sophomore.

Red took me out with three minutes to go and the fans in the Garden gave me a standing ovation, quite a tribute. I was awed. I've heard a lot of ovations, but these people were really stomping.

Then the crowd started yelling, "We want Clyde!" Red said he hadn't realized how many points I had; he was sort of apologizing for taking me out. I told him in my noblest tone of voice, "It doesn't matter, just as long as we won the game."

I doubt if I would have tried to break any records anyway because I am not the kind of player who would just go in a game and pump, pump, pump.

I would like to have done all that heroic stuff in front of my family, but they still got to read about it and most of them wrote me to congratulate me.

I think that 43 psyched me up. Whenever we played the Rockets I thought I was a big scorer. It seems like everybody in our league has a pet team they really do well against and San Diego must be mine. Everybody takes a turn guarding me, Stu Lantz, Hambone Wlliams, Bernie Williams. The nights we play the Rockets I seem to penetrate well; I don't know if it's because they don't help out on defense or what. For instance, later in the season I had 32 points and 11 assists against them in an easy 13-point win.

We had won eight straight when we came into L.A. early in November. Wilt Chamberlain had hurt his knee, the first serious injury he's had in the pros. He had been operated on the day before the game. I didn't know what to feel. It would help us to have him out of there, but you don't want to see a player as great as Wilt out of the sport. I was sort of depressed because he draws a lot of people and he brings a lot of interest to basketball. The same thing could happen to me, it could happen to anybody. While we were on the west coast, people kept comparing it to Elgin's knee injury, but I believe Baylor was only 30 when he had his operation. Wilt was 33 and then, too, he has a lot more weight than Elgin to carry around with him. The doctors weren't so optimistic, but Wilt was. He said he'd be back in six to eight weeks.

The irony of the whole thing was that a lot of people said he was licking his chops this season with Bill Russell gone. And he had been playing great ball, averaging something like 35 points a game.

The Lakers were still tough for us because they had Elgin and Jerry West. And Bradley, only 6 foot 5, had to guard Mel Counts, a 7 footer and a pretty fair shooter. Then Dave DeBusschere got his nose broken. It happened early in the second half on a defensive rebound. Somebody, I think West, took a shot and missed, Dave got the rebound and he had the ball out in front of him, ready to pass it off. I was about ten feet away from him, standing at the sideline in front of the Knick bench. He was about at the free-throw line and Rick Roberson, a big rookie from Cincinnati, reached for the ball and—I mean it sounded like WHACK! You could hear it all over the place. Everybody in the stands moaned and groaned. Dave went down and I thought he was knocked out, but later the public-address announcer said he had a broken nose. I didn't run over to look because I can't stand to see injuries like that.

The ball rolled away when he fell and they got a basket! Mel Counts just picked up the ball and made a lay-up. There was no foul called. We argued with the official and he said, "I heard it, but I didn't see it." Man, the bodies in Inglewood Cemetery *heard* it. In spite of losing Dave the rest of the game and giving up that free basket, we won 112 to 102.

I didn't see Dave until the next day in the hotel when we were ready to get on the bus. His nose had not swelled much and you couldn't even tell it had been busted, except that his eyes were blackened a little. He didn't have any trouble breathing. It was a clean break. All they had to do was just snap his nose back in place, a little operation I'm glad I missed seeing. Pro basketball is a tough sport.

We had a day off, then Dave played a great game against San Francisco, pulling us out near the end with his shooting and rebounding. Maybe he scared the Warriors with the weird mask he had to wear.

We won our 11th straight game against Chicago 114 to 99 and I was bubbling in the dressing room. I couldn't wait for the next game. We really thought we couldn't lose.

The more you win the harder it is to lose and the Knicks just kept on winning. Generally the games weren't even close until we arrived at the Spectrum in

Philly late in November to go for our 14th straight win. On paper it figured to be easy because the 76ers had lost four in a row and *six* in a row at home. We had a bad night, though, and it was nip and tuck at the end.

Twice I had chances to ice the game in the last 15 seconds, but in that short space of time I made only two of six free throws. When you get three chances to make two from the foul line and you blow all three, it's what we call "doing the hat trick." We were leading 94 to 92 when I got fouled and missed the second and third free throws. Billy Cunningham put in a sort of jump hook to bring Philly to within one point, then I got fouled again. This time I missed the first two and had the hat trick staring me in the face, but I made the third. We hung on to win 98 to 94 when Reed intercepted a pass, was fouled and made two free throws. After that game the guys gave me the concrete hands bit.

The NBA record for consecutive victories was 17, set by the Washington Capitols in 1946 and tied later by Boston. We wanted to go down in the record books, and our chance for the 17th straight couldn't have come in a nicer place, Atlanta. My mother, all of my sisters and my brother were there. It cost me a little money because John Warren has relatives down there and some of the other guys have gotten to know some Atlanta people. It's not so easy to get extra player tickets now. (Each player gets three tickets for Garden games and two tickets for road games. When we go to Atlanta, I try to collect everybody's comps; DeBusschere's big in Detroit, Cazzie in Chicago and Bradley has a lot of friends in Boston.)

We live in the Marriott in Atlanta, which isn't far

from my house, maybe a 15-minute ride by cab. So I go home and maybe go up to Howard to see my highschool coach and mess around. It depends on how I feel. If I'm tired, I stay in and just call them on the phone and tell them how many tickets I've got. I set a record one game: 17! My mother, my aunts, my grandmother, my sisters—I had a whole cheering section that game.

So far in Atlanta I've played well, but up to this game for our 17th straight you'd never know I was from there. They never write anything in the paper, never say anything in reference to me being from there. "Did you go to school here?" Red used to ask me. "Did you really live here?"

In Detroit and Chicago they're all for Cazzie because he played at the University of Michigan and Carver High in Chicago, but those two are more basketball-conscious towns. Maybe if I were white, I'd be spread all over the Atlanta papers. Even when I was a highschool hotshot at Howard, the papers didn't have much coverage of our games. It's not much different with Cleon Jones and Tommie Agee of the New York Mets, both from Mobile, Alabama. It took them a lot longer than it should have to be recognized in their hometown.

"I must have asked twenty or thirty people about you in the white community and only two or three knew you were from here," an Atlanta sports writer told me early last season. "The blacks all knew and were proud that you'd made good."

Then a local radio station called me the day of the game and said they were going to give me a trophy for being an inspiration to the community, to the kids. I thought they were just going to come to the arena and send the trophy to the locker room. I was a little surprised that it was a ceremony before the game, but I should have realized the station wanted to get some publicity out of it, which was fine with me. I gave the trophy to my brother Keith. I could see in his eyes that he wanted to keep it. From the way he was hugging it, I don't think he would have let me have it anyway.

The Hawks were leading the western division, but they might as well have been the Howard High Rams the way we blew them out in the third quarter. We outscored them 38 to 12 in that period and, although the official box score said Atlanta had only 22 turnover, Leonard Lewin of the New York *Post* had me down for 15 steals alone, 7 in the third quarter. Even Richie Guerin, the Hawks' coach, didn't believe the official stats and said, "Frazier showed the best individual effort and the Knicks showed me the best team performance that I have ever seen. He stole everything but our sneakers."

The chance to break the victory-streak record came in front of more than 10,000 fans at Cleveland Arena, the first neutral court we had played on all season. We played Cincinnati, which had won three in a row and was going pretty good. It turned out to be the most exciting basketball game I've ever been in.

The Royals played well and when their coach, Bob Cousy, coming in for little bits here and there at the age of 41, hit two free throws to make it 105 to 100, all I could think about was that the streak was over and we'd have to start a new one. With 16 seconds to go, Reed made two foul shots. It was 105 to 102 and still hopeless. Then Cousy threw the ball in, DeBusschere intercepted and went all the way in to score. I was thinking, "This is just making it worse because we're getting close but still can't win."

Cousy inbounded the ball to Tom Van Arsdale. I've wondered since what their hurry was. They could have killed a second or two in the backcourt. But no, he rushed out of bounds and threw the ball to Tom, who rushed it up court. Just out of sheer habit, I guess, I was trailing the play, running lackadaisically. I saw Willis tip the ball and it came to me in a crowded tangle of players near mid-court.

I had to make one behind-the-back dribble to get by Norm Van Lier. I didn't know how many seconds were left on the clock. I could have hit DeBusschere with a pass, but I figured the clock would run out, so I dribbled as close as I could to get off a shot and threw it up. My momentum carried me toward the basket. The ball hit the back of the rim and came straight out—it went over Connie Dierking's head and Willis' head to me. I was on the way up with the rebound to shoot when Van Arsdale fouled me. If he hadn't, it might have gone in because I had enough time to catch it in midair, pause and shoot with good aim.

There I was lying on the floor thinking, "Why me?" I wished the jumper had gone in. I would have felt a lot better. Scenes from the Philly game were dancing in my head. I had three chances to make two and I never doubted I was going to make one of them, but the big thing was making the first one. I knew I had to come through. If I missed those shots I wasn't going back to the dressing room. My two free throws hardly tickled the net. No concrete in these hands. After the game I remember kidding with with the press. "I've got ice water in my veins!" I said.

Two seconds were all that were left and Willis intercepted their inbounds pass. We had won, 106 to 105.

We ran off the court and one of the guys on the team kissed me on the way to the dressing room! It was chaos in there. After it was over we couldn't believe it. We'd actually won 18 in a row.

Chapter Thirteen

Nothing on Ice but Beer

RED so thoroughly indoctrinated us with team defense and all-around team play that it even got into our hair, like greasy kid stuff. Since Madison Avenue is pretty close to Madison Square Garden, it was natural when we were going so well that Vitalis would want to use us in a color television commercial. Originally it was for the five starters, but Red insisted that everybody had to be in on it, so that's the way it was, with all of us sharing, including Red and Danny Whelan. It would have been a lot of money for five guys because even when it was split 14 ways each man got $500. Lucky we weren't a football team.

For team morale it was a good thing, but I couldn't see doing it for everyone. Teamwork can go too far.

The commercial, shown over and over on national TV, starts with Barnett, DeBusschere, Reed and me being introduced before a game. Then the fifth starter, Donnie May, comes out to the free-throw line and we all slap hands and we notice May's hands are greasy. Willis checks out Donnie's hair and discovers he's still using that greasy gunk. Back he goes to the bench, all downcast, and Red sends in Mike Riordan, who presumably has his handsome Irish head soaked in non-greasy Vitalis. (A better idea would be for some ad agency for a packing house to case Mike in a hot dog commercial.)

Well, a couple of questions came out of this. Why May and Riordan in staring roles instead of Cazzie and Stallworth? Obviously because Vitalis wanted to have another white guy in the starting lineup with DeBusschere. It wanted sales promotion aimed at both races.

Second, why wasn't Bradley in the original starting lineup instead of May, who didn't get to play much during the season? Because Bill doesn't do commercials or endorse anything, or at least he hasn't so far. I think there's something in his contract that if he appears in an advertisement the Knicks get most of the money, or anyway half of it. Bill is willing to do some things for nothing if they're good causes, fighting poverty, things like that.

Bill did get involved in one business venture with the team, the Bench Warmers Club. In fact, he came up with the plan and presented it to us before the season. We told him it sounded good and he should go ahead. The idea was for the Knick players to be the board of directors of the organization and charge members $200 a year. We would send five boys to basketball camp and make ourselves a little money, too. The ad in *The New York Times* sports section said:

"You could be one of 100 New York executives who will attend private lunches with the Knick players. . . . This is *not* a group of fans or boosters. It is a Charter

Club run by the Knick players themselves. They will be present at every superb luncheon.

"From the beginning, you'll be first-naming each other. You'll get to know each other the way only fellow players usually do. Better than just reading about them, or watching them on TV.

"The Club meets eight times between mid-January and the end of the regular season. The players have reserved a private floor at New York's most dapper restaurant: Spats!

"The players will all be there. You'll rub elbows, bend elbows (maybe even cross swords). . . ."

The applications deadline was January 14 and I guess not enough came in because we dropped the project. Bill said it had cost about $5,000. I think he was doing the Bench Warmers thing for the good of the team, not for himself. It's too bad it didn't work out. I didn't put out any money on it. I think Bill did.

But basketball was still our main business. After that 18th straight win at Cleveland we came home to lose to Detroit 110 to 98, our only loss the entire month of November. We hardly stole a ball all night and didn't put on any of our usual scoring bursts. We came out on the floor for the start of the game and the Garden fans, many of whom had seen the record-breaking game on television, gave us a terrific ovation, and at the end, when it was certain we were going to end the streak, they actually applauded us.

We should never have lost to the Pistons. It was unlikely they would make the play-offs or even come close. Boston, too, didn't seem to have a very good chance, especially after we made up for some of the wrongs the Celtics had done us in the past and smashed them 113 to 98 on November 15 in the Garden. At one time we led by 25 points.

I was surprised we beat them so easily. It was never a contest. They showed nothing of the old Celtic spirit. You could see they really missed Russell—it's amazing how one man can leave a team and it just goes to nothing. Bailey Howell, Satch Sanders and Larry Siegfried weren't playing too well and I thought the whole Boston system was centered too much around John Havlicek. He had to bring the ball up, he had to shoot, he had to go to the boards and play defense. It was asking a lot of him. They played us much better in later games, but up to then they were weak.

It was disappointing (speaking as a fan) that the season Russell decided to leave sports and go to Hollywood was the same season Alcindor arrived on the scene. It wasn't a case of Bill ducking a challenge. He certainly didn't run away in 1959 when Chamberlain came into the league with a big reputation.

I saw Lew in the summer before the season started, up in the Catskills, at the Stokes benefit game, and he looked damn good to me. He was quick, and he could go around an opponent from about eight feet out and stuff the ball—with just one giant step.

Moving left to right across the key, he could reach out and drop it in, like a normal person would throw a wadded-up piece of paper in a wastebasket. He stuffed the ball once against Wilt in the Stokes game. And the first time Wilt got the ball *he* stuffed, too. He took it right to the rookie, but there wasn't much body contact under here. They didn't keep Lew in for that long, so he and Wilt couldn't really go at it, but the times he was in there Lew looked good.

The first time we played Milwaukee in the regular season was in the Garden before a typical Saturday-night sellout house. Willis got in early foul trouble. Nate Bowman played for 27 minutes and did a good job: 12 points and 8 rebounds. But Nate eventually got six fouls and Willis, with five came back in. We had a big lead late in the second half, but we blew it and almost blew the game because the Bucks went into a good press. Lew ended up with 36 points and Flynn Robinson had 34.

The Bucks had won only 27 games the previous season, which is why they had a shot at drafting Lew (they were last in the East and Phoenix was last in the West, but the Bucks won the coin flip for first pick). We had beaten them six straight times in the pre-Lew days. After that first game with Lew, though, I realized they would be tough. They were well coached by Larry Costello and they had a good running game. Flynn had been troublesome for the Knicks at both ends of the court, Jon McGlocklin was playing good ball and they had a good rookie, Bob Dandridge, a fourth-round draft choice from Norfolk State (in Earl Monroe's old college league). I still felt they had too young a team and that as the season went on it would tell.

The following Monday night in Milwaukee, Willis destroyed Alcindor, socking it to him good. He made Lew look bad, probably the worst he looked all year. I guess Willis was psyched up for him. We played them again December 6 and Dollar Bill and I scored 29 points apiece (I hit 13 of 17 from the floor) and we won going away 124 to 99. It was our 26th win in 28 games, tying the record start of the 76ers in '66-'67. A few nights later we beat them again, the tenth straight time over two seasons, but with 8:24 to go I had to leave the game with a groin injury.

I faked a shot before going up, then took the shot and as I came down I felt the pull. I only missed one game, versus Seattle, but we lost the next three in a row and people were beginning to feel we were human after all.

The Bucks began to pick up steam in December, won quite a few in a row and on January 2 finally beat us 118 to 105 in Milwaukee. I had 27 points and 13 assists, but Willis, bothered by stomach pain that was diagnosed after the game as hyperacidity, got outplayed by Lew, 41 points to 16, 16 rebounds to 9. The Bucks were getting experience fast and Lew's offense was improving rapidly. The 13-point margin made it our worst loss up to that time, a crummy way to end the first half of the season.

On January 14 each member of the Bucks got a nice bonus, ten shares in Milwaukee Professional Sports and Services Inc. (the parent company of the club), which had closed the previous day at 13½. Two coaches, the trainer and the equipment man also got ten shares.

The team that seemed to be the slump breaker for us was Baltimore. After our 18-game winning streak we won only five of ten games. We were a little down when we got the Bullets in the Garden five days before Christmas. We came alive and won by 37 points, 128 to 91, which meant that in the calendar year 1969 we had beaten them 10 out of 11 games. Barnett and I combined for 55 points and I also had 14 assists and 8 rebounds. The Bullets were not passing well or playing good defense.

Baltimore turned up on our schedule again eight

games later, just when we badly needed another boost. We had lost at Milwaukee January 2 and the following night Boston Coach Tom Heinsohn had the Celtics running like their old selves in the Garden. They beat us 111 to 104. So we had lost two games in a row, Willis was still bothered by stomach cramps—although the team doctor said it was nothing serious—and we were about to start on a potentially dangerous road trip: 8 games in 15 days.

Keeping us out of New York for two weeks was not a plot by the commissioner's office. It happens to us every season when the Ice Capades come into town and take over the Garden.

The first game on the trip was in Baltimore's Civic Center and we poured it on against the Bullets again. DeBusschere hit 9 of 11 shots from the floor and held Gus Johnson to 14 points. Willis outrebounded Westley Unseld in a battle of linebackers, 22 to 20. I scored 19 points and had 10 assists. Red had mostly subs in for the final 12 minutes and we won in a breeze, 129 to 99.

It was in Baltimore that I found out I had been named to a starting guard's spot in the annual NBA All-Star game. Willis told me. There was a newspaper strike down there then, but he heard it on a news broadcast. The other East starters were going to be Willis, John Havlicek, Billy Cunningham and Oscar Robertson. DeBusschere was on the second team. Pretty good company. It was an honor and a thrill for me, but I'll have to admit I wasn't surprised. I knew I had a good chance because we were in first place.

The easy win over the Bullets and the All-Star news got us off to an exciting start on the road trip and the

15 days didn't turn out to be such an ordeal after all. We won six of the eight games, and although we were gone a long time we had quite a few days off. I kept the up-coming All-Star game out of my mind and just tried to keep up with what city we were in.

What messed up the trip somewhat was a convention in Detroit that hogged all the hotel rooms. We had to stay across the river in Windsor, Ontario, for four days. Try finding excitement in Windsor, Ontario. We were there from Tuesday to Friday and all I did was walk downstairs to eat and go back up to bed. It was a nice little holiday for DeBusschere because Detroit is his hometown.

Actually we had staggered through a far more trying trip late in December—a quickie, no-sleep tour of the Far West. We beat Detroit in the Garden by one point Christmas night, then caught a midnight flight to Los Angeles. We arrived at L.A. International Airport at 3:30 A.M. (6:30 New York time). We lost by 12 points that night at the Forum. We were up at 6:45 the next morning for a flight to Vancouver that arrived at 11:15 A.M. That night we beat Seattle by two. We were rousted out of bed at 5:45 A.M. for a six-hour, three-stop flight to Phoenix and beat the Suns that night by 19. How, I don't know. We flew home, finishing off a trip of more than 7,000 miles. We changed our name from the Knicks to the Zombies.

That trip was unusually brutal, but constant travel is one of the serious drawbacks of working in the NBA. (Baseball players have to travel all the time, too, but their sport is much less demanding. They don't have to be constantly running, stopping and starting.) Sometimes it seems like I'm living out of my Adidas bag. In and out of buses, airports, hotels and arenas, not to mention time zones.

We usually fly tourist, and tourist sections were not built for extra-long men. If a flight is more than two hours, we're supposed to go first class. Most of the time we're traveling at night with no one else on the plane except the crew. We get the aisle seats and stretch out—our legs a menace to anybody trying to reach the lavatories.

Most of the guys kill time on flights by reading. Some guys sleep. Cazzie is always horsing around, talking to the stewardesses, other passengers or whoever will listen to his chatter. He and Bowman and Barnett sometimes get to reminiscing about their off-court exploits. I'll usually read a magazine, sleep or think about the next game. Sometimes I'll get restless and stand in the aisle to relax. I'll do that on a bus, too, when my legs are tight.

Having the press travel with us is great. The Ratpack we call them, because they're always in a group. When we're winning we have more writers than players. For instance, on the 18-game streak we must have had 18 writers with us—the regular men on the Knicks beat, columnists, magazine writers, guys working on pro-basketball books. At half time at some of the games they'd introduce the New York press: Lewin from the *Post,* Tom Rogers from the *Times,* Murray Janoff from Long Island, Bob Harding from New Jersey and on and on.

I accept the lack of privacy that goes with having the Ratpack along. If you're nobody, nobody wants to know your life. If you're somebody, you have to pay the price of being in the limelight. The writers don't follow us around after games and they usually give us good write-ups, so there are few complaints from the players. The more you keep your name in the public eye, the better off you are for endorsements and business opportunities, but some athletes can't take it. Roger Maris, when he was hitting home runs like crazy for the Yankees, maybe blew a fortune because he couldn't, or wouldn't, talk to the writers. They cut him up and ran him out of town. Each of them has a newspaper and you haven't, and that makes it senseless to feud.

The great thing about having them along is that the fans in New York will know how we're playing. They won't have to rely on shorter AP and UPI reports. This kind of keeps us on our toes. I confess I like to know what the writers are saying about me, but I never knock them if they knock me. The New York writers, as in most places, can be cold. When the team is losing, they sometimes get down on us. I know they have to write what the people want to read. This is their job. Somethings I might not like, but I don't speak up. At least I haven't so far.

My roommate on the road most of last season was Donnie May. He's similar to me in that he's quiet. We didn't get in each other's way, even though he likes to get up early and I love to sleep late. He had been away in the Reserves the previous summer, so he had this insane idea about getting up at eight o'clock, even without reveille, and going down to breakfast. I never ate breakfast. He'd come back up and I'd still be in bed. He'd wonder if I was ever going to rejoin society. A nice, quiet-spoken, conservative guy. We got along very well.

Guys on the team joked all the time with him and Bill Hosket about their hometown, Dayton, because there's nothing going on there. Both of them love Dayton, though, and love to go back there. I don't think they like New York. Too much of a rat race. Donnie and Bill played on the same high-school team but went to different colleges, May to the University of Dayton and Hosket to Ohio State, where his father had been a basketball star. Bill tries dressing like May, conservative style. His real first name is Wilmer.

The two of them hung around together most of the time on the road and were always telephoning each other. Donnie would call Hosket at two o'clock in the morning and Hosket would leave a wake-up call for Donnie at five in the morning, which of course woke me up, too.

I don't know exactly how Red decides who's going to room with whom. It's probably the players' own choices most of the time, with veterans getting first pick. I was the only black with a white guy (the Knicks had seven blacks and five whites, so there had to be at least one "integrated" room). There are some guys on any team who can't get along living in the same room, like Nate used to room with May and they couldn't hit it off. Nate likes jazz music, and Donnie probably doesn't. So for this one trip, management changed things around and I moved in with Donnie and Nate moved in with my roommate, Stallworth. It worked out and it was kept that way (we usually keep the same roommate for the entire season).

I take along a radio-tape recorder on trips, but I'm very versatile and I'll listen to a station that plays black, white and in-between music, so we didn't have a problem. Most of the time Donnie was out anyway.

The radio-tape recorder is my best friend on the road. I usually tape different sounds from different cities and it keeps me occupied because most of the time during the day in these NBA towns there's nothing on TV but soap operas. I get out of bed at about 11 A.M., go down to the lobby and get a newspaper or two and go back up to the room, where I can ad-lib until maybe it's time for the pre-game meal, which we don't all take together. I like to eat early, maybe around two or three o'clock. Some other guys like to eat at four or five. (We get $16 a day for meals.)

San Francisco is the choice town of all the players. It's beautiful. One reason we like it so much is that we stay at the Jak Tar downtown, right where the action is, not far from Union Square, North Beach and Fisherman's Wharf. One time I went down to Fisherman's Wharf with Willis and watched him put away two and a half steaks. The one drawback is that the Warriors play one time in Oakland, the next time in the Civic Auditorium, the next in the Cow Palace. No steady home court. But I guess that's more of a disadvantage to the home team than to the visitors.

The worst place in the league to visit is Chicago. It seems to be always snowing and cold and it used to be that the fans didn't come out. It was like playing in front of ghosts until attendance picked up last season. Chicago is the best place for me, though, because I can visit Walt III. He's doing fine, growing fast, talking all the time. "I saw you on television, dada," he told me. "You had the ball."

In so many cities that might be fun to visit such as

L.A., San Diego, Phoenix and Philly, we stay in motels out in nowhere land and we can't walk around. They're out on freeways lined with nothing but motels, franchise coffee shops, fried-chicken take-out places and pancake houses. The players don't like it.

Getting back to the eight-game road trip, it actually was a *nine*-game trip for Red, DeBusschere, Willis and me because the All-Star game was wedged in there between visits to Boston and Chicago. Red was the East coach because the Knicks were in first place as of January 12.

Just like in baseball, the All-Star is a big social event, a showcase for the sport. Everybody is there: owners, general managers, coaches, fans, writers. It's a big mid-season convention of professional basketball. The players didn't mingle that much because we didn't show up until the day before. The one practice was more like a press conference. We got suited up and went out on the court but didn't do much of anything. We didn't have plays, so we had to just play basic, fundamental basketball. That's about all you can do in a game like that, play it by ear. Because of that I don't think All-Star games are too exciting. Players are reluctant to do things because they don't know what the other guys are going to do.

The 20th annual NBA All-Star game was in Philly on January 20, on a snowy, miserable night. I didn't like the game itself too much because there were so many substitutions and time-outs that I couldn't pick up the tempo. We couldn't keep up the momentum. Two times we lost interest when we were far ahead and the West closed the gap. We got a little lackadaisical out there.

The East won 142 to 135, but you've got to remember that the West didn't have Chamberlain (he was still out with his knee injury) or Thurmond. Nate tore some cartilage in his right knee a few days before the All-Star and was lost to the Warriors for the season. He was averaging 23 points and 18 rebounds a game when he got hurt.

So the starting West center was Elvin Hayes of San Diego. He did very well, making 24 points for highman honors. Oscar scored 21 and passed Bob Pettit as the All-Star game's all-time leading scorer. It was the tenth such game Oscar had played in. Willis, with 21 points, 11 rebounds and a very strong first quarter, was named most valuable player. The voting wasn't close at all.

In the locker room afterward the players were being interviewed and signing each other's programs for souvenirs. In walked Willis with a big grin on his face, lugging the MVP trophy. You'd never have known by his appearance or his play that he had been having stomach problems off and on or that some people thought he had an ulcer.

He was in so much pain after one game that we had to help him lie down in the locker room and relax. He took some tests before the All-Star, got some medication to take and he seemed all right after that. Maybe he had some roots and herbs sent up from his relatives in Louisiana.

Willis was not ulcerated. We had survived the long road trip. We had a comfortable lead in the eastern division. It seemed all we had to do was play halfway decent ball, avoid serious injuries and we could coast in. We won 10 out of 11 after the All-Star break.

Things were breaking right for us, but there were some aches and pains.

Fortunately we had a fairly durable team. Some guys in the league are just accident-prone, like Nate Thurmond and Gus Johnson. These men are strong, but they seem to be hurt every year. Jerry West seems to have the most things happen to him. One time in my second year West got his nose broken in a game against us. The game was over for all intents and purposes and somebody tapped the ball away from him with only about three seconds left. He ran by Willis and Willis happened to raise his elbow. Bang—West had another broken nose, one of many. The Knicks in '69-'70 were luckier.

DeBusschere had a sore back late in January and missed three games. Stallworth stepped into the starting slot. I think Red's thinking at the time went like this: Cazzie gives us instant scoring. He's probably the best shooter on the team, but there are things he doesn't do. He's pretty bad on defense and he doesn't rebound— he's better coming off the bench whenever the team bogs down.

However, in the third game DeBusschere missed, January 25 at Boston, Cazzie came in off the bench and was just filling the basket with balls. He scored 25 points, his season high, on 12 of 17 field-goal attempts. We broke away from the Celtics in the fourth quarter and it was Russell's shooting that was mainly responsible.

Bradley's left ankle was the most serious problem we had in the second half of the season. He hurt it against Boston late in January and missed all but 86 seconds of the next two games. Then he came back. He shouldn't have been playing on that ankle. He was taping it very tightly and this only made it worse. If we had just waited two or three days, he would have been all right.

After he played in five games despite the swollen ankle, it started hurting too badly. He had to give up and become a spectator. He missed the next 14 games, including four against Philly and two against Baltimore, but none against Milwaukee, our closest eastern rival. We're lucky it happened then and not later.

It was Cazzie, not Stallworth this time, who stepped up to the first string, the first time he had started since he broke his ankle the previous season. I guess Red felt DeBusschere was around to stop the toughest opposing forwards, so Cazzie could just concentrate on taking Dollar Bill's place in the scoring column.

By this time the guys on our second team were getting a fair share of the acclaim, including a humorous cover of *Jock New York* showing them sitting on a Central Park bench. Our bench strength was very important. Players like Riordan, Cazzie and Stallworth came in and did great jobs most of the time. It's hard to stay in shape when you're not playing. They had to run on their own, they had to stay alert and involved even while not getting the playing time they might have wanted. What I objected to was the notion that the whole secret of the Knicks' success was the second string.

There were times when they hurt us, too. They came in and lost ground. I remember an early game versus the Bulls when Red was very upset because they didn't move the ball. All the subs came in and just wanted to shoot. Nobody played defense. Our lead was in jeopardy for a while. Most of the time, though, they came in and kept the heat on the other team. They ran hard and made good use of their own options, many of which were designed to free Cazzie.

One of the things that helped Barnett throughout the season was Riordan coming in for him and playing good ball. That way Dick could get a longer rest on the bench, come back in fresh and get us lots of points in a short time. Riordan played well, pushing the ball to the middle on fast breaks. He's a great driver anyway, but when he started hitting the open men, too, he was dangerous.

I had a touch of the flu in February. I felt weak. We had a game with Boston that night. I talked to Red on the phone and he told me to go over to the Garden and try to work out, which I did. About two o'clock I tried to run up and down the court and I was too weak. I went back to bed, git up in the evening to go over to the Garden to get some pills and went back to bed again. We lost to Boston.

I was okay for the next game, February 13 versus Philly at the Spectrum, and I'm glad I was. We killed them 151 to 106, a 45-point margin, the worst defeat in 76er history, even going back to when they were the Syracuse Nationals. There were seven Knicks who scored 10 points or more. We had 80 in the first half! I had 17 points and 7 assists, pretty good considering I was getting over an illness. I didn't feel tired at all. It was like an easygoing practice session out there.

When I'm playing in a laugher I don't always realize what's going on right away. I didn't realize that night that it was such a rout until all of a sudden I looked at the scoreboard and we were leading by 20 points, which is actually not too many against the 76ers because they make fabulous comebacks. Red took the starters out and the second team did a great job, so then it was 30 points, then 40. Nobody could miss. Barnett was filling it up and Cazzie ended with 35 points, hitting 15 of 23 shots from the floor and 5 free throws.

Everybody played a fantastic game. It got sort of comical because we could do no wrong. Philly's fans were booing and laughing.

We played the 76ers again the next night, this time in the Garden. It was a much closer game, which didn't surprise me. I knew it would be tough. Any team with pride would have been way up for the game and the 76ers were. We won 116 to 114 and kept our 6½-game lead over Milwaukee.

One thing that characterized our team in the regular season was our dominance of the weaker teams, which in baseball you would call the "second-division clubs." We swept 12 our of 12 games against Chicago and Phoenix. I think we had more manpower than either club and it was simply a matter of time in each game before we wore them down. They only had five guys playing every night. Phoenix did pretty well against other teams, but we matched up well against them. The Suns didn't have a good center, so there was nobody to hamper Willis. Their guards were small except for Dick Van Arsdale, who is really a forward.

We did not dominate Atlanta, I think when we humiliated them earlier in the season it woke the Hawks up. Every time we met they got psyched up. They were a hustling, very physical team. Joe Caldwell and Lou Hudson did most of the scoring and Bill Bridges hit the boards. After they beat us, they'd let down and lost four or five games. Walt Hazzard would have a fine game aginst us and versus some other team he'd score maybe two points.

Detroit traded Walt Bellamy to the Hawks early in February and his first game in an Atlanta uniform was against us. I thought at the time that if he decided to play all out he could be a big help to them. To beat L.A. in the western division play-offs, they had to have a big man to offset Chamberlain if Wilt could make it back. Bells, when he was with the Knicks, always played well against Chamberlain and Bill Russell. The Hawk players talked themselves into thinking Bellamy was their saviour. They rolled out the red carpet for him and immediately made him feel right at home.

They beat us badly in Bellamy's first game, 111 to 96, ending our post-All-Star winning streak. At the start of the fourth quarter Willis made a free throw to tie it 76 to 76. Then Hazzard and Hudson got hot and they zoomed away from us. Caldwell, very fast and a tough defensive player, took me right out of the game. Bellamy, not familiar with the system, still had 10 points and 12 rebounds. The whole team did a good job of following Coach Richie Guerin's firm instructions:

"Keep the play away from Frazier."

That 15-point loss was our worst of the season up until then. Atlanta did even better on February 21 in the Garden, beating us 122 to 196. Guerin was doing flip-flops he was so happy. Even a sore left toe from kicking a chair in the fourth quarter didn't dampen his spirits.

Bellamy was supposedly crying in the dressing room even though his team had won. He had fouled out with eight points and nine rebounds. I guess he had been stoked up to put on a rousing show in front of the New York crowd and was disappointed. Or he felt the referees were abusing him, which is how one report had it. I couldn't picture him in tears. It was hard for me to believe he would be so upset over something an official had done. I hadn't seen him motivated too often. Bells was always the kind of guy who shrugged things off and said, "That's the way it goes."

We had such a solid lead in the East that it got to be very difficult for us to get excited about the games. Other teams were fighting for play-off berths or battling to improve their standings. And they were goaded by all the publicity the Knicks had been enjoying. We were just coasting, although that didn't make Red too happy. At least there were a few comedy acts and controversies down the stretch to help keep us entertained.

In a Saturday-night game against the Baltimore Bullets, we lined up for the tap at the start of the fourth quarter. Leroy Ellis of the Bullets tipped the ball back *away* from his basket and Dick Barnett caught it in perfect stride going toward *our* basket. He had an easy lay-up, but he stopped, obviously confused because it seemed far too easy. Baltimore was just as confused because its guards were guarding him the wrong way.

At first I had no doubt he was going to the right hoop, but when he hesitated I started thinking, "Where's our basket?" I ran down to help him and the sonofagun threw me the ball, figuring if I scored for the other team, I'd get the blame, and if I scored for us, he'd get an assist. But from the fan reaction I was pretty sure it was our basket and as I went in to make the lay-up I remembered I had made the last field goal of the third quarter at the end.

Still, I was a little leery after I made it and started looking around. I didn't want to be the "Wrong-Way Riegels" of pro basketball. Everybody in the place was laughing, including Barnett and me, the other players on the floor and the guys on both benches.

In Philly we saw a fan fistfight that might have been the daddy of them all. Willis had blocked a shot and the referee had called a foul on him; then all of a sudden we heard all this commotion like the place was falling down. Guys were spilling out on the court and everybody started running and hollering, so I went and sat under the basket and just watched the action. I didn't want to get hit by any stray punches.

The guys fighting, I heard later, were transit policemen dressed in civvies and apparently one had been spilling beer on the other. The press table went over and our bench was knocked over. It was chaos, a wild scene, and it broke our momentum because we had an 18-point lead. After the fight the 76ers caught up with us.

So these two guys were flailing away at each other and Willis went up to the official and said, "See what you started. That was a clean block!"

In a nationally televised game in the Garden one Sunday Archie Clark of the 76ers crashed into an ABC courtside camera early in the first quarter (I've heard of close-up shots, but there should be a limit) and had to be taken to St. Clare's Hospital for X rays. It turned out he had no broken bones, just a badly bruised hipbone, which was bad enough because it was so damn unnecessary. I didn't see the accident and I don't think Archie saw it either. He was going full tilt and he was looking back, I think on a fast break, and all of a sudden he hit the camera. The cameraman didn't really have enough room to operate, so it wasn't entirely his fault, but we told the officials to get him out of the way.

Later in the game Nate Bowman ran into the camera and got a big welt on his thigh. Guys in both dressing rooms after the game were upset. What if Archie's career had been ended by that ABC camera?

I've banged into Nate Thurmond and Rudy LaRusso and Bailey Howell and some other big obstructions, but never into a camera or a 24-second clock. Maybe it's because I'm under control most of the time, not going so fast that I can't stop if something looms up. Still, I can remember in my second year, at the end of a play-off game in Boston, I dived for a ball and slid into the stands on my chest. I survived that okay. All my injuries have been on the court, not off it.

Another little fuss was kicked up by Johnny Most, the Boston broadcaster. It became apparent fairly early that Boston wasn't going to make the play-offs, which I expected without Bill Russell. Maybe Tom Sanders and John Havlicek and the others expected it, too, but they were still definitely disappointed after all those winning years.

It was disappointing to Most, too, I guess, because when we ran over the Celtics 133 to 100 he ranted and fumed over the air and called it bush. I couldn't understand his reasoning because our starting five only played 30 minutes apiece. The substitutes really ran it up, not us. I don't understand those bitter Celtics fans— their heroes bombed the Knicks out plenty of times. I guess they're envious now and they shouldn't be, man, after they've enjoyed a zillion championships. I figure it's time somebody else had to win, but these guys were still griping. They couldn't forget.

We were in L.A. when word leaked out that Willis had been named the NBA's most valuable player in a vote by the players themselves (you couldn't vote for anyone on your own team). The points went like this: Reed 498, Jerry West 457, Lew Alcindor 335, me 50, Billy Cunningham and Connie Hawkins 27 apiece, Lou Hudson 23. West and the Laker fans were upset he hadn't won it and Jerry spoke out with some bitterness. I was surprised because the *players* voted. Maybe I could see him getting mad if the writers did it, but these are the guys you play against every night, and they voted for Willis. The night we played the game in Inglewood's Forum, the fans were booing Willis. They were really vindictive.

UCLA Coach John Wooden got into the act, saying West was "the best player in basketball" but there was "no question" that Alcindor was the most valuable. Even though he had been Lew's college coach and might be accused of bias, his argument was better than West's. Lew really didn't come on until half the season was over, so that's probably why he didn't get it. I think at the end of the season he was the best player in the league. Before that he was just learning the ropes and wasn't so great.

It's a big man's game, so any MVP votes I got were like icing on the cake. It made me feel great, knowing that some of the players cast votes for me.

There were troubles and tragedy at the end of the season, too. We played a TV game in Baltimore on Washington's Birthday and lost (we had also lost the night before in the Garden to the Hawks). We were pretty dejected when we trooped into the dressing room. Then we were hit with the news that the team physician for the Knickers and the New York Rangers, Dr. Kazuo Yanagisawa, had died of a heart attack at his home in New Jersey. He was only 55.

Anytime somebody that young dies, you're surprised, but I had noticed that Yana had lost a lot of weight. When he was treating me for the flu, he didn't seem to have much life to him. Most of the time I knew him he was strongly built and in a good frame of mind, but I guess this had been eating at him for a long time.

"I should be in bed myself," he told me.

He treated all my injuries, including my ankle when I hurt it my rookie year. He operated on Barnett for an Achilles tendon injury and Dick's still playing. He worked on Bill Hosket's knee last summer and Bill played without a brace last season. He was in charge of several spinal-fusion operations on hockey players and he was the one who fixed Phil Jackson's back.

At least one ex-Knick had a clause in his contract stating that if he had a back injury his new club had to pay his way to New York so Yana could work on him.

Yana didn't baby anybody. He didn't believe in injuries. He'd look at you and say, "You'll be all right." If you had a day's rest, then he figured the next day you should be ready to go.

All the guys wanted to go to the funeral. Emmette Bryant of the Celtics, who was injured and not with his team, came down from Boston and we all met in front of the Garden on Eighth Avenue. We had limousines, but Tom Hoover, an ex-pro who does some broadcasting now, came, and Emmette, Eddie Donovan, Red and Danny Whelan, so we were crowded.

Hoover was going to take a group of guys in his car, at least that's what we thought when we took off for New Jersey in the limos. At the last minute they decided they'd go in Stallworth's car, but Bowman had left the parking-garage ticket for Stallworth's car upstairs in the Hotel New Yorker and went up to get it. When he came back downstairs the cops had Hoover, Bryant and Stallworth handcuffed. They had guns drawn on them.

It turned out that Hoover's car, borrowed from some girl he knew, had last year's inspection sticker in the window. Some cop checked it out and found it was a stolen car. It took about five hours at the police station to straighten things out and those guys never made the funeral. When they were released, the Knick officials had a press conference at the Garden to explain everything. I don't know what happened with Hoover's lady friend.

We clinched a tie for the division championship by beating Seattle 117 to 99 in the Garden March 10, while Atlanta was beating Milwaukee. It was the 25th time we had held the other team to less than 100. The game was interesting mostly because of the miserable shooting of DeBusschere. Dave hit only 2 out of 17 shots! It was a tribute to his defense and his rebounding (he had 26 rebounds) that Red let him stay in for 34 minutes.

Red had just added another hat to his collection, the general manager's, because Eddie Donovan had left to take the GM spot at Buffalo, one of three new NBA cities with Cleveland and Portland. I was happy for Eddie because he got more money and was able to work closer to his home in upstate New York. And I was happy for Red. After the win over Seattle we asked Red to leave the dressing room for a few minutes. We were more polite about it than usual because now he was an executive.

We were about to leave on a four-game road trip, playing Seattle, San Diego, L.A. and Detroit. We realized we hadn't flinched anything but a tie. It was still a touchy situation, so we had to buckle down and try to put those games away as soon as possible.

"We can't blow it," Willis said at the meeting. "Everybody should take care of himself and be ready to play ball so we can win it."

I agreed, not that I was going to be screwing around anyway.

We played Seattle in Portland and everything seemed set up perfectly for us. We were meeting a weak team on a neutral court, Bradley was back in uniform and the game was being televised back to New York on Channel 9. Phil Jackson, still on the injured list, was along so he could be in on the kill. We had champagne on ice and we were ready to celebrate. But we blew the game.

The Super-Sonics were still hoping for a spot in the western division play-offs and they simply wanted the game more than we did. They were behind only once. Captain-Coach-Star Lennie Wilkens had a great game. Dollar Bill didn't get in, and we didn't play like we *wanted* to clinch it.

We didn't play much more inspired ball the next night in San Diego, but we beat the Rockets 119 to 103 for New York's first division title in 16 long years (on March 13, 1954, the Knicks beat Syracuse 67 to 60 to win the eastern championship). It should have been enough to thrill us, but we were passive, just like it was another game, one out of 82. There was no shouting, no horseplay, no throwing Red and Danny in the showers, nothing on ice but beer. I think if we had won in Portland we would have staged a little party, but somehow losing that game took all the glamour away. Then, too, it was no surprise because we had been leading for five months. I mean I don't think anybody was exactly shocked.

The New York Mets were jubilant when they won the pennant because they never expected to. We had.

As a matter of fact, my memories of that night are not too fond. After the game we were supposed to fly to Los Angeles. At the San Diego airport we waited for about an hour for our flight and then the man announced the plane had a flat tire. They couldn't find anybody to fix it and they didn't have another crew to fly the only other plane on hand. We had to wait a long time for our luggage and went back to the hotel around midnight for a few hours sleep.

While we were waiting on the plane, a lot of guys were eating pizzas. Plus we had a wheelchair race featuring Stallworth and Cazzie, using the wheelchairs that airports keep around. Cazzie won because Rave got off too fast and spun his wheels.

I'll bet we're the only NBA team in history to celebrate a division championship with beer, pizza and a wheelchair derby.

Chapter Fourteen

Forget About Tomorrow

My FAMILY in Atlanta keeps a close watch on the pro basketball box scores. If I have what they consider to be a sufficient number of assists, rebounds and points, they know I'm feeling fine. If I fall down in any department, they start worrying about the state of my health. I guess it's a lot easier for me than writing home every day.

So in the midst of the play-offs the phone rang in my Manhattan hotel room. No doubt it would be another old acquaintance from Southern Illinois or somewhere else calling me up to chitchat as if just yesterday we were out on the town together. Eventually the subject would coincidentally get around to tickets and I'd have to turn him down. Thanks for calling. Operator no more calls until 3 P.M., please.

But this time it wasn't any long-lost pal. It was my Uncle Eddie Wynn—Chello—calling from Georgia, and he sounded worried.

"Are you sick?" he asked.

"No," I said.

"You hurt, then?"

203

"No."

"Well, I saw you only had two points," he said. "I thought maybe you got injured. What's going on?"

What was going on was a delicate retuning of the Knicks' engine by chief mechanic Red Holzman. Some people might have considered it a major overhaul. The Knicks are a team that depends on balance. We help each other on defense. We do certain things to cause chinks in the opposition's defense, then quickly wiggle through those chinks. When we're on our game—moving constantly, shooting well and being stubborn on defense —we have quarters and halves and sometimes whole games of clever, beautiful basketball.

When things get out of balance, Red sees it first. It was after the fourth game of the eastern division semifinals against Baltimore that he and I had a conference. He called me aside before a practice session and told me that to a certain extent he thought I was looking for my shot too much. I told him I didn't think I was, or I wasn't aware of it if I was. I thought I was playing well, though we weren't winning as consistently as we should. I wouldn't have thought of changing if no one had said anything.

When we played against the Bullets Earl Monroe was giving us trouble, scoring points at a fantastic rate. I thought that if we were going to beat them he had to be contained (and I had to be the guy to do it). But I also thought I should be firing it up with Willis, Barnett and the rest of the other end. Red changed my ideas. He wanted me to play good defense on Earl the Pearl and concentrate on hitting the open man on offense. I said okay, and it paid off.

There were games in the play-offs when I scored two

measly points and we won, and games I scored 6 or 10 and we won, so obviously he was correct.

Baltimore was our first opponent because they finished third. Following NBA rules, second-place Milwaukee was rewarded with the easier draw, fourth-place Philadelphia. I though the Baltimore series would be difficult even though we had beaten the Bullets four straight in the '68-'69 play-offs (when their Guy Johnson was out with an injury) and even though we had dominated them 5 to 1 in the regular season (average margin of victory: 19 points). Chicago Coach Dick Motta had said of us back in November:

"There's no doubt that they'll win the eastern division championship, but in a short series they'll have trouble in the play-offs against either Baltimore or Milwaukee."

Baltimore had other pluses besides Gus Johnson. Guard Kevin Loughery, who had been out because of four broken ribs and a punctured lung, said he was ready to play with the aid of a protective corset. The Bullets were not worn down from protecting their division lead as they had been the previous year. And their chief tormentor on the Knicks, Willis, gave in to the doctor and consented to have a cortisone shot above his left kneecap before the first game. There was some question as to how mobile he'd be.

That opener, which went into double overtime and lasted 58 minutes, was a fairly accurate sample of the kind of pressure in store for us in practically every one of the 19 play-off games.

Most of the game the pearl ate me up. I had my hand in his face, I had my body right up with his, we were double-teaming him whenever possible—and he just kept hitting. Thirty-foot turnaround jumpers! I don't think he even saw the basket on some of his shots, but he's that kind of shooter. There wasn't a thing I could do with him. I don't think anybody ever scored so many points on me—39. The confrontation might have been fun to watch, but it wasn't fun to play.

Despite his heroics the game was extremely close at the end. He hit a long turnaround to give Baltimore a 101 to 100 lead. Wes Unseld traveled and we got posession with 63 seconds left. Reed missed. I purposely fouled Monroe and he made the free throw: 102 to 100. Time out New York. Bradley drove along the base line for a lay-up to tie it. The Pearl went one-on-one with me. He had scored the Bullets' last eight points. Just before the buzzer his shot hit the rim and bounced away. He had thought it was the end of the third period and was surprised to see five minutes posted on the scoreboard.

The Bullets led 110 to 108 at the end of the first overtime when I jabbed the ball away from Monroe. Barnett grabbed it, drove in and was fouled. He made both free throws to tie the game. Monroe again went into his one-on-one show, and again I knocked it away, and again Barnett scooped it up and barrelled in for lay-up, pursued by rookie Fred Carter. The ball hit the right side of the rim and was pulled down at the buzzer by Carter—we thought he had pinned it on the backboard. Goaltending? Referee Mendy Rudolph said no. Second overtime.

It was a tight again. With 33 seconds to go, I fed a bounce pass to Willis underneath and his basket gave us a 119 to 117 lead. Now the Pearl had to go one-on-

one against me to *tie* the game rather than win it. With 18 seconds left he shot and missed. Unseld's follow shot was not good. We got possession and DeBusschere was fouled with four seconds to go. He made the second free throw and we won 120 to 117.

I felt those steals helped me redeem myself. Some of the newspapers said, "Monroe wins the battle, but Frazier wins the war." I thought that was appropriate.

The Pearl wasn't nearly as effective in the second game, probably because it was played the next night (in Baltimore) and his aching legs hadn't enough rest. He played 41 minutes but made only 6 of 16 shots. The time he was on the bench he held ice packs to his knees. Riordan did a good job on him in the fourth quarter. In face, Coney Island Mike was the star of the game.

We beat the Bullets 106 to 99 with a good second half. In the fourth quarter, while Bradley was making every one of his 15 points, Baltimore got only 5 baskets. Mike ended up with 13 points and 8 rebounds, which made him the combat hero of the 274th Mobile Communications Squadron.

Mike and Cazzie, both members of the National Guard, were called for emergency duty during the nationwide mail strike and they didn't practice for two days. We were worried we'd have to play without two of our top subs, but fortunately we had them for all the games. There was a lot of kidding. Mike was assigned to drive a jeep. We insisted his jeep had been seen in front of the Blarney Stone bar. We accused him of putting letters in the wastebasket so he wouldn't have to deliver them.

Cazzie caught it, too. The papers carried a picture of

him all decked out in military regalia—gun, helmet, canteen. You'd have thought he was somewhere in Vietnam.

I knew the series was going to get rougher. It did. The Bullets surprised me, though, because they played with a lot of confidence and poise despite being two games down. They didn't fold and they didn't play wild-eyed, foolish basketball, either. Except for Kevin Loughery.

Between the first and second quarters of the third game he took off his protective corset and from then on he played unencumbered. In 19 minutes, even though he wasn't back in good condition, he scored 17 points. (The previous year he had a pulled groin muscle, so they said. He played anyway.) I wasn't surprised he shed the corset, although it sounded as if he was taking a big risk. It was hard to understand why a guy would do that just to have more freedom of movement. The threat of a second punctured lung must have been scary.

We were flat and uninspired in that game, so flat that Unseld's 34 rebounds were more than the entire Knick team had! We let them get off too well in the third period. Monroe was tough again and Reed, bothered by his sore knee, had only five rebounds in 29 minutes. It was a nationally televised Sunday game, too, and we never seemed to win those. They blasted us, 127 to 113.

They beat us again 102 to 92 in Baltimore, playing excellent defense and letting the Pearl dribble out the clock at important times before casting in impossible, leap-twirl-and-heave jumpers. It was peculiar about Monroe. During the season we contained him well. I think he only averaged 16 points a game against us. Then in the play-offs he went wild. We played good defense, but he still put the ball down the hole. It's hard to explain.

I guess a guy can get psyched up for a short series. Also, at the beginning of the season he wasn't in good shape. We played against him in exhibition games and he seemed to be overweight. As the season progressed he came into his own and by the end he was at his peak. It carried over to the play-offs. People in Philadelphia, his hometown, call him "Magic." A fitting nickname.

In the fourth game, while he was scoring 34, I had 25 points, 7 assists and 6 rebounds. But we lost and I guess that's when Red decided I should pass more and shoot less.

Willis took another cortisone shot in his left knee before the fifth game and the drug must have been from a potent batch. In rebound battles the first four games Unseld had beaten him badly, 110 to 58. The captain decided to put a stop to it, which he did with 36 points and 36 rebounds (the latter a Knick record). He chased Unseld right off the court and Wes' replacement, Ray Scott, was no more effective.

I hadn't seen Willis play like that since the previous year's play-offs versus Baltimore when he destroyed Unseld. This particular night he shot well and was moving forcefully to the basket to follow up the few shots he missed. He was out of sight.

The rest of us were back to our old selves, double-teaming, rebounding and running. I had 16 points and 16 rebounds. Earl the Pearl had one basket in the second half.

Unfortunately we were also our old selves in the sixth game on Sunday national television and lost 96 to 87. That made our ABC-TV record a sizzling 1 to 7. The Bullets' Coach Gene Shue should have paid several ABC cameramen to bring their equipment to the Garden for the seventh game. They wouldn't have had to plug the cameras in, just aim them at us.

The Pearl was at it again in that last game, scoring 32 points. I was tired of thinking about that cat. But the Pearl's man, Dick Barnett, burned him for 28 points. We ran our best offense of the year and beat them 127 to 114.

DeBusschere was as pleased as anybody to see the series end because he and Johnson had played each other to a standstill—almost canceled each other out. It was a good match-up—both are strong, both are good shooters. Gus might be a little stronger, but Dave is a little quicker. Both like to play physical, bumping defense. Several times they wore each other down to the point where they were too tired to shoot. One game Gus would be the best, the next time it was Dave. I think Dave came out on top in the last game with 12 of 20 field-goal attempts and 13 rebounds.

I wasn't sure I could stand two more best-of-seven series. I told somebody I would rather play one game for everything because a tough series goes to 3 to 3 anyway and boils down to a seventh game for all the marbles. But it was tired, locker-room talk. After thinking it over, I figured the longer the play-offs went the better chance the best team would have of avoiding upset. And I felt we had the best team.

Milwaukee defeated Philadelphia in the other eastern division semifinal and played us for the eastern play-off title. It was a short series and the highlight, I think, was the sight of jazzy Cazzie Russell going in for a lay-up all alone, trying to stuff and missing!

At the time it wasn't a laughing matter because we needed a basket badly. It was the second game and we were up by one point with just a few minutes left. We came up with a steal, that's what led to it. I was in the backcourt and I saw Cazzie going in by himself. I thought, "We've got it." He went up to stuff and not only didn't make it but damn near missed the whole hoop.

The Garden crowd went wild, sort of giving out with a giant gasp. Half laugh, half moan, if that's possible. Caz wears fancy blue and orange sweatbands on his wrists, yet he said he missed the dunk because his hands were sweaty. He didn't have to apologize because he came back and made a big basket right after that.

And if that wasn't enough, in a Sunday game in Milwaukee he was all alone for another stuff shot and blew that one, too. This time it was funny because it was early in the game. His mother and some of his family were there, up from Chicago, so he had to be embarrassed. The next time he had a chance to stuff he just made an orthodox lay-up and the crowd applauded his good sense.

Another highlight of the series was the good defensive job we did on Lew Alcindor and their two best outside shooters, Flynn Robinson and Jon McGlocklin. With Flynn, I think I had some help from their coach, Larry Costello. Flynn started the first game and shot poorly in our 110 to 102 victory. He had 19 points but was only 4-for-16 from the floor. He had hurt us all year, but in that game he was psyched out and missed some open shots.

Costello put a lot of pressure on him by not starting him in the second game. The guy lost his confidence and that made my job much easier. My basic strategy with Flynn was to keep him going left, prevent him from coming down the middle. Then, too, I discovered he didn't like body contact. I stay off guys normally, but this series I got more physical. When I shoved and bumped, Flynn wasn't as aggressive, he passed the ball off and didn't look for his shot as much.

In Costello's favor, he needed a man who could play good backcourt defense. That was Freddy Crawford, the ex-Knick.

Our strategy against Lew was to sag on him and hope their outside shooters couldn't go to the rescue. We were trying to keep him out from the basket because if he gets close he can just turn around and stuff the ball. Unlike Wilt, he can go either right or left. He's not as strong as Wilt, but he's a lot more agile and he's much quicker, so he presented quite a problem. Whenever the Bucks cleared out one side and it was just Lew versus Willis, it was very difficult for Willis to stop him.

We didn't try to penetrate much against Alcindor. If you let him block a few of your shots, his team gets stirred up. It's similar with L.A. and Wilt, but it's more pronounced with Milwaukee because Lew is their life. Not penetrating hurt us, but not much because we're basically an outside shooting team anyway.

The Milwaukee series was when I really retired my shooting arm. I knew Red wanted me to concentrate on Robinson and give up the ball on offense. I took only nine shots in the first game and left the scoring to Willis and the rest (three forwards scored 18 points apiece, an oddity). The Bucks made some rookie mistakes, such as Lew holding the ball when we sagged on him. He should have slipped it out quickly to somebody else. But maybe the outside shooting had disappointed him and he felt he had to do it himself.

The second game, featuring Cazzie's sweaty-handed stuff attempt, was a great battle of centers. Lew had 38 points and 23 rebounds, Willis had 36 points and 19 rebounds. Lew missed two foul shots with 52 seconds remaining, which cost Milwaukee the game. We won, 112 to 111.

We were flat for the third game, in Milwaukee, and lost by five, but then we beat them soundly in the fourth and fifth games. 117 to 105 and 132 to 96. Cazzie came in off the bench in the fourth game and gave us a great lift, and Milwaukee didn't seem to care when the series moved back to New York for what turned out to be the final game.

I played a good, all-around game against the Bucks but averaged less than ten points. I scored only two in the last game.

Lack of experience killed the Bucks. They needed one guy who could stabilize them, a guard who could score, play defense and keep them organized. If they needed a ball handler, they sent in Guy Rodgers. If they needed a defender, Freddy Crawford went in. For scoring they had to have Robinson.

Their attitude afterward was, "We're a young team and we'll be back," which is probably correct. Lew and Bob Dandridge, a forward with octopus arms, are sure to improve. Lew, for instance, will no doubt improve his rebounding. Against us he didn't block out well and didn't go hard to the boards. Also, I don't think he was as good a shot-blocker as he should have been with his height.

You've got to feel the Bucks are a team of the future. I said *a* team, not *the* team. Most of our players have a few years left, too.

Not long after we beat them, the Bucks traded Robinson and 6 foot 8 Charlie Paulk (serving in the military at the time) to Cincinnati for Oscar Robertson. When I first heard about it, I thought here was the three-in-one guard Milwaukee was pining for. Down the stretch he'll keep things organized if anybody will.

Then I got to thinking. Alcindor is not a pick-and-roll center and that play is what Oscar does best. I can't see Lew out there setting a lot of picks for Oscar. The club wants its young giant as close to the basket as he can get. It will be interesting to see how those two superstars adjust to each other.

Now we were in the world series of professional basketball (I don't care what the American Basketball Association says). I wasn't feeling run down from the long season. Not counting exhibitions, we had played 94 games, and I figured, "We've come this far, why stop now?"

Our opposition was Los Angeles, which had beaten Phoenix and Atlanta to get there. L.A., the team with three superstars—Jerry West, Elgin Baylor and Wilt Chamberlain. The way they handled Atlanta, beating the Hawks four straight, they had to be good.

It was a meeting of two clubs with histories of frustration. In the previous 23 seasons New York had made the finals only three times, in '51, '52 and '53, losing to

Rochester once and Minneapolis twice. The Lakers moved from Minneapolis to L.A. for the '60-'61 season and kept the Lakers nickname, even though most of the lakes in Southern California dried up thousands of years ago.

L.A. was even more frustrated than the Knicks because it had such fine teams almost every year, had gone to the finals six times in nine seasons, yet had never won the championship. In 1962 the Lakers pushed Boston to seven games but lost 110 to 107 in overtime. L.A.'s Frank Selvy could have won it with three seconds to go in regulation time, but his shot barely missed. West says he still dreams about that shot. The Celtics and Bill Russell beat them again (and again and again) in '63, '65, '66, '68, and '69.

Now Russell was gone. It was Willis Reed and the Knicks standing in their way.

I was pleased that my old Southern Illinois teammate, Dickie Garrett, was in the finals as a starting guard with West. We both could use the money. I was married when Dickie came on the scene at SIU, so I didn't hang around with him or the other players too much. I was the oldest guy on the team and Coach Hartman relied on me to keep the others in line. Still Dickie and I were pretty good friends.

We talked several times during the season and he told me he was going back to Carbondale for the summer.

"All right," I said, "we'll hook up down at the school. We'll give a party, a reunion-type thing."

At that time I had no idea L.A. would get Wilt back from injury in time for the play-offs and beat out Atlanta, putting Dickie and me head to head in the finals. I saw him in New York before the first game and we agreed that the guy on the losing team would sponsor the party back at school. It added some spice to a series that already had plenty.

Another reason I was pleased it was L.A. and not Atlanta was the Forum in Inglewood, my favorite after the Garden. It's a plush place with a good seating capacity. I think the locker rooms are the best and most spacious in the league, about a third larger than the Garden's.

Atlanta plays its home games in Georgia Tech's gym, outdated, small, poorly lighted and, because of a hard floor, bad for your knees. The permanent floor has no "give" or resiliency. If the Hawks keep playing in that place, some of the guys on the team will have shortened careers. I know it couldn't have helped Wilt in the Hawk-Laker series. Anybody with a bad knee has got to be in trouble on that floor.

It's surprising how many bad features some NBA arenas have. Sometimes the shooting backgrounds make things tough. While you're shooting free throws at one end in Cincy, an advertising sign on the scoreboard is reflected in the glass backboard. In Milwaukee and Boston, if it's a game televised in color, the extrabright lights hamper your vision and make it very hot out on the court. It's like being on a Hollywood set. I have no complaint about the Forum, though.

Just before the series started, the NBA office announced the '69-'70 All-Star team, picked by writers and broadcasters in the 14 league cities. West, Billy Cunningham, Connie Hawkins, Willis and I made the first team, which didn't include Oscar Robertson for the first time since he turned pro in 1960. The NBA all-defensive team was announced, too. The coaches picked Gus Johnson and DeBusschere at forwards, Willis at center (beating out Alcindor in a close vote) and West and me at guards. All but one of the 14 coaches named me for the first team; one put me on the second. I wonder who it was.

I was the top vote-getter on the defensive team, so Norm Miller of the *Daily News* asked me how I felt about it. "Great," I said. Then he asked me if I wanted to guard West. I said yes. I thought I should take Jerry because I was sacrificing my offense anyway and by taking him that would leave Barnett with plenty of energy to work on getting points. I'd be playing the same game I played against Monroe and Robinson.

I didn't claim I could stop West. I've tried to figure out a way to stop him cold—break his nose again or something—but I can't. At least I thought I could contain him so he wouldn't go berserk on offense.

Red didn't commit himself until we were going out on the floor before the first game. Then he told me I had my wish, I was guarding West. I felt good about it—for a while anyway.

West is a guy you can't gamble on most of the time. You usually have to play him straight up, try to make your presence a nuisance and force him to his left. When he goes up to shoot, which is difficult to anticipate, keep a hand in his face and pray. My mistake was wanting to put pressure on him right away. Instead I put pressure on myself. I tried to steal from him at the beginning, got careless and was called for fouls.

Willis got off to a big start, making 25 points in the first half, many of them from outside where men 6 foot 10 don't belong. Wilt wasn't coming out on him. But

Reed collided with Happy Hairston while going in for a dunk and hurt his left shoulder—his shooting shoulder and wasn't quite as hot after that. The game was tied 52 to 52 at half time.

We led by as much as 15 in the third quarter, but the Lakers fought back to a 5-point lead. In the fourth period they simply pooped out. Coach Joe Mullaney had not used many substitutes and it showed in the end. Cazzie came in fresh from our bench and made four quick baskets, and the Laker turnover rate went up sharply. One of our steals, the result of double-teaming Keith Erickson, led to a four-point play: I made the layup after the steal and got fouled by Baylor. I missed the free throw, the rebound was knocked back to me and I passed to DeBusschere, who made a basket.

Counting the basket they *didn't* get because of the steal, it actually was a six-point play and probably was the turning point.

I felt pretty bad until then because I had let the team down by getting into foul trouble. I played only 30 minutes and had six points. When L.A. ran out of gas, we went on to win 124 to 112.

It was a poor game for Wilt despite his 24 rebounds. It seemed to me he had lost a great deal of mobility because of his knee injury. His comeback was surprising. I had thought the Lakers were full of baloney when they said Wilt would be back. "If he hurts that knee again, he's through for sure," I thought. "If he lays out he could play two or three more years." But he fooled me by working out hard, playing volleyball at the beach and returning to action in time to save the season for L.A. Rick Roberson was a pretty good rookie, but he wouldn't have helped much under play-off pressure.

Wilt's knee gave out a couple of times that first night against us in the Garden. He would move to the basket, start to dip down and then stumble. He got called for traveling several times.

The second game, also in the Garden, was much closer and more exciting for a variety of reasons. Wilt concentrated and did a better job on Willis, plus he was more under control by using his strong leg as a crutch for the bad one. He kept his feet closer together while he was getting ready to jump. Again I was assigned to guard West and again I got in early foul trouble. And L.A. was much more deliberate in its attack, following Mullaney's instructions not to play racehorse style with us.

With 46 seconds left, it was tied 103 to 103 and West went to the line on a three-to-make-two situation. He made two. Wilt blocked Reed's subsequent shot, DeBusschere got the ball and missed, and Stallworth grabbed the rebound but was caught for being in the lane too long. Two difficult offensive rebounds but no points. Eighteen seconds left.

Riordan and DeBusschere hemmed in Garrett just inside the mid-court line and the rookie threw a bad pass which Willis intercepted. We still had a chance. Barnett took the shot that could have tied it and missed. Erickson got the rebound. L.A. had beaten us on our floor 105 to 103.

We didn't make too many mistakes, but the ones we did make came at costly times. I was convinced the series would go the full seven games, but we had to pay them back by winning one at their place.

The first game at the Forum will stick in my mind for a long time because Jerry West made the most incredible shot I've ever seen in an important series.

Red went back to our regular-season strategy of Barnett on West because he didn't want me in any more foul trouble. It freed me to do some other things —help Dick out with West, for one. Red gave me a free hand to roam and cause trouble. West knew every time he dribbled down in a corner that I'd be coming. He had to keep wondering, "Where's Frazier?" because I love to double-team. I guess he wasn't wondering too hard, though, because he scored 34 points and had 9 assists.

Barnett went zero for seven in the first half and the Lakers went off at the intermission with a 14-point lead. Erickson made a 40-foot shot just before the buzzer that was only a tame preview of what was to come.

All through the third period we whittled down their lead. Barnett and DeBusschere, both cold earlier, joined Willis in a scoring spurt and the game got tight. Wilt tied it at 100 to 100 with a free throw. (He does make them sometimes.) We came down on offense and I fed DeBusschere, who put up a forced jump shot from 17 feet away and luckily made it. There were three seconds left and despite all the twists of a long season of surprises, we thought we had the game won.

Wilt took the ball out of bounds and I saw he was straddling the line instead of standing outside it as the rule book insists. In the excitement nobody else noticed it. He passed the ball in to West. Jerry dribbled a short way, moved past Willis and I saw a determined look in his eyes. I said to myself, "Is he crazy?"

He heaved the ball and I watched it soar 55 feet and drop right through the net without touching the iron.

I was totally amazed. DeBusschere was under the basket and was so stunned he fell over, like a comicstrip character. My immediate feeling was, "Let's go home. Let them have the game after a shot like that." I stood there for what seemed like two minutes.

"Come on, Clyde," yelled Red, "we've got an overtime to play."

It seemed as if we always had an overtime to play those last few weeks.

The Lakers couldn't get going in the extra period and West was zero for two—from much closer range. We were ahead 109 to 108 and had possession with less than 30 seconds left. Barnett hit a jumper to clinch it 111 to 108. Willis had 38 points and 17 rebounds.

Neither team played well in the fourth game, which also went into overtime. West was supposed to be bothered by a jammed thumb on his left hand, but he ended up with 37 points and 18 assists. I wish he'd show me how to jam my thumb exactly the same way. The game was close throughout. When it was 99 to 99 we ran the clock down until nine seconds were left and called time out. Red gave us a play.

The play was to get the ball to Bradley coming along the base line for a jumper, but he was covered. Right away I should have made my move to the basket. Instead I waited, wasting four seconds standing there. Erickson was all over me. I was trying to get some momentum going and then jump into him and maybe draw a foul, but he didn't go for it, so at the last second I had to force up a shot. It hit the front of the rim, short by inches.

That missed shot took everything out of us and they came on in the overtime to demoralize us. They never trailed. Journeyman John Tresvant, playing for his fifth NBA team, had a fine game. He was the one who made is too tough for me to get that pass to Bradley. And in the overtime he scored, stole passes and played good defense. Where had he been the first three games? On the bench, spectating. He was the difference as L.A. won, 121 to 115.

Back to New York we flew for the fifth game, which turned out to be the most important in the series. It was the game in which our captain and leading scorer and rebounder was so painfully injured. We had to play without him.

I was the other end of the court when Willis went down. Somebody threw the ball to him, he turned around and Wilt moved up closer on him. He started to drive to his left, which is the way he usually goes, and it seemed to me his right foot got tangled with Chamberlain's. By the way he fell I could tell it wasn't his knee. He landed on top of the ball and grabbed his side.

"It's all over," I thought. "This kills us."

We kept on playing. Wilt picked up the ball, which had rolled away from Willis, and passed to somebody. The Lakers came down quickly and drew a foul. While Willis was writhing in pain, there was nothing we could do but wait until they scored or we recovered the ball and could take a 20-second time out for injury. It's an NBA rule that in situations like that, play isn't stopped automatically. If we hadn't called time out and instead had come back on offense ourselves, Reed probably would have been called for three seconds in the lane!

When he went out we were behind by 10 points; at half time we were down by 13. The first thing Red did in the locker room was check with the doctor on Reed's availability. Willis was lying on a table, looking depressed.

"No," said the doc, "not in this game."

"All right, then, let's go," said Red, and he talked to us as calmly as if nothing had happened.

We decided to use a different offense, a 1-3-1, to get some movement. I was the man at the head of the key, Bradley (whose idea it was) played in the middle, Cazzie and Barnett were on the wings and DeBusschere was on the base line. Red didnt replace Willis with Bowman because we needed some offensive punch, and Nate isn't that good a shooter.

Another reason we went to the 1-3-1 was that it was one of the best ways to combat a zone defense, and we thought the Lakers were using a zone despite the league rule against it. Red had argued with the refs about it just after the second period was over. You could go through the middle in the first half and nobody would follow you. They weren't even trying to get through our picks; they'd sort of pass the dribbler on to the next defensive man. By using the formation we thought they would be forced to play a tighter man-to-man against us. Without Willis we were terribly weakened in most departments, naturally, but at least we had more speed and ball-handling finesse.

They should have buried us in the second half. If they had stretched their lead to 20 or 25 points, we would have given up and the world championship probably would have been L.A.'s in the sixth game. It seemed hopeless anyway. But they kept being overcautious and we kept coming back until we got psyched up and convinced ourselves we could really beat them. We pressured the passers and kept them from getting the ball in to Wilt, who was being guarded by comparative midgets, DeBusschere and Stallworth. By the end of the third quarter, aided by nine Laker turnovers, we had cut the margin to seven points.

I thought we had it won when we closed it to 80 to 84, and I was right. With a swarming, gambling defense we caught up with them and won going away 107 to 100. Our press helped considerably. The Lakers must have thought they were living a nightmare. They didn't know what to do. If they did get through the press they kept trying to go to Wilt and we kept picking off the passes. We stole the ball from them eight times in the fourth period. I stole it three times in the last 12 minutes.

We led the series 3 to 2 and wanted to put them away for good in the Forum on Wednesday night, May 6. I was fairly sure Willis would not be back, so it was up to the rest of us. We wanted to clinch it that night, but it was conforting to know there was another game—at home.

While the most valuable player in the NBA sat on our bench in street clothes, Chamberlain went wild: 45 points and 27 rebounds. He only made 5 of 14 freethrow attempts or it would have been worse. Bowman, Hosket and DeBusschere couldn't stop him.

L.A. got off to a strong start, 36 to 16. Garrett, shooting mostly from the left side just as he did at Southern Illinois, hit his first eight shots in a row. The Lakers spoiled our double-teaming strategy by moving the ball around well (44 assists, 13 by West), and

Dickie benefited. He shot 9 for 11 from the floor for 18 points. West had 33. Bowman, maybe a better shooter than I thought, finished with 18 points. They beat us 135 to 113.

There was little talk on the flight home from Los Angeles. We weren't hopelessly down in the dumps or anything like that, just quiet. I was glad they had beaten us badly because if we had played them a close game and lost, it would have taken a lot out of us. By losing the way we did, what did it mean? Plus I think they got overconfident. They were sure Willis wouldn't be back by Friday in one piece, so they figured they could wipe us out again. Our guys felt confident because there was still a tomorrow and we were going home. I know I was very confident.

Still, the night before the game I was restless. The traffic noises blaring up from Eight Avenue to my room seemed louder than usual and I was having dreams both good and bad. There were times when I saw us really blowing L.A. out of the gym and then there were times when the game we had played Wednesday night haunted me and I saw Chamberlain destroying us. I only got about five hours sleep, if that much.

"Maybe I'll never come this way again," I said to myself. "I want to go all the way right now. Forget about tomorrow, I want it today!"

The reason for the restlessness was the pride at stake, not the money. Sure, a load of endorsements and public appearances were waiting for some of the winners, but the actual difference in prize money between winning losing and the championship was only a bit more than $1,000 a man. On a per-game basis in the play-offs, we were making peanuts. Many of the players, especially a few of the Lakers, were already getting gigantic salaries. West, he'd have given anything to win the title. Ditto Chamberlain and Baylor. It wasn't money motivating *them*, that's for sure.

On game day I ate about three o'clock, hung around the lobby of the hotel for a while and went for a walk. Erich Barnes, the pro football player, is a friend of mine, so I stopped by his off-season office. He wasn't in. I waited for him half an hour and gave up.

("If Willis does play he'll only be fifty percent of his usual self. He probably won't be in the game long enough to be a factor.")

I went home and read a newspaper, killing time. I dressed casually in a Clyde outfit: dark-brown bell-bottom pants, beige coat pinched in tight at the waist and beige boots. It was pretty cool, I thought. I grabbed my bag and went out. I was relaxed, considering everything.

("If we stay close, we can win it. In that last game on the coast we let them jump out to a big lead. It took a lot out of us trying to catch up.")

I wasn't nervous until I hit the street. People on the sidewalks were calling out from all sides, "Good luck, good luck." In front of the Garden there were about a hundred kids, each of whom considered it his sacred duty to slap me on the back.

"Wait a minute, wait a minute," I said. "If you keep hitting me, I won't be able to play the game tonight."

I was one of the first guys in the locker room. Willis was in on the rubdown table getting treated when I arrived. He had been around the Garden most of the day, working out and being fussed over. He wasn't exactly in a happy-go-lucky mood. I just said, "What's happening?"—not really wanting him to answer the question. I didn't ask if he was going to play or not.

"Clyde, you're ahead of your schedule," said Red when he saw me.

"Yeah," I said, "I'm going to be ready tonight."

Red seldom lets me come or go without a joke. For instance, he's always on me because I take a long time to comb my hair, I'm always looking in the mirror. "Clyde, nothing will help you," he'll say. It relaxes me. I get loose by joking.

When the time came for the team meeting, Willis was in there with the rest of us holding a heat pack to his side. I guess in a situation like that Vince Lombardi would have ranted and raved and talked about hate. Knute Rockne would have used some gimmick to inspire us.

Red Holzman came in and said, "Well, it's a big game tonight."

There was no new strategy. Red wanted us to play a 1-3-1 offense with Willis on the base line and me at the top of the key to quarterback the team.

Then we went outside, without Willis, for the warmups. Bradley spoke for the team when he said how we felt when Willis finally appeared on the court. He said, "It gave us all about a ten-foot lift just to have him there."

The pandemonium died down a little, but when Willis made his first two or three practice shots, the cheering rose up again. All this hoopla was psyching the team up. This was actually the turning point of the game, *before* the opening tip-off. We couldn't have written a better script ourselves. Yet it wasn't planned that way. Suppose he had received his injections first and been out on the court with the rest of us all the while. Nothing would have been dramatic about that.

The starting lineups were introduced and when his turn came he got another tremendous ovation from the 38th sellout crowd of the season. It was very inspirational for me, too. It wasn't *for* me, but I got chills. It was a great feeling.

The game began and he hit his first shot. Right away I said, "We're going to beat them." He came down and hit another jump shot! That set the tempo of the game right there. Four points were all he scored, but those four points got us off to a beautiful start.

Through a combination of our good shooting and defense and their turnovers, we jumped off to a 13 to 6 lead. Garrett was on me and quickly got three personal fouls, so I tried to take advantage of him all the more. DeBusschere and I finished the first period with 25 points, one more than the whole L.A. team. It was almost a perfect quarter for me: 15 points on 5 of 5 from the line and 5 of 5 from the floor, 4 assists and 4 rebounds. Garrett had two points and I was already thinking about what caterer he would hire for our party in Carbondale.

Each time I shot I was so confident I was on target that if the ball didn't drop through I was shocked. And I was constantly trying to make steals simply because I was sure I could.

We knew we had to help out Willis by sagging more than usual on Chamberlain. L.A. helped us sometimes by standing around. When they passed into Wilt they didn't cut around him or break straight to the hoop. They just stood there, giving us golden opportunities to double-team the big man. Willis was operating with only one sound leg and had little mobility, but Wilt couldn't take that much advantage, apparently because he was afraid to put the ball down on the dribble. One or two Knicks were usually waiting down there by his ankles.

Early in the second quarter West passed to Chamberlain and Wilt didn't see me sneaking up on him. I had to sneak because I'd never be able to outmuscle him for a ball—I'd get killed. He was getting ready to cradle it and I snatched it right out of his arms, raced up the middle toward our basket and fed Bradley for a lay-up. We were ahead by 17 points.

Then I missed several shots in a row and got mad at myself. That's when I stole the ball from West. To be fair, I should mention that Jerry, like Willis, had received injections before the game. He had jammed his left thumb in the third game and hurt his right hand in both the second and fifth games, so he had to have shots in both hands. It didn't affect his shooting that much, he said, but it hurt his ball handling.

The two opposing sets of guards were facing each other at about mid-court, with Riordan and me on defense. I saw West feint toward the middle, then get up a full head of steam to try to go outside Mike. He didn't notice me off to his left, so I moved away from my man, darted in front of West and swooped the ball away. I drove in with it and out of the corner of my eye I saw him coming and I jumped into him. That's why the lay-up rolled around and almost didn't go in. I continued off the end of the court and circled around almost to the corner before the shot dropped through. The free throw went in, too, and we had a 20-point lead, 51 to 31.

Near the end of the half Baylor had the ball and my man cleared out an area for him at the top of the key. So I faked as if I was going to follow my man off to the right corner, taking a few steps with him. Elgin dribbled into the area we had just vacated and all of a sudden I broke back on him and took the ball away.

As I raced down to our end for another lay-up, I heard him say, "God damn!"

(I've thought back to that moment several times since. Here was Elgin Baylor—a cinch for the hall of fame, the man who scored 71 points in an NBA game and, by most accounts I've ever seen or heard, a fine person—watching perhaps his last chance for a world championship slipping away. Elg was 35. Neither he nor West came in our locker room afterward to congratulte us. Wilt did.-

We led by 27 points at half time and the Garden brass might just as well have ordered that ice-cold champagne right then so Bowman could get a head start bathing me in it. (Man, that stuff was freezing!) We weren't completely sure at the time, of course, but the game was won. Everybody was congratulating everybody else in the locker room and saying, "Let's keep it on them."

We came out for the third period and were kind of shaky. Bowman was ready to jump center until Willis (after getting another injection) came running out just in time to report to the scorer's table and get in. The Lakers outscored us 7 to 2 and things were a little tense. We were missing our shots and we knew as well as anybody that a big lead in pro basketball is about as durable as a Popsicle in hell.

With Garrett in foul trouble, L.A. put West on me in

the second half. He has quick hands and comes up with a lot of loose balls, plus he gambles a lot because he knows Wilt is backing him up. Get by West and it's like out of the frying pan into the fire. But I figured Jerry wouldn't exert himself that much on defense. The Lakers needed points in a hurry and he was the chief point-getter. He had to concentrate on offense.

Their little flurry at the start of the second half cut our lead to 22 points. I hit a jump shot, but that didn't slow them down because West got a three-point play and our lead was 21. Then we enjoyed one of our best spurts of the game. I made a free throw. I stole the ball from Dickie and went all the way in for a lay-up. I hit a jump shot, and was fouled and made a free throw. A few seconds later Wilt missed two free throws (he ended up one for 11 from the line), DeBusschere threw in one of his typical long jumpers and we had a 27-point lead again. We led 94 to 69 at the end of the third quarter and coasted through the fourth for an easy 113 to 99 victory.

The Garden fans were unreal. They screamed when Willis appeared, they screamed when he was introduced, they screamed when we got off to a great start and they screamed when any one of us paused to retie a shoelace. They made so much racket in the beginning that they had no lung power left at the end. They were relatively quiet and limp in the final minutes, no doubt storing up energy to storm the court. I ducked out with four seconds left because I knew they would try to mob us. I was in the safety of the locker room—exhausted and numb—by the time they broke past the police and covered the floor. After 23 seasons of frustration, they deserved a little Mardi Gras.

It was a great team victory, and I don't care how corny that might sound. DeBusschere, who probably hustled and battled more consistently all season than anybody else on the Knicks, had 18 points and 17 rebounds. At one point in the third quarter he took a defensive rebound and drove the length of the court for a basket. Dollar Bill, playing in the middle of our 1-3-1, scored 17 points and had 5 assists.

Barnett scored 21 points, quite a few of them on twisting, unorthodox drives to the basket in which he somehow got the ball over Chamberlain's long arms. He said he kept seeing dollar signs up on the backboard. (Many people thought Dick would be put up for the post-season expansion draft because of his advanced age, 33, but the club wisely protected him. The new clubs took Donnie May, Bill Hosket and John Warren, the three guys with the least playing time on our team. I think with a chance to play, they'll all do well.)

I don't know how much pain Willis endured to play his 27 minutes, but it must have been a great amount. He was determined to try his best no matter how much it hurt and that was the whole story. For his courage and his excellent performances earlier, there was no doubt he deserved the Most Valuable Player award for the play-offs and the new car that went with it. Also, for being the most valuable Knick in the play-offs he won the use of an Avis rental car anytime, anywhere, for a year.

As for me, I think it was my greatest game, especially considering the circumstances and the competition. I scored a game-high 36 points, but the funny thing was I went into it thinking defense. I said to myself, "Stay with Garrett and forget about double-teaming West." I took the shots as they came, and they went in. In addition, I was 12 for 12 from the free-throw line and had 7 rebounds and 19 assists (tying a final play-off-series record for a single game).

I think the game was destiny, it was meant to be. The Knicks could have beaten anybody out there that night. There was no way we could lose, no matter who they put out on the court against us. A collection of the greatest players in the NBA—we could have beaten them.

We play a very together game.

Epilogue

In the end our pot was filled with $118,000. It had mounted up this way: $5,000 for finishing the regular season with the best winning percentage (.732 to Milwaukee's .683), $20,000 for winning the regular-season eastern division title, $20,000 for participating in the semifinals versus Baltimore, $25,000 for beating, Milwaukee in the division finals, $48,000 for winning the NBA championship.

We had a little gathering the night after the final Laker game to celebrate and divvy up the loot. We gave three office secretaries and six ball boys $250 apiece, Scout Dick McGuire $750 and the two publicity men, Frankie Blauschild and Jim Wergeles, $2000 apiece. The club took care of Phil Jackson, who had missed the season because of his bad back, so the remainder could have been cut up into 14 full shares (12 players, Red and Danny Whelan).

Instead, we voted unanimously to divide it 15 ways and give a full $7,400 share to Dr. Yanagisawa's widow and her five children.

WALT FRAZIER'S CAREER STATISTICS

New York Knickerbockers

	G	Min.	FGA	FGM	Pct.	FTA	FTM	Pct.	Reb.	A	PF	Disq.	Pts.	Avg.
1967-68	74	1588	568	256	.451	235	154	.655	313	305	199	2	666	9.0
1968-69	80	2949	1052	531	.505	457	341	.746	499	635	245	2	1403	17.5
1969-70	77	3040	1158	600	.518	547	409	.748	465	629	203	1	1609	20.9
TOTALS	231	7577	2778	1387	.499	1239	904	.721	1277	*1569	647	5	3678	15.9

NBA Play-Offs

	G	Min.	FGA	FGM	Pct.	FTA	FTM	Pct.	Reb.	A	PF	Disq.	Pts.	Avg.
1967-68	4	119	33	12	.364	18	14	.788	22	25	12	0	38	9.5
1968-69	10	415	177	89	.503	57	34	.596	74	91	30	0	212	21.2
1969-70	19	834	247	118	.478	89	68	.764	149	156	53	0	304	16.0
TOTALS	33	1368	457	219	.479	164	116	.707	245	272	95	0	554	16.8

Southern Illinois

	G	Min.	FGA	FGM	Pct.	FTA	FTM	Pct.	Reb.	A	PF	Disq.	Pts.	Avg.
1963-64 (freshman)	14		225	133	.591	85	52	.612	129		46		318	22.7
1964-65 (sophomore)	24		353	161	.456	111	88	.793	221		64		410	17.1
1966-67 (junior)	26		397	192	.483	126	90	.714	310		66		474	18.2
#TOTALS	50		750	353	.471	237	178	.751	531		130		884	17.7

*An average of close to seven assists per game
#Not including frosh season; Frazier did not play senior season

Frazier Honors

All-NBA, first team, '69-'70 (selected for the league by writers and broadcasters in 14 cities)

Sporting News All-NBA, first team, '69-'70 (selected by the NBA players)

All-NBA Defense, first team, '69-70 (received 27 of 28 possible votes from NBA coaches, more votes than any other player)

Professional Black Athlete of the Year, 1969 (selected by Association of Black Athletes)

All-NBA Defense, first team, '68-'69 (received 25 of 28 possible votes, more than any other player including Bill Russell)

East All-Stars, first team, '69-'70

NIT Most Valuable Player, 1967

Southern Illinois University Most Valuable Player, '66-'67

Little All-America, first team, '66-'67 (Associated Press and United Press International)

Little All-America, second team, '64-'65 (Associated Press)

Walt Frazier's Greatest College and Pro Games

May 8, 1970: Knicks 113, Lakers 99 at Madison Square Garden. N.Y. wins world championship with minimum service (at least minimum *physical* service) from injured Willis Reed. Clyde plays tough defense on ex-college teammate Dickie Garrett. 36 points, 19 assists (tying final series record), 7 rebounds, 5 steals.

March 21, 1970: Royals 136, Knicks 120 at Garden. Clyde returns after missing three games because of injury. 29 points on 10 of 15 field-goal attempts and 9 of 10 free throws, 9 rebounds, 7 assists.

Jan. 31, 1970: Knicks 123, Bulls 104 at Garden. N.Y.'s seventh win in a row. 35 points on 12 of 16 field-goal attempts and 11 of 14 free throws, 8 assists, 6 steals.

Jan. 24, 1970: Knicks 127, Rockets 114 at Garden. N.Y. plays without Dave DeBusschere. 32 points, 11 assists.

Dec. 30, 1969: Knicks 128, Bullets 91 at Garden. N.Y.'s eighth straight victory over Baltimore. 29 points on 11 of 22 field-goal attempts and 7 of 8 free throws, 14 assists, 8 rebounds.

Nov. 28, 1969: Knicks 106, Royals 105 at Cleveland Arena. N.Y. trails by 5 with 16 seconds left and wins the game! Clyde's two free throws just before the buzzer decide it. N.Y.'s 18th straight victory, breaking NBA record. 27 points, 7 rebounds, 5 assists.

Nov. 2, 1969: Knicks 138, Hawks 108 at Alexander Memorial Coliseum in Atlanta. After the game Coach Red Holzman said of Clyde, "I never saw a guy play a game like that." 15 steals, 33 points, 12 of 16 field-goal attempts, 8 rebounds.

Oct. 30, 1969: Knicks 123, Rockets 110 at Garden. Clyde receives tremendous ovation when he leaves the game. San Diego Coach Jack McMahon says of Walt afterward, "He is a coach's dream." 43 points on 14 of 22 shots from the field and 15 of 19 free throws, 9 assists.

Oct. 21, 1969: Knicks 140, Suns 116 at Garden. Clyde plays just 29 minutes. 28 points on 8 of 11 field-goal attempts and 12 of 14 free throws, 8 assists.

Feb. 26, 1969: Knicks 92, Celtics 88 at Boston Garden. Clyde and Dick Barnett score N.Y.'s last 25 points. Clyde hits 12 of N.Y.'s 18 points in a stretch where Knicks go from 67-76 down to 85-82 up.

Feb. 22, 1969: Rockets 108, Knicks 104 at Garden. 30 points, 11 rebounds, 12 assists.

Feb. 18, 1969: Lakers 113, Knilcks 109 at Garden. 30 points on 11 of 18 field-goal attempts and 8 of 9 free throws, 10 rebounds, 16 assists.

Feb. 15, 1969: Knicks 98, Warriors 92 at Garden. In third quarter, when N.Y. goes from 4 points behind to 11 points ahead, Clyde steals ball 3 times, blocks a shot and scores 9 of Knicks' 15 points. 20th straight Garden victory. 8 steals (6 of which lead to baskets), 24 points, 14 rebounds, 13 assists.

Feb. 10, 1968: Knicks 115, 76ers 97 at Garden. Last game in old Madison Square Garden at 50th St. and 8th Ave. 23 points, 15 assists, 15 rebounds.

March 18, 1967: Southern Illinois 71, Marquette 56 at Garden. Salukis win NIT championship to cap their greatest basektball season ever. ". . . In the end, it was the superb resources tapped by Southern's Walt Frazier which turned the tide," wrote Terry Bledsoe in the Milwaukee *Journal.* "Frazier seemed able, as champion athletes often are, to come up with a big play when a big play was required." 21 points, 11 rebounds, 5 assists.

March 16, 1967: Salukis 79, Rutgers 70 at Garden. 26 points on 10 of 18 floor shots and 6 of 8 free throws, 18 rebounds, 4 assists.

March 9, 1967: Salukis 103, St. Peter's 58. SIU runs previously high-scoring Peacocks right back across Hudson River to New Jersey. 24 points, 14 rebounds.

Jan. 16, 1967: Salukis 52, Kentucky Wesleyan 51 at Owensboro, Ky. Panthers' first loss in 10 games. Walt hits long jump shot with 1:27 left, steals the ball at midcourt and barrels in for a lay-up, gets key last-second rebound. 18 points, 13 rebounds.

Jan. 11, 1967: Salukis 53, Louisville 50 at Carbondale, Ill. Ends Cards' win streak at 13. 16 points on 5 of 11 field-goal attempts and 6 of 9 free throws, 9 rebounds.

Dec. 7, 1966: Salukis 69, St. Louis U. 59 at St. Louis. Salukis outrebound Billikens despite decided height disadvantage. 21 rebounds, 14 points.

Game-by-Game March to the NBA Championship '69-'70

REGULAR SEASON

1) Knicks 126, Seattle SuperSonics 101 (Stallworth, recovered from heart attack that kept him out more than two years, gets big reception; Clyde has 16 points and 12 assists).

2) *Knicks 94, Cincinnati Royals 89 (Clyde and Willis score 22 apiece).

3) *Knicks 116, Chicago Bulls 87 (Willis 18 rebounds, Clyde 20 points and 9 assists).

4) Knicks 99, Los Angeles Lakers 96 (despite Jerry West's 42 points).

5) Knicks 140, Phoenix Suns 116 (Clyde paces runaway with 28 points).

6) San Francisco Warriors 112, Knicks 109 (first loss of season).

7) Knicks 128, Baltimore Bullets 99 (Bradley 23 points; Clyde 21 points, 12 assists, 6 rebounds).

8) *Knicks 116, Detroit Pistons 92 (Clyde's 7 assists put him over 1,000 mark in slightly more than two NBA seasons).

9) Knicks 128, Atlanta Hawks 104 (Reed 28 points; Adam Clayton Powell appoints himself team's official chaplain).

10) Knicks 123, San Diego Rockets 110 (43 points for Clyde).

11) Knicks 112, Milwaukee Bucks 108.

12) *Knicks 109, Bucks 93 (Reed dominates Alcindor).

13) *Knicks 116, Suns 99 (N.Y. record now 12-1).

14) *Knicks 129, Rockets 111.

15) *Knicks 112, Lakers 102 (DeBusschere's nose is broken).

16) *Knicks 116, Warriors 103 (DeBusschere 24 points, 16 rebounds).

17) Knicks 114, Bulls 99.

18) Knicks 113, Boston Celtics 98 (17th victory in 18 games, best start in NBA history).

*Away game

19) Knicks 112, Royals 94.

20) *Knicks 98, Philadelphia 76ers 94 (N.Y. plays poorly, wins anyway).

21) Knicks 128, Suns 114 (Willis 37 points, 15 rebounds).

22) Knicks 103, Lakers 96 (Clyde 26 points, 13 rebounds, 9 assists).

23) *Knicks 138, Hawks 108 (Willis and Clyde 33 points apiece; N.Y. steals Atlanta blind).

24) #Knicks 106, Royals 105 (18th straight victory, an NBA record; Clyde wins it with two free throws).

25) Pistons 110, Knicks 98 (obvious letdown).

26) Knicks 129, SuperSonics 109 (Clyde 30 points, 7 assists).

27) *Knicks 116, Bullets 107 (N.Y. record now 25-2!).

28) Knicks 124, Bucks 99.

29) Royals 103, Knicks 101.

30) *Knicks 95, Bucks 75 (Clyde suffers groin injury).

31) *SuperSonics 112, Knicks 105 (Clyde doesn't play).

32) 76ers 100, Knicks 93 (Clyde 18 points, 8 rebounds, 7 assists).

33) Hawks 125, Knicks 124 (overtime: Clyde 14 assists; third straight loss).

34) *Knicks 108, Bulls 99 (Clyde 20 points, 11 assists, 12 rebounds).

35) Knicks 128, Bullets 91 (Clyde 29 points, 14 assists, 8 rebounds).

36) Knicks 112, Pistons 111 (Clyde throws length-

*Away game

of-the-court pass to Willis, who scores winning basket as buzzer sounds).

37) #Lakers 114, Knicks 106 (West 40 points; in Vancouver).

38) *Knicks 119, SuperSonics 117.

39) *Knicks 135, Suns 116.

40) Knicks 116, Bulls 96 (Holzman is named East All-Star coach).

41) *Bucks 118, Knicks 105 (N.Y. ends first half of season with 33-8 record).

42) Celtics 111, Knicks 104 (poor N.Y. defense).

43) *Knicks 129, Bullets 99 (9th victory in a row against Baltimore over two seasons).

44) *Knicks 99, Warriors 94 (Barnett 25 points).

45) *Knicks 123, Warriors 93 (20th time this season N.Y. has held opponent under 100 points).

46) *Rockets 123, Knicks 115 (N.Y. tired and fouls too much).

47) #Knicks 130, Suns 114 (Clyde 13 assists; at Salt Lake City).

48) *Knicks 104, Pistons 102 (Reed 29 points, 14 rebounds, 8 blocked shots).

49) *Celtics 109, Knicks 102.

ALL-STAR GAME
East 142, West 135 (Willis wins MVP trophy).

REGULAR SEASON CONTINUED

50) *Knicks 120, Bulls 117.

51) Knicks 127, Rockets 114 (Clyde 32 points, 11 assists).

*Away game
#Neutral court

52) *Knicks 102, Celtics 96 (Cazzie comes off bench to hit 25 points).

53) Knicks 133, Celtics 100 (fine team ball; 8 Knicks score in double figures).

54) Knicks 127, Pistons 106 (Bradley's injured ankle puts him on bench).

55) *Knicks 104, 76ers 100 (Bradley sits out; Willis 18 rebounds).

56) Knicks 123, Bulls 104 (Clyde 35 points, 8 assists, 6 steals).

57) *Knicks 117, Pistons 111 (Willis 30 points, 16 rebounds).

58) Knicks 118, Warriors 98.

59) *Hawks 111, Knicks 96 (worst defeat of season so far).

60) *Knicks 135, Royals 92 (Oscar out with groin injury).

61) Knicks 121, Royals 114 (Clyde 31 points, 9 assists).

62) Celtics 125, Knicks 118 (Clyde out with flu; Bradley still out).

63) *Knicks 151, 76ers 106 (Cazzie 35 points; worst defeat in history of 76ers' franchise).

64) Knicks 116, 76ers 114.

65) Knicks 114, Lakers 93.

66) Hawks 122, Knicks 106 (Joe Caldwell does another good job on Clyde).

67) *Bullets 110, Knicks 104 (Monroe scores 37 points).

68) Knicks 121, Suns 105 (38 assists for N.Y., two short of club record).

*Away game
#Neutral court

69) Knicks 115, Bullets 101 (N.Y. record now 54-15).

70) Knicks 115, Warriors 100 (Reed 21 rebounds).

71) Knicks 107, Rockets 103 (DeBusschere 30 points, 16 rebounds).

72) *Knicks 111, 76ers 104 (Willis 29 points, 15 rebounds).

73) 76ers 133, Knicks 116 (Cunningham 39 points).

74) Knicks 117, SuperSonics 99 (N.Y. clinches tie for East title).

75) #SuperSonics 115, Knicks 103 (champagne stays on ice at Portland).

76) *Knicks 119, Rockets 103 (N.Y. clinches East title).

77) *Lakers 106, Knicks 101.

78) *Knicks 122, Pistons 106 (Bradley returns to starting lineup and scores 19 points; Clyde misses game because of slight groin injury).

79) Bucks 116, Knicks 108.

80) *Hawks 110, Knicks 102.

81) Royals 136, Knicks 120.

82) *Celtics 115, Knicks 112.

EASTERN DIVISION SEMIFINALS

1) Knicks 120, Bullets 117 (double overtime; Monroe 39 points).

2) *Knicks 106, Bullets 99 (Riordan comes off bench to spark victory).

3) Bullets 127, Knicks 113 (Unseld outrebounds whole N.Y. team).

4) *Bullets 102, Knicks 92 (Monroe 34 points).

*Away game
#Neutral court

5) Knicks 101, Bullets 80 (Willis goes wild with 36 points, 36 rebounds).

6) *Bullets 96, Knicks 87 (Monroe and Gus Johnson tough in second half).

7) Knicks 127, Bullets 114 (Clyde 15 points, 10 rebounds, 8 assists).

EAST DIVISION FINALS

1) Knicks 110, Bucks 102 (Alcindor 35 points; Clyde clamps down on Flynn Robinson).

2) Knicks 112, Bucks 111 (Alcindor has 38 points but misses two free throws in last minute).

3) *Bucks 101, Knicks 96 (Alcindor 33 points, 31 rebounds).

4) *Knicks 117, Bucks 105 (good outside shooting by N.Y.).

5) Knicks 132, Bucks 96 (Reed 32 points, Barnett 27, Bradley 25).

NBA FINALS

1) Knicks 105, Lakers 112 (Willis 37 points, 16 rebounds).

2) Lakers 105, Knicks 103 (West 34 points; Chamberlain 24 rebounds).

3) *Knicks 111, Lakers 108 (West sinks long shot at buzzer to force game into overtime).

4) *Lakers 121, Knicks 115 (John Tresvant comes off bench to spark L.A.).

5) Knicks 107, Lakers 100 (Reed hurt in first half, N.Y. presses and steals its way to victory anyway).

6) *Lakers 135, Knicks 113 (Wilt goes wild in Reed's absence).

*Away game

7) Knicks 113, Lakers 99 (36 points, 19 assists and five steals for Clyde; Willis makes inspirational appearance but plays little).

"I've only been here a few days. I would have gotten to you eventually."

Rising from the bench, she took a few steps forward until she was mere inches from him. "I'm here now. So…why don't you go ahead and interrogate me?"

Resting one foot on the tree stump, Dan kept the ax safely between them. Knowing that Olivia was every bit as stubborn as her cousin, he decided it would be easier to humor her. "Very well, then. I'll ask you the same question I asked everyone else. Do you have any idea who would want to kill Simon?"

"None whatsoever and I can't believe you bought Jill's ridiculous assumption that he was murdered. Nearly everyone I know adored him. The man was an icon, for God's sake. One more good deed and he would have qualified for sainthood."

"Is that how you thought of him? As a saint?"

"Hell, no. In my opinion he was a cunning, selfish bastard, and I liked him about as much as he liked me, which isn't saying much."

"Not to mention that you didn't see eye to eye when it came to the running of B&A."

Her eyes narrowed. "Who told you that? Jill? Is that bitch trying to pin a murder on me now?"

"Relax, Olivia. Nobody is trying to pin anything on you. You're the one who wanted to be questioned, remember?"

"What motive would I have for killing Simon?" she said.

"Money. I understand you stood to gain quite a bit of it in a buyout Simon had opposed."

"Oh, that." Olivia gave a careless shrug. "Everybody on the board was opposed to the buyout idea.

You don't see me killing them all off, do you? Although that might not be a bad idea." She inched closer. "Now, why don't you ask me something interesting—like what was I doing the night Simon died."

Dan played along. "Okay. What were you doing the night Simon died?"

"I was in my bed. Sleeping between red-hot silk sheets and dreaming erotic dreams." She gave him a wicked smile. "Would you like details?"

"I'd rather know if anyone was with you."

She threw him a sly smile. "No, or the dream would have been a reality." She held up her hands. "Want to slip a pair of handcuffs on me?" she purred.

"College professors don't carry handcuffs."

She batted her eyelashes. "I do."

Before he could stop her, she lifted herself on her toes and kissed him on the mouth. "So long, handsome. If you need me for anything—and I do mean anything—you know where to find me."

Shaking his head, Dan watched her walk across the patio and down the path that circled the house. Moments later, the sound of a powerful engine roared to life and Dan picked up his ax again.

He had always thought of Olivia as a lost soul, a young woman no one had ever taken the time to understand, and because of that he had always felt a little sorry for her. One of these days, if she wasn't careful, her craving for attention would get her in trouble.

As for being a suspect in her uncle's murder, the thought may have crossed his mind at first, but not anymore. Olivia Bennett may be a lot of things but she was no murderer.

Eighteen

Arms folded against his chest, Dan stood in his old bedroom, studying the case chart he had tacked on the wall. A replica of the one he had used as a homicide detective, it was divided into three columns. In the left column he had written down the name of every possible suspect. In the center column he had detailed that person's motive and opportunity to commit the crime, and in the last column he had jotted down his own personal thoughts.

Of the seven names on the chart, Pete Mulligan topped the list. He had a strong motive for wanting Simon dead, and while his wife claimed he was in bed with her that night, she could have lied to protect him.

And after what Al Metzer had told him, the contractor's motive seemed even stronger. According to the private investigator, Pete Mulligan was very much in love with his beautiful wife, more so than she was in love with him. He had courted her for years before she had agreed to marry him, and rumor had it that the only reason she'd finally said yes was that Pete had saved her father from bankruptcy.

Vivian Mulligan, whose name appeared beneath her husband's, was also a possibility, and so was Amanda, by virtue of the fact that she hadn't been completely honest when Dan had questioned her.

Cyrus, on the other hand, presented a conflicting challenge. Physically, he could have done it. He was strong and in remarkably good shape for a man who had just celebrated his sixty-first birthday. And he had been home alone that night, with no one to provide him with an alibi. Not to mention that he had flatly refused to talk to Dan about Simon. He hadn't even bothered with an excuse.

"I'm not thrilled at the thought of you stirring up trouble for our family," Cyrus had told him bluntly. "And even less thrilled that you're back in my niece's life. You've hurt her badly. Simon may have forgiven you for that, but I haven't."

Yet no matter how hard Dan tried, he couldn't think of a single reason why Cyrus would want to kill Simon. While another man would have resented living in the shadow of his more talented brother, Cyrus had always seemed happy just as he was. And he had never shown the slightest desire to run B&A.

The same reasoning applied to Paul Scoffield and Philip Van Horn. Both were wealthy, with no apparent grudge against their flamboyant boss. Both lived alone, and their alibis couldn't be confirmed, hence the reason for their presence on the list.

The last entry on the chart was Joshua, but until Dan questioned him and learned more about the caretaker, he had nothing to go on.

A knock at the door broke his concentration. Not waiting for Dan to say "Come in," Joe Santini opened the door and ducked his head into the room.

Dan waved him in. "Come on in, Joe."

"I just got off duty and came to see how you were doing." A detective with the Brooklyn narcotics squad, Joe had offered to get whatever information he could gather on Mulligan or any other suspect.

Of the three Santini brothers, Joe was the one who had inherited their father's dark good looks and jovial personality. At thirty-five, he had a head of thick black hair, laughing dark eyes and dimples that had once earned him the much-despised nickname of "Cheeks."

Looking at the wall chart, Joe quickly read the information Dan had compiled and chuckled. "I swear, Dan, no one can come up with a list of suspects faster than you can."

"Coming up with suspects is easy, Joe. The hard part is sorting through the mess and finding the killer."

Joe's gaze moved up and down the chart, stopping at the top. "I made a few discreet inquiries and found out something interesting about your number-one man."

Dan leaned against the bureau and folded his arms. "What's that?"

"Word on the street is that he was once tight with Gino Pugliese."

"That two-bit punk in Jersey?"

"He's expanded now, not in status—he's still a two-bit punk—but in territory, which now includes Lower Manhattan."

"What is he doing exactly?"

"A little bit of everything. Loan-sharking, drug pushing, pimping. You name it, he's got his dirty nose in it."

"Any convictions?"

"Not Pugliese. The weasel is too slippery to get caught."

"You said Mulligan *was* tight with him. How do you know he still isn't?"

"I don't. That's why I want you to be careful."

"I will. Thanks for the info, Joe." Dan didn't tell him about his confrontation with the contractor the previous night. Knowing Joe, he'd put a twenty-four-hour guard on him.

"Don't mention it." Joe gave him a boyish grin. "What's that we used to say when we were kids? All for one, one for all, right?"

Dan smiled at the familiar saying. Once the Santini brothers had been known around the neighborhood as the Three Musketeers. Then at nineteen, Nino, an incorrigible adventurer, had joined a mountain-climbing team and had gone to conquer the Himalayas. He and two fellow climbers were killed on the second day of the journey, leaving behind grieving parents and two heartbroken younger brothers.

Joe glanced at his watch. "I've got to take Nick to basketball practice, but you remember what I said and watch your back. If Mulligan and Pugliese *are* buddies, there's no telling what either of them might do."

Dan took his blue felt pen from the bureau and underlined Mulligan's name—twice. "I always watch my back, little brother."

When Jill returned from Washington later that day, her first call was to Dan. "That cabdriver was wrong after all," she told him. "I talked to the director of the clinic himself, as well as his head nurse. Both told me my father was never there.''

Dan sounded skeptical, which didn't surprise her. Cops, even ex-cops, were suspicious by nature. "Are you sure they told you the truth? Doctor-patient confidentiality is pretty sacred stuff. You breach that and your business goes down the tubes.''

"Dr. Laken and Nurse Parson didn't lie. They even checked the clinic's records for me. The only abortion Dr. Laken performed on October 3 was on a young woman who came in with her husband. Both were nineteen years old. There was no other surgery until the following week.''

"Still, it wouldn't hurt to have Al run a check on the doctor and the nurse, just to be sure. In the meantime," he continued, "we could take a drive to Livingston Manor and talk to Joshua. Wally called to say he was back. Is tomorrow good for you?''

Jill glanced at her calendar. "I'm free at four.''

Dan agreed to pick her up at the entrance of the Vangram Building.

Olivia woke up with a start. Eyes wide open, heart pounding, she held her breath. Something wasn't right. A scent—sweet, cloying, unfamiliar—hung over the bed, filling her nostrils and making her nauseated.

Someone was in her room.

As her eyes became accustomed to the darkness, she saw the shape at the foot of the bed.

Swallowing a scream, Olivia bolted to a sitting position, pulling the sheets over her bare breasts. She tried to speak but a knot of fear had lodged in her throat, blocking out all sound.

Suddenly, the shape leaned forward, reached for the bedside lamp and turned it on.

A man dressed in black sat looking at her. In his forties, he was short and wiry, with cold, pale blue eyes, a thin mouth twisted into an ugly grin and shiny black hair he wore slicked back in a ponytail.

Her terrified gaze was riveted to the switchblade he held in his right hand.

"Hi, Livy."

Pressing her back against the headboard, Olivia felt her whole body tremble. "How..." Her voice broke.

"How did I get in?" The man gave a careless shrug. "I have my ways." When Olivia opened her mouth again, he leaned forward and pressed the flat part of the blade against her mouth. "Shh. I do the talking, Livy, okay? You do the listening."

His eyes hardened. "Now about that little favor you're supposed to do for my good friend Pete. You've got twenty-four hours. If you keep messing around..." The blade moved to Olivia's cheek, its point lightly sinking into the flesh.

Olivia held her breath.

"Talk to me, Livy."

Not daring to nod for fear the knife would sink in deeper, Olivia blinked furiously.

"Say it," the man ordered.

"The bids. He wants the bids."

"In twenty-four hours."

"Twenty-four hours."

"Good girl." Smiling now, the man let the blade move downward to Olivia's neck, stopping long enough over her pulse to make her break into a sweat.

It continued downward until it reached the top of her right breast.

"I'd hate to cut up a pretty number like you." There was a sort of longing in the man's voice as if the thought of cutting her excited him. "But if you give me reason to come back, that's exactly what I'll do, and then you won't be so pretty anymore." The smile widened, exposing small, ferretlike teeth. "You get my drift?"

Unable to do much more than moan her agreement, Olivia pressed harder into the headboard.

Almost reluctantly, the intruder pulled the blade away. There was a click before it disappeared inside the handle.

"One more thing. Don't go squealing on me, okay, Livy?" He leaned closer until all she could see were those pale, cold eyes. "Because if I hear you went to the cops, you're going to find yourself in the bottom of the East River with the fishes feasting on that beautiful bod of yours, *capisce?*"

The image brought another shudder. Olivia nodded. "I won't say anything."

Transfixed, she watched him move quickly and silently across the room. At the door, he turned around. "Oh, and don't worry about George downstairs. He should wake up in about an hour, feeling as fresh as a daisy."

Before she could expel another ragged breath, he was gone.

It was only then that she began to tremble. Clutching the sheets against her, she didn't even try to fight the spasms that rocked her body, but went with them, letting the fear work its way out of her system.

She wasn't sure how long she sat there, shaking and crying. When she looked up again, the clock on her bedside read 2:10 a.m.

Knowing she wouldn't be able to sleep, she got out of bed, tested her legs to make sure they'd support her and went into the living room to pour herself a stiff drink. This time she didn't bother with ice cubes.

She took a big gulp of the liquor, coughed, then drank again. When she was relatively calm, she sank into a chair.

Oh, Olivia, she thought as she closed her eyes. What mess have you got yourself into now?

A layer of new-fallen snow covered the area when Jill and Dan arrived in Livingston Manor the following evening. On the narrow walk that led to Joshua's cabin, the snow had already been removed and salt granules twinkled in the moonlight.

"Now don't forget," Jill told Dan as they prepared to knock on the door. "He's wary of strangers. He might even refuse to talk to you, so let me start, okay? He'll trust you more if he knows you and I are friends."

As Dan had expected, Joshua's timid smile turned into a frown the moment he saw him.

He was a big man, Dan noted, with a powerful body, thick callused hands and unruly mousy brown hair that fell to his shoulders. Dan estimated his age to be anywhere between thirty and forty.

"Hello, Joshua," Jill said gently.

"Hello, Miss Jill."

"Joshua, this is my friend." Jill took Dan's arm and

pulled him forward. "His name is Dan Santini. You can call him Mr. Dan if you like."

"Good evening, Joshua."

Joshua didn't return the greeting. Nor did he make eye contact with Dan.

"Did Wally explain why we're here?" Jill asked.

"He said you wanted to ask me questions."

"That's right." She rubbed her hands together. "Is it okay if we come inside, Joshua? It's awfully cold out here."

As the caretaker moved aside to let them in, Dan took a quick inventory of the cabin. It was scrupulously clean, from the small galley kitchen across from the living-dining area, to the small bedroom alcove on the far side of the room. Wall shelves were filled with an odd assortment of dismantled radios, alarm clocks and blenders. A woodstove with a kettle on it kept the place cozy and warm.

"Joshua likes to fix things," Jill explained. "Don't you, Joshua?"

Joshua went to the sink and started to wash his dinner dishes, a task Dan and Jill's arrival had apparently interrupted.

"I like to fix things, too," Dan said.

In lieu of a response, Joshua ran a plate under the water faucet, then set it on a wooden rack to dry.

Not looking the least bit disturbed by the man's unreceptive behavior, Jill moved closer to him but was careful not to invade his space. "Dan needs to ask you a couple of questions about the night my father died." She spoke slowly and gently as one would to a child. "Is that all right with you, Joshua?"

He puzzled over that for an instant then nodded.
"Okay."

Trying to look as unthreatening as possible, Dan
leaned one elbow on the kitchen counter. "It was raining pretty hard that night, wasn't it, Joshua?"

The caretaker nodded and began to scrub a pot.

"Do you remember looking out?" Dan glanced at
the small window above the sink. In the dark, the main
house was just a huge, dark shadow. "To watch the
rain?"

Joshua nodded but still didn't look at him.

"Do you like the rain, Joshua?"

"Yeah."

"So do I." Dan waited a beat, not wanting to crowd
all the questions together. "Did you see anything besides the rain? Like maybe…another car? Or a person?"

Joshua's mouth tightened as he continued to wash
the pot. "I didn't see nothin'."

"But you saw Mr. Simon's Jeep, didn't you?"

Joshua looked up then, his expression confused and
frightened. He shot Jill a quick glance as if expecting
her to come to his rescue.

"It's all right, Joshua. You can tell Dan anything.
He's a friend, remember?"

"Did you see Mr. Simon's Jeep?" Dan repeated.

Joshua set the pot on the drying rack and shook his
head.

"My father probably parked in the garage," Jill offered. "That would explain why he didn't see it."

Dan kept his gaze on Joshua. "You didn't hear another car drive up?"

The caretaker's expression suddenly turned hostile

and his movements became more brusque. His face was now flushed as he started to wipe the counter with a green sponge. "I told you I didn't see nothin'. I was busy," he added. "I was trying to fix something." He pointed at a toaster at the end of the counter.

"Oh." Dan went to take a closer look at the appliance, which lay on its side. "What's wrong with it?"

Joshua shrugged. "Needs a part. A heating co…"

"A heating coil?" Dan asked.

"Yeah, but I can't find one."

Picking up the toaster, Dan turned it upside down and noted the model and serial number on the back of a business card he took out of his wallet. "I'll tell you what," he said. "I know a man in Brooklyn who might just have what you need. I'll talk to him and let you know, okay?"

Joshua cast him a suspicious look. "Mr. Simon told me they don't make toasters like that no more."

"That's true, but my friend owns a hardware store. And he never throws anything away, no matter how old it is." He waited until Joshua had dried his hands on a dish towel before adding, "Did Mr. Simon have a lot of visitors when he was here?"

Joshua shrugged. "Mr. Wally comes here sometime and when there's a holiday, Mr. Simon's family comes, too." His face turned sad again. "Now they won't come no more."

"Oh, Joshua, that's not true," Jill said quickly. "I plan to come here a lot and so does my mother and my uncle Cyrus."

But Joshua didn't look convinced. Dan tried to draw him back into a conversation but it was useless. Joshua had suddenly erected a wall and retreated behind it.

Jill sensed it, too. Glancing at Dan, she shook her head before addressing the caretaker again. "Thanks for talking to us, Joshua." On an impulse, she walked over to him and hugged him. "That was very nice of you."

The man's expression softened as he looked at Jill. "I'll take good care of the house, Miss Jill."

"I know you will, Joshua."

Once they were outside, Jill turned to Dan. "Well, what do you think of him?"

"He doesn't trust me."

"That's because he doesn't know you."

"And he didn't tell me the truth."

"Oh, Dan, how can you say that? I was right there and he sounded completely truthful to me—"

Dan took Jill's hand. "Hold it," he whispered as he brought her to a stop.

Instinctively, she moved close to him. "What is it?" she whispered.

"Someone just came out of your father's house."

Holding her breath, Jill peered through the trees. Dan was right. A small figure dressed in black was hurrying down the walkway. "Who could it be?" Jill's heart beat erratically. "And what would they be doing here at this hour?"

"That's what I'm going to find out. You stay here."

Letting go of Jill's hand, Dan moved quickly toward the main house until he had intercepted the intruder. When he realized who it was, he stopped dead in his tracks.

Nineteen

Looking like a trapped animal, Lilly stared at Dan, then at Jill, who, at the sound of Dan's exclamation, had rushed over. "What are you two doing here?"

"We came to see Joshua." Jill's gaze went to the black purse her aunt held pressed against her chest. "What about you, Aunt Lilly? What are you doing here at this hour?" A feeling of uneasiness spread through her. "How did you get into the house?"

"I borrowed Amanda's keys." Lilly's smile was unnaturally tight. "I lost a valuable pair of earrings the last time I was here and I came back to look for them."

"Did you find them?"

"Yes. As a matter of fact...I did."

"Why wouldn't you ask *me* to look for your earrings?" Jill's voice was gently persistent. "You know I come up here all the time."

Lilly didn't say anything.

Intrigued by the actress's obvious nervousness, Dan continued to observe her. The possibility that Lilly could somehow be involved in Simon's murder was not one he had considered, and yet, here she was, looking guilty and frightened. "I wasn't aware you had a car," he said, looking around him. "You did drive, didn't you?"

"Yes, of course." Lilly nodded toward her left. "It's in there. A rental. I hid it."

Following her gaze, Dan saw a midsize sedan pushed into the underbrush. "Why would you hide it?"

"Because I didn't feel like getting into a long discussion with Joshua. You know how he is. The man guards the house like a rottweiler." She laughed, a brittle laugh that betrayed her nervousness. "He probably would have shot me on sight."

It had begun to snow heavily again, thick flakes that settled on Lilly's dark mink coat like small puffs of cotton.

"Well, you can't drive back to New York in this weather," Dan said as he looked up at the dark, snow-laden skies. "So why don't we all go inside and have something hot to drink. Then we'll talk."

"I have to get back—"

Before Lilly could protest further, Dan had claimed her arm and was helping her up the walkway. Jill was right behind them, already searching for her keys.

Once inside the house, Dan went straight to the fireplace to start a fire while Jill busied herself in the kitchen. Within moments she had prepared a pot of tea, located a tin of shortbread cookies, milk and sugar. Thanks to Joshua, who replenished supplies whenever needed, essential staples were always on hand.

Walking back into the living room, Jill set the tray on the coffee table and threw a quick glance at her aunt. Trembling from what must have been a combination of fear and cold, Lilly had remained huddled in her mink coat and was still holding on to her purse.

Jill's dismay grew. There was a lot more inside that purse than a valuable pair of earrings. But what? What could Lilly possibly want from this house that she couldn't get by simply asking?

She filled a cup and handed it to her aunt. "Here, drink this. It's hot and strong, just the way you like it."

As she took the cup from Jill, Lilly's grateful smile went straight to Jill's heart. She adored her aunt. As a teenager, Jill had often talked of becoming an actress someday and following in her aunt's famous footsteps. In time that dream had made room for another one— that of becoming an architect—but the close bond between the two women was still there.

"Are you warm yet, Aunt Lilly?" she asked. "Would you like to take off your coat?"

Glancing at the roaring fire, Lilly nodded. "I will, in a minute." She looked from Jill to Dan, who had come to join them on the sofa. "I guess I didn't make much sense out there, did I?"

Jill smiled. "Now that you mention it, it wasn't one of your best performances."

Lilly put down her cup, and as she started to slip out of her coat, Dan helped her. "Do you trust Jill and I enough to tell us the truth now, Lilly?"

"I know how bad this looks, but I swear to you both that I didn't kill Simon."

"I know you didn't, Aunt Lilly."

Lilly looked at Dan, as if expecting him to echo Jill's statement. He didn't. "What's in the purse, Lilly?" he asked gently.

An awkward silence fell over the room. Lilly's beautiful, expressive face was taut with tension as she stared into the distance. After a while, she lowered her gaze to her purse, then, as if finally making up her mind, she opened the clasp and pulled out a white, business-size envelope.

She handed it to Jill. "You'll find the answer to that question in here. Go ahead," she said as Jill hesitated. "Take a look. You, too, Dan."

Somewhat apprehensively, Jill opened the envelope. Inside was a newspaper clipping dating back to November 30, 1986. It had been taken from the *Weekly Gazette,* a British tabloid that printed only the most sensational, outrageous stories, from royal gossip to imminent UFO invasions.

A paparazzo had apparently photographed Lilly in the arms of a man whose face Jill recognized instantly. His name was Yussef Abrahim and he was suspected of having masterminded the bombing of several Parisian restaurants in the fall of '86, killing sixteen people.

Because of the man's wealth and powerful connections, French law enforcement agencies, as well as Interpol, were never able to charge him. He had died in a helicopter crash in 1993.

The headline spoke volumes: Blood Money.

Sitting side by side, Jill and Dan read the short article together.

American stage actress Lilly Grant was seen cruising the Greek Isles this week in the company of Yussef Abrahim. A well-informed source reveals that Abrahim, one of Libya's richest men, and a known terrorist, will finance Ms. Grant's new play *A Rose on My Pillow,* due to open in London in December of this year.

Dan looked up. "Is that true, Lilly? Abrahim financed your play?"

She nodded.

"But why?" Jill asked. "You had to know who he was, what he had done."

"I did." Lilly's eyes remained downcast. "But I hadn't had a decent part in more than two years. I thought my career was over. Then one night, while I was appearing in a small play in London, my agent told me that Yussef was in the audience and wanted to meet me.

"In spite of his reputation, which he swore was grossly exaggerated, the man was an absolute charmer. He told me he loved the theater and that he was a great admirer of mine. One thing led to another and two days later, he had made the necessary arrangements for me to star in this wonderful new play." She looked up. "The same play, which, as you know, put my career back on track."

"Did the producers know who he was?"

"The producers were all friends of his, people whose plays he had financed before and who didn't care where the money came from."

Jill glanced back at the clipping. "Why didn't we hear about you and that man here in the U.S.?"

"I'm sure you would have, but as I said, Yussef's influence extended far and wide. He stopped the story from going any farther. If he hadn't, my career would have been over. I even doubt I would have had the courage to return to the United States.''

Dan glanced at the article again. ''How did that clipping end up in Simon's house?''

Lilly sighed dramatically. ''He had me investigated.''

Jill gaped at her aunt. ''*Investigated?* Why?''

Lilly gave an adamant shake of her head. ''There's no need to go into that. You wanted to know what I was doing here and now you know. Let's leave it at that.''

''No, let's not.'' Jill dropped the envelope on the table. ''You're making it sound as if my father was blackmailing you, and if he was, I want to know why.''

''It will only cause you pain—''

Jill's tone turned bitter. ''I'm getting used to pain, Aunt Lilly, so please, don't let that stop you.''

''Very well.'' This time Lilly met her niece's gaze without flinching. ''Simon called that clipping 'insurance,' a guarantee that I'd keep my mouth shut.''

''About what?''

''About something I wasn't supposed to have seen.'' She took a deep breath. ''Earlier this year, I think it was late spring, I was having dinner with a gentleman friend in a secluded but famous inn on the Chesapeake Bay. To my surprise, Simon was there, having dinner with a woman.''

Jill looked at Dan, then back at her aunt. ''Did he see you? Did you talk to him?''

''He saw me, but we didn't talk. I just went about my business as if I hadn't seen a thing, but he knew I had. When I got back to New York a couple of days later, there was a message on my machine. It was from Simon. He wanted to see me.

"At first, he tried to make light of the situation, claiming the woman was a business acquaintance. When he realized I didn't believe him, he asked me not to tell Amanda."

"And you never did?"

"Of course not. It would have destroyed her. But Simon didn't trust me, so he hired a private investigator. He figured actors were bound to have a few skeletons in their closets, and in this case, he was right."

Feeling almost dizzy from the shock, Jill kept shaking her head. They couldn't possibly be talking about the father she had known and loved all her life, the father who was turning into a stranger, a man who had schemed and deceived and even blackmailed a member of his own family.

"I'm sorry, Jill," Lilly said softly. "I didn't want you to find out."

"I thought he loved her," Jill murmured to no one in particular. "I thought they had the most perfect marriage in the world."

"He did love Amanda, darling. That's why he didn't want her to know."

Jill found no comfort in those words. Her father was an adulterer, a common, vulgar skirt-chaser who had committed the ultimate betrayal, apparently more than once, unless, of course, the woman Lilly had seen him with was Vivian Mulligan. "Do you know who the woman was?" she asked.

"No."

"Can you at least describe her?" Dan asked.

Lilly shrugged. "Not very well, I'm afraid. The restaurant had no overhead lighting, only candles on each table, so I wasn't able to have a good look at her. But I could tell she was beautiful, with very long blond hair, and well dressed. The only thing I can't be sure of is her age. In such flattering lighting, she could have been anywhere between twenty and forty."

Lilly's small, delicate hand touched Jill's. "You believe me, don't you, darling? You believe I had nothing to do with your father's death."

"Of course I believe you, and I'm sorry Daddy put you through this hell. I..." Despite her determination not to cry, a tear ran down her cheek. "I don't know why he...why he did all those things."

Dan, who hadn't yet spoken, finally did. "I'm curious, Lilly. How did you know the clipping was here?"

"I didn't. After Simon died, I searched the town house as best as I could with Henry and Amanda always there. When I didn't find it, I figured the damn thing had to be here." Her cheeks colored slightly. "Earlier today, I took Amanda's keys, knowing she wouldn't miss them, and came here. I didn't dare turn the lights on for fear Joshua would see them, so I used a flashlight."

Her hands tightened into fists. "If only I had found that envelope sooner, I would have missed you and you would have never known."

Feeling sick and cold, Jill rose and moved to the window. The snow was coming down harder now. Soon the narrow mountain roads would be impassable.

Behind her, Dan had come to the same conclusion.

"We'll spend the night here," he said, laying his hands on her shoulders. "Okay?"

Not trusting her voice, Jill nodded. She heard Dan ask Lilly if she was okay to stay the night. Her aunt quietly agreed.

Dan gave Jill's shoulders a gentle squeeze. "Everything's going to be all right, Jill. You'll see."

She wished she could share his optimism, but with all she had learned in the last while, she felt as though nothing would ever be the same again. Her father was not the man she thought he was, her favorite aunt had shared the bed of a terrorist and her mother was still keeping secrets from her.

Was one of those secrets her husband's affair? It had to be. No matter how discreet a man was, how many precautions he took, there were signs a woman never failed to recognize.

When Jill finally turned away from the window, the room was empty. Only the dying embers were left in the fireplace and a Good Samaritan had cleared away the tea tray.

Jill smiled. Dan hadn't lost his touch. He still knew when she needed comfort and when she needed to be alone.

Walking over to the single lamp he had left burning, she turned off the switch and went upstairs.

Twenty

By seven o'clock the following morning, Dan was up, showered and dressed. Outside his window, snow had blanketed the landscape and he could already hear the rumble of busy snowplows as they made their way up and down Johnston Road.

Jill was already downstairs, sitting on the sofa and staring at the dark fireplace. He was glad to see that her cheeks had regained their healthy glow and that her eyes no longer had that haunted look about them.

In a gesture that seemed as natural as breathing, he sat next to her and wrapped an arm around her shoulders. "Slept okay?"

"Oddly enough, yes. It took me a while, but once I closed my eyes, I never reopened them until I heard the first plow."

"Wally claims it's the mountain air."

She laughed, a sound that warmed his heart. "Wally thinks his mountains can cure anything."

"Would you like to put his claim to the test and stay here awhile longer? It's Saturday."

"Can't. I have tons of work." She leaned into him. "Maybe we could come again, do some skiing? With a little advance planning, I might be able to arrange it."

"I'm going to hold you to that."

There was a long silence, but not an awkward one, rather the kind of silence friends understood. "Did you have any idea my father was so different from the man we knew?"

"No. And it's not your cross to bear, Jill."

"Then why can't I get what he did out of my mind? And why am I feeling so betrayed?"

Afraid to say the wrong thing, Dan treaded softly. "I can't tell you that what he did doesn't matter, because it does, or that it shouldn't change how you feel, because it already has." When she turned her head the other way, he touched the underside of her chin, forcing her to look at him. "But the father who loved you didn't change. The man may no longer measure up to your expectations, but he was still a good man in many ways. He did good things for people, Jill, things that mattered, things that made a difference. And you must admit, that as a father, he was beyond reproach."

"I feel like a fool for not seeing what was going on."

"You weren't meant to see it."

"That woman Lilly saw, she fits Vivian Mulligan's description, doesn't she?"

"The long hair doesn't unless she cut it since then. But just to be sure, I plan to ask Vivian."

"And if it's not her but someone else?"

"Then we'll find her."

"But how? There must be about a million blond, beautiful women between here and Maryland."

Above, in one of the bedrooms, a door opened and closed. Lilly was coming down. Rising, Dan held out his hand. "Come on, Red. I'm starved. Let's go see what we can wrestle up for breakfast."

After Dan had cleared the snow from around both cars, Lilly kissed them both goodbye and left. Within minutes, Dan and Jill were also on their way. Knowing Jill had a lot on her mind, Dan respected her silence. He spun the radio knob, and found a station that played velvet-smooth R&B, which he could tell by the way her shoulders relaxed was still her favorite sound. He turned the volume down low.

Halfway to New York, he took advantage of the slow-moving traffic to turn to her. "How would you like to have Sunday dinner with us?"

The question obviously took her by surprise because she seemed speechless.

Dan laughed. "You look as if I just dropped a bomb on your lap."

"Well...you did."

"They only want to see you, Jill, not eat you alive."

"I don't know. I'd feel awkward."

"Awkward? With my folks?" Dan shook his head. "That's an oxymoron. Besides," he added, when Jill didn't answer, "the invitation comes directly from my mother. And you know how she is. If you say no, she'll blame me."

It was only a dinner, Jill thought. And Dan was right, she had never felt awkward with his family. Why should she now? Just because she hadn't seen them in twelve years. "Tell Angelina I'd love to come for dinner."

As she spoke those words, she wondered what kind

of magic spell Dan had put on her to make her lower her guard this way.

Jill had always found work to be the perfect antidote for stress. Thanks to the Church Hill project, which she had spent most of the day working on after returning from Livingston Manor, last night's events were no longer intruding on her mind with such alarming frequency.

Stifling a yawn, she glanced at her watch. Seven o'clock. She had just enough time to stop at the video store and make it to Ashley's apartment for their usual Saturday-night ritual—pizza and a movie. Now that the Summerfield wedding was over, Jill looked forward to spending a few relaxing hours with her friend.

Wearing her black coat with Dan's whimsical pin on the lapel, Jill walked down the deserted hallway where the executive offices were located. As she turned the corner and neared her uncle's office, she noticed that the door was closed, which was unusual, and that a light filtered from beneath it. Was he also working late? Or had the cleaning crew simply forgotten to turn off the lights?

Puzzled, she gave a light knock, then, because she hadn't expected an answer, she swung the door open. And stopped.

Her cousin sat at Cyrus's desk, her mouth open in shock.

"Olivia. What are you doing here?"

Never one to be tongue-tied for long, Olivia snapped right back. "I could ask you the same question."

"I was passing by and saw the light." Jill glanced at the letter in her cousin's hand. "What's that?"

"Not that it's any of your business, but it's that memo you wrote the other day regarding expenses." She held the paper so Jill could see it. "I lost my copy and couldn't find one on Cecilia's desk so I tried my father's office. I knew he'd have a spare copy."

"Oh—"

"What's the matter, Jill?" Olivia's tone dripped with sarcasm. "Disappointed? You were hoping to catch me committing some unspeakable crime perhaps?" She tapped a crimson-tipped finger against her bottom lip. "Let's see now, what could that be? Stealing from petty cash? Or something more serious, like…photographing B&A's latest designs so I could sell them to a rival firm?"

"Oh, stop it, Olivia. You're so damn paranoid."

"And you're so damn perfect." Olivia dropped the memo into her open briefcase. "Queen Jill, the perfect daughter, the perfect niece, the perfect VP."

Jill blew out an irritated sigh. "That's always what it comes down to, isn't it? That stupid jealousy of yours."

Olivia laughed. "Me? Jealous of you? You're flattering yourself."

"I don't think so. You've resented me ever since I graduated from college and came to work here on a full-time basis."

"Oh, and you don't think I was justified? Especially after all the hype that surrounded your royal arrival? Having to listen to your daddy's bragging, as if you were some sort of demigod."

"No one else at B&A seemed to mind."

"Would they tell you if they did? And risk Simon's wrath?" Olivia's smile was condescending. "Really, cousin, dear, for all your smarts, you can be awfully dense at times."

There was no point in even trying to argue with Olivia when she was in such a foul mood.

Turning around, Jill marched out of Cyrus's office. "Good night, Olivia."

Watching her disappear, Olivia let out a sigh and fell back against her chair. That was close. Too close. But how was she to know that Jill would be working this late on a Saturday? Lucky for her, she'd had the presence of mind to bring that memo with her, in case someone came in unexpectedly.

Using the key she had taken from her father's key chain earlier, she opened the drawer where the bids were kept, aware that her hand was shaking.

Apex Construction, one of Pete Mulligan's fiercest rivals, was the low bidder with 5.2 million. The next bid came at 5.5 million. The other three were all in excess of six million dollars.

After making a mental note of the numbers, she put the bids back in the drawer and locked up.

There, she thought with another sigh of relief, it was done. And except for that little scare with Jill a moment ago, it had been painless. Now all she had to do was call Mulligan with the numbers and collect the rest of her money.

Ninety thousand dollars.

Twenty-four hours earlier, the thought of all that cash would have been enough to make her salivate. Today, all she could think of was the way that blade had felt against her skin and the dispassionate expression in the man's cold blue eyes. She never wanted to experience that kind of terror again.

And the best way to insure she wouldn't was to end her partnership with Pete Mulligan.

After she collected her money.

At the news that Jill was having Sunday dinner with the Santinis, Ashley's mouth dropped open. "You're going *where?*"

Perched on a stool in Ashley's tiny kitchen, Jill accepted a glass of Chardonnay from her friend. "Don't make it sound like a visit with the pope. It's only a dinner. And the offer came from Angelina, so how could I say no?"

"You couldn't." Ashley's smile was gently teasing. "Scared?"

"Terrified." Jill stole a lettuce leaf from the big wooden bowl and munched on it. "It's been a long time since I've been around the Santinis. They're bound to have changed."

"Good people don't change, Jill."

"But what about Dan's nephews? You know how awful I am with little kids. I never seem to know what to do with them, or what to say."

Ashley uncapped a bottle of olive oil and drizzled it over the baby greens. "You're great with Sally."

"How can you say that? The last time your little niece stayed with me, I set fire to her hair, and the time before that, I lost her in a New Jersey mall."

"But you found her. And you were awfully quick with that fire extinguisher."

"I nearly drowned her in all that foam."

Laughing, Ashley handed her the salad bowl. "Toss. And stop worrying so much. You'll be fine. The boys are going to love you. All you have to do is be yourself." Setting a French baguette on a cutting board, she started slicing. "How are things between you and Dan?"

Pretending not to understand the question, Jill widened her eyes. "What things?"

"You know damn well what things. Are there any sparks between you two, any vibes, any...sexual tension?"

"No. I've already told you, my relationship with Dan is purely business, so get that silly grin off your face."

"And I suppose that sexy, outrageously expensive perfume you've started wearing again, that same perfume Dan always claimed could reduce him to mush, is purely business as well."

"Oh, that." Jill shrugged. "I was ready for a change, that's all."

"Bull. I think you're falling for him again. Hard."

"You're dreaming."

With a smug look, Ashley walked over to her purse, which hung on a peg on the wall, pulled out a twenty-dollar bill from her wallet and slapped it on the counter. "Twenty bucks says I'm not."

Jill looked from the bill to Ashley. "What are you doing?"

"I'm betting you twenty dollars that any day now you're going to realize that you and Dan are an even better match than you were thirteen years ago."

"We were a lousy match thirteen years ago."

"Bet me."

"No. I hate gambling."

"Coward."

That did it. No one called Jill Bennett a coward. Rummaging through her own purse, she found two tens and laid them on top of Ashley's twenty. "You're on."

Twenty-One

The Santinis were just as Jill remembered them—warm, good-humored, inquisitive and noisy. Even noisier now that Dan's nephews had joined the clan.

Nine-year-old Nick was the oldest and was his father's spitting image. Frankie, who had just turned seven, looked more like his mother with lighter hair and Maria's mischievous smile. He also had Dan's hazel eyes and, though Jill tried hard to overlook this detail, she kept being drawn to the boy.

Much to Jill's relief, the entire family had welcomed her with open arms and was genuinely thrilled to see her. Whatever reservations Jill had had about accepting Angelina's invitation had dissipated the moment Angelina had rushed to meet her, greeting her like a long-lost daughter.

The boys were fascinated to learn she designed skyscrapers, especially Frankie, who wanted to know if she had designed the Empire State Building. Nick, who loved to show off his superiority, rolled his eyes.

"What a stupid question to ask, Frankie. Can't you see she's not *that* old."

Everyone burst into laughter.

While they waited for desert to be served, Dan entertained his nephews with magic tricks, the same ones that had delighted Jill during their short marriage. He'd learned most of them from his maternal grandfather, Guido, who, at the tender age of thirteen, had left home to join a traveling circus.

Having a big family had always been one of Dan's most fervent wishes. Unfortunately, Jill hadn't shared his enthusiasm. There was so much she'd wanted to do in those early days, so many dreams she'd had yet to fulfill. How could she even think of becoming a mother?

Now, at thirty-four, she had realized nearly all her dreams but had no hope of ever getting remarried, much less having children of her own. And maybe that was just as well, she thought not without a touch of regret. Some women were cut out to be mothers, others were not. Jill had always felt she belonged to the latter category.

She watched Nick's and Frankie's concentrated attempts to make a pencil float. Those two didn't intimidate her as much as other children did. In fact, they had melted her heart the moment she laid eyes on them. Frankie even more so because he reminded her of Dan.

"I'm sorry I didn't keep in touch after your divorce," Maria said as Jill helped her bring the desert dishes to the table. "I should have. Brooklyn isn't that far from Manhattan."

Because Jill seldom committed to anything that wasn't work-related, her own reply surprised her. "Maybe we could make up for lost time and get together for lunch once in a while."

Maria beamed. "I'd like that very much." Her gaze

fell on Jill's blouse and the angel brooch. "What a pretty pin, Jill. Is that an antique?"

Jill felt herself blush. "Dan said it wasn't."

Maria's eyebrow went up. "Dan?"

"Yes. He saw it in a window and…well, you know how impulsive he can be sometimes."

Jill could see that Maria did her best to keep her face neutral. "Yes, I do. And how nice of him to do that." But Jill could tell by the expression of sheer delight on Maria's face that the wheels of speculation were already spinning in her fertile mind.

As Jill sat down again, Frankie turned his big hazel eyes on her. "Jill, is it true you used to be married to Uncle Dan?"

The question earned him another stern look from his older brother and a nudge in the ribs. "*Frankiiie.* Didn't Dad tell you not to talk about *that?*"

Jill laughed, delighted by the boy's candor. "That's all right, Nick. I should have realized you'd both be curious." She threw a quick glance at Dan, who, from the amused gleam in his eyes, was enjoying himself immensely. "It's true, Frankie. I was married to your uncle once, but that was long before you were born."

"So that makes you our aunt."

"Ex-aunt," Nick corrected.

"Oh." Frankie looked disappointed.

"But I'm still Dan's friend, which makes you your friend as well."

Frankie plunged his fork into a luscious slice of tiramisu. As he chewed, he glanced back at Jill. "Then, maybe, since now you're our friend, you could take us snowmobiling one day."

"Frankie!" his father admonished. "You can't ask something like that. Jill is a busy lady."

The boy's shoulders slumped. "Sorry." He threw Jill an apologetic look. "I heard you tell Mom you hadn't used the snowmobiles for a long time and I thought..." As Joe continued to glare at him, the boy shrugged. "Forget it."

"Actually," Dan interjected. "I think it's a great idea. Jill used to be quite a sled rider if I recall. You even won a couple of races once, didn't you, Jill?"

"You raced?" Nick was clearly impressed.

"That was a long time ago, Nick."

"Why don't you and I take the boys up one day this week?" Dan suggested. "After what Cecilia told me about your schedule, you could use a day off."

Mildly alarmed, Jill tried to signal him with a discreet shake of her head. That's all she needed, to play mother to a couple of rambunctious boys.

But Dan, apparently propelled by some maniacal desire to drive her crazy, plowed on. "How about tomorrow? Wally tells me another foot of fresh snow fell on the area last night. The conditions are perfect."

"I can't do it tomorrow. I have a job that has to get out."

The expression on Frankie's face was enough to make her heart sink. She took a deep breath, wondering what she was getting herself into. "I tell you what." She looked from one boy to the other. "Tuesday is good for me. We could go then if it's okay with you two—and your parents, of course."

It was Nick's turn to be disappointed. "I have basketball practice on Tuesday and I can't miss it. The coach says I need to work on my foul shots."

Frankie's head snapped toward his father. "I don't have anything, Dad. So, can I go with Jill and Uncle Dan?" His eyes turned imploring. "Please?"

Maria looked concerned. "Are you sure you want to do that, Jill? Frankie can be a handful, even by himself."

Jill wasn't sure of anything, except that she didn't want to disappoint the little boy. "As long as Dan is with me, we'll be fine." She turned to Nick. "Let me know when you have a free day, okay? We'll arrange something."

His face split into a big grin. "Cool."

Later, as Dan was taking Jill home, he gave her a friendly pat on the knee. "Thanks for being such a good sport, Jill. I know my suggestion to take the boys snowmobiling took you by surprise."

"You can say that again." Up ahead, the lights of the Brooklyn Bridge glittered against the night sky, pretty as a postcard. "What got into you?"

Dan shrugged. "Oh, I don't know. A spur-of-the-moment thing, I guess. I remembered how much you used to like the sport." He merged onto the bridge, blending smoothly into the heavy Sunday-night traffic. "And I thought the boys would get a kick out of it."

She turned to looked at his profile. "You love them a lot, don't you?"

"They're great kids."

"Do you regret leaving New York?"

"A week ago, I would have said no. But after spending these past eight days with my family, surrounded by all the love, laughter and hectic pace, the thought of returning to my quiet, orderly Chicago apartment doesn't hold much appeal."

"Have you ever thought of coming back?"

In the semidarkness of the Land Rover, their gazes met. "Once or twice."

"Maria told me how upset you were over what happened in that barrio three years ago. With that young boy?" Jill glanced at him to see if she was venturing into forbidden territory.

His expression didn't change. "Eddy Delgado."

"He's the reason you left the force, isn't he? And New York?"

"He had a lot to do with it."

She could hear the strain in his voice and realized that even now, after three years, the death of that boy still haunted him. "It wasn't your fault, Dan," she said in a whisper. "I read every account of that accident, listened to every news broadcast, morning and night—"

He glanced at her. "Did you really?"

"Yes. And I know you had no choice but to do what you did."

"Thank you."

"And it shouldn't keep you from coming back to New York if that's what you want to do."

A slow grin spread over Dan's face. "Are you saying you'd like me to come back to New York, Jill?"

There was a brief fluttering inside her chest, but she thought it best not to analyze its meaning. "No." She stared straight ahead. "I just want what's best for you, that's all."

They rode in silence until they reached MacDougal Street. Thanks to Carol Kranski, the thoroughfare was now well lit and no longer looked as ominous as it had on that cold, frightening night.

Spotting a parking space halfway down the block, Dan slid into it and brought the truck to a stop.

Because it wasn't as bitterly cold as it had been in recent days, a few pedestrians were walking at a more leisurely pace and with their coats wide open, as if spring was just around the corner instead of months away.

"I hope you had a good time," Dan said as they reached the front door. "We all certainly did."

"Everything was wonderful, Dan, the food, your family, the way they made me feel. I didn't realize how much I'd missed them until tonight." She took her keys from her purse. "Did Maria tell you we plan to—"

The rest of her sentence died on her lips. Without warning, Dan pulled her against him roughly and kissed her. This time there was more to the kiss than the simple brushing of his lips against hers. And this time, oh, God, this time she wanted it.

Responding to the yearning, she coiled her arms around his neck, parting her lips. His mouth was hot and hungry, his need as urgent as her own, his hands impatient as they roamed over her body in those all too familiar strokes.

This was crazy, she thought as she returned his fiery kiss. And not at all what she had meant to do. So why wasn't she pushing him away? Why was she clinging to him, pressing her body against his so shamelessly?

"God, Jill, I've wanted to do that ever since I first saw you eight days ago." Holding her head between his hands, Dan ran his mouth over her face, along her throat where her pulse beat wildly, before dragging it back to her lips, crushing them in another deep, heated kiss.

"Stop!"

He released her instantly. One moment they were clinging to each other, the next he was drawing back, resting his brow against hers. "Sorry." He took a deep breath. "I got carried away."

She laughed self-consciously. "I can't let you take *all* the blame." Her own breathing was slowly returning to normal but her emotions were on a roller coaster she feared would never stop. "Let's not do this again, okay? Neither of us is ready for that kind of relationship."

The light did strange things to his eyes. "That's not the way it felt a moment ago."

"That was a mistake."

With trembling fingers, she tried to insert her key into the lock. At the third try, Dan took it from her, unlocked the door and pushed it open.

His gaze skimmed her face, settling briefly on her lips, which were still moist from his kiss. For a moment, she thought he was going to kiss her again. She held her breath, wondering if she would have the strength to push him away this time.

Unexpectedly, he took her hand and dropped the keys inside her palm. "Sweet dreams, Red."

Twenty-Two

Using the level he'd had since his shop days at Evergreen High, Dan held it flush against the wall. Then, taking the pencil from between his clenched teeth, he drew three short lines and backed off. Damn. It was still too high. His mother was only five foot two. She'd never reach this shelf if he kept lowering it half an inch at a time.

He was about to try again when the phone rang. It was Al Metzer with news about the abortion clinic in Fairfax. Dan had asked him to put a rush on it and by God, he had.

"Dr. Laken is one of the area's most prominent OB-GYN doctors," Al told him. "He's sixty-three, a graduate of Harvard Medical School and runs a squeaky-clean operation. His clientele is upper class and includes many of Washington's elite."

"What about his staff?"

"We may have hit pay dirt there. Cynthia Parson, the nurse you asked me to investigate, has a rather interesting background."

"What kind of background?"

"Her husband died a little over a year ago and left her with a mountain of debts. Following his death, her little girl developed separation anxiety disorder. Cynthia put the kid in therapy, but the treatments were expensive and when the insurance ran out, she couldn't afford to continue the sessions.''

"Not on a nurse's salary.''

"Ah, but here's the interesting part. Three weeks ago, Cynthia started paying off some of her debts and resumed her daughter's therapy. And, according to a gossipy neighbor, Cynthia and her daughter leave for Walt Disney World on Wednesday morning, another luxury she couldn't have afforded a month ago.''

"Where did the money come from?''

"Don't know that yet. It didn't come from family because Cynthia doesn't have any, and since her husband died a year ago, I doubt it's a life insurance policy, but I can check for you if you'd like. It'll take a little time.''

"That's okay, Al. I can take it from here.''

Well, well, Dan thought as he hung up. Things were certainly looking up for Nurse Parson. With a little luck, he'd find out why.

After he'd made his plane reservation to Washington for the following day, Dan called Jill at B&A. He'd have to tell her he couldn't go to the Catskills with her and Frankie. "Meet me outside the Vangram Building at noon,'' he told her. "I'm taking you to lunch.''

New York at lunch hour was a sight Dan had always found exhilarating. A metropolis of perpetual motion and energy, the city truly came alive at noon, as throngs of office workers poured out of buildings, aggressive street vendors pushed their dubiously legal wares and busy intersections turned into a clogged nightmare.

Leaning against a lamppost so he could watch the revolving doors of the Vangram Building, Dan took it all in—the vitality, the pace, the excitement. No wonder Jill loved it here, he thought. This city seemed to be made for her.

"Dan!"

Across the sea of people, Jill waved at him as she emerged from the building. She looked stunning in an apple green coat and black boots. As if to welcome her, the sun had come out from behind a cloud, turning her hair a burnished shade of gold. Catching the gleam of admiration in a passerby's eyes, Dan felt a pang of jealousy.

He waved back, pulled away from the lamppost and shouldered his way through the crowd, making it a point to bump into the gawker, hard.

"Hi." Jill tilted her head up, squinting against the sun. "Where are we going?"

"It's a surprise."

"Good. I love surprises." As another man slowed down for a better look at Jill, Dan took hold of her arm and led her to the curb where they crossed Fifth Avenue and headed north toward Central Park.

Jill turned to him, her eyes gleaming with pleasure. "Lunch in the park? Wait, don't tell me. Hot dogs with the works and two orange sodas."

"You remember."

How could she forget? While Jill was interning at B&A during the summer months, she and Dan had met in Central Park two or three times a week for lunch and a stroll. The menu was always the same but

Jill had loved it. "You don't suppose our vendor is still there, do you?"

"Why don't we check and see?"

The old Irishman with the easy smile was gone, and his cart had been replaced by a newer, larger model, but the hot dogs were still as good as ever. At the park entrance, a guitarist in moody black was strumming a rock-and-roll version of "Jingle Bells" as tourists tossed quarters into a hat.

Jill and Dan walked slowly as they ate, strolling along the winding path that bordered the bird sanctuary.

"So," Jill said, licking mustard from her fingers, "what did I do to deserve such a treat?"

"Finish your lunch first."

"Uh-oh, bad news again." Trying not to anticipate the worst, she popped the last of her bun into her mouth and washed it down with orange soda. "Okay, I'm ready."

"I can't come with you to Livingston Manor."

"What?"

"Al called—"

Jill wasn't listening. "I don't believe you're doing this to me. The only reason I agreed to this insane idea was because you were coming, too, and now you're telling me you're not, that I'm going to have to take care of Frankie all by myself?"

"I can't help it, Jill." Dan told her about Al's phone call.

"If I don't talk to Cynthia before she leaves for Florida," he added, "I'll have to wait until she gets back, and I'd rather not do that."

"Darn."

Dan gave her an amused look. "What's the matter, Jill? You're not scared of a harmless seven-year-old, are you?"

"You know damn well I am."

"Why? Frankie's crazy about you."

"And I'm crazy about him. But when it comes to children, I'm a total klutz."

"You've got instincts. Rely on them. The rest will take care of itself."

The thought of canceling the trip came and went quickly. She couldn't disappoint Frankie. Not after Maria had gone to the trouble and expense of buying him a complete ski outfit.

"He's so excited about tomorrow," she had told Jill on the phone earlier. "We can't shut him up. If he keeps this up, we'll have to put a muzzle on him."

But what if he got hurt? Jill thought, remembering the mishaps with Ashley's niece. Or if he became sick? Or had a temper tantrum?

"Actually," Dan continued, "Frankie is a lot easier to handle than you realize. And he's pretty self-reliant."

Dan was right. Hadn't she been the first one to marvel at the boy's maturity and quick wit? At the way he cleared the table without being asked? Really. How much trouble could a seven-year-old be?

Still, just to be sure there wouldn't be any problem, she would ask Ashley to come along. She, too, could use a day off. And her friend was terrific with kids.

It wasn't until six o'clock that evening, just as Jill was preparing to leave the office, that she thought of using her uncle's Suburban to drive to the mountains.

Her old BMW could have handled the trip, but with a child in the car, she didn't want to take any chances.

She went to her uncle's office to ask him for the keys, but when she realized Cyrus was in a meeting with Paul Scoffield, she started to turn around.

"Jill!" Cyrus called out. "Come on in."

"You're busy. I can come back later."

"Nonsense." He waved her in. "We were just discussing the new leasing contract for our offices."

Paul, who took care of the company's money as if it were his own, gave her a smug grin. "We've managed to hold them to the old prices for another four years."

"Great."

Cyrus's gaze shifted back to Jill. "Are you all set for your big adventure tomorrow?"

"What big adventure?" Paul asked.

"Oh, that's right, you don't know yet." Jill made a face. "I'm taking Dan's young nephew snowmobiling."

"That's mighty brave of you, Jill." Paul chuckled. "Considering your track record with children."

She groaned. "Please don't remind me."

"She thought Dan was going to be helping her," Cyrus said, watching her with a mixture of fondness and amusement. "But as it turns out, Dan can't go, and our intrepid Jill here will have to face this challenge all on her own."

"You think I can't do it, don't you?" she replied. "You think I'm going to let this little kid get to me, or that some disaster will strike."

"I didn't say that."

"Good, because I'm going to be just fine. I do, however, need a favor."

Cyrus, clearly not ready to give up yet, feigned alarm. "You're not going to ask *me* to go with you, are you?"

"Are you offering?"

"Hell, no. I'm no better with little kids than you are. Why don't you ask Paul here? He's got five grandchildren. And he's still alive."

Paul raised both hands in protest. "Oh, no you don't. I still bear the scars from the last time I took Evan hiking."

Jill shook her head in mock disgust. "You're both pathetic, you know that? I wouldn't ask either one of you for help if you were the last two souls on earth."

Cyrus laughed. "All right. We've teased you enough. What do you need?"

"The Suburban. I'd feel better with a four-wheel drive."

"Good idea." Cyrus was already reaching into his desk drawer for a spare set of keys. When he found them, he tossed them to Jill. "When will you be back?"

"Tomorrow afternoon some time. I promised Frankie's mother I'd have him home for dinner. Are you sure you won't need the truck?"

"Positive. I'll catch a ride to the AIA dinner with Paul."

Jill dropped the keys into her purse. "In that case, if you two gentlemen will excuse me, I have to go home and check my snow gear, make sure I have everything I need."

Paul smiled at her. "Good luck with the boy."

* * *

The early blizzard that had blanketed the East Coast from Maine to North Carolina had finally ended, leaving five inches of snow over the state of Virginia and a razor-blue sky.

Sitting in the car he had rented at Washington National Airport, Dan looked at the small yellow Cape Cod home at the end of the cul-de-sac. With its jolly Santa in the front yard and the Christmas-scene cutouts in the windows, it was obvious that a small child lived there.

He waited until a UPS truck had driven away before getting out of the car. The young woman who opened the door was trim and neat and had a friendly look about her.

"Mrs. Parson?"

She tilted her head, a smile on her lips. "Yes. May I help you?"

"My name is Dan Santini, Mrs. Parson. I'm a friend of Jill Bennett's."

The smile disappeared. "If you're here to inquire about her father, I'm afraid you've come a long way for nothing. I can't help you, Mr. Santini, any more than I was able to help Miss Bennett. Believe me, I sympathize with her, but the fact is, I don't know any Simon Bennett. I never even heard of the name until she mentioned it the other day."

"That's not what I was told."

The woman's grip on the door tightened just enough for Dan to catch it. "I'm not sure what you're insinuating but—"

Remembering the nosy neighbor Al had mentioned, Dan said, "May I come in, Mrs. Parson? I'd rather not discuss the matter on your doorstep."

She glanced uneasily at the quiet street, then back at Dan as if trying to decide whether he was friend or foe. In spite of her efforts to remain calm, it was obvious she was badly shaken.

After a few more seconds of indecision, she opened the door wider and let him in. "Who are you?"

"I'm a former homicide detective. A persistent one." This time he caught the quick flash of fear in her eyes.

"I don't know what you want with me."

"The truth, Mrs. Parson. Nothing more."

She hugged her arms as if to ward off a sudden chill. "I told you, I don't know anything."

"Then may I tell you what *I* know? You can correct me if I'm wrong."

Cynthia Parson licked her lips and said nothing.

"You lost your husband a year ago last Thanksgiving," Dan began. "You work hard, support yourself and your daughter adequately, but sometimes you find it difficult to make ends meet, especially with your daughter's illness. Then three weeks ago, your situation changed. You paid off a few debts and started taking your daughter to an expensive therapist. How am I doing so far?"

Nurse Parson, whose face had turned a sick shade of gray, remained silent.

"You want to tell me where the money came from, Mrs. Parson?"

Cynthia's hands pressed against her stomach and for a moment, Dan thought she was going to faint. Whatever secret she was hiding was taking its toll on her.

"I know this isn't easy for you, Mrs. Parson." Dan spoke in a gentle, unthreatening tone. "You are scared and you feel trapped. But the truth is already coming out, and denying it will only get you in deeper trouble.''

Dan saw the young woman's shoulders sag as if they could no longer support their own weight. He felt sorry for her. She was a good woman who had allowed herself to get caught in a maze of lies and deceit for the sake of her child and was now beginning to pay the price for it.

Her face ashen, the woman all but collapsed in one of the oversize chairs. "What do you want to know?"

Dan sat down and leaned forward, his hands hanging between his knees. "Were you acquainted with Simon Bennett?"

She nodded.

"He came to the clinic?"

"Yes. He met a young woman there on October 3 and introduced her as Julia Banks, but I don't think that was her real name."

"You don't require real names?"

"No. We cater to a rather upscale clientele and many of our patients prefer to remain anonymous."

Dan watched her hands, which were tightly clasped on her lap.

"Was Julia Banks pregnant?"

"Yes. She was in her first trimester."

"A local woman?"

"She gave us a Georgetown address, but that, too, could be false."

"Can you tell me what she looked like?"

"Slender, long blond hair, very pretty."

"Age?"

"She might have been in her late twenties, certainly no more than thirty."

He thought of Vivian Mulligan. What would she look like, he wondered, with longer hair falling down her shoulders? Could she pass for a woman in her late twenties? "What else can you tell me about this young woman?" he asked.

Cynthia was silent for a moment, then said, "I had the impression that she didn't want to terminate the pregnancy, so I explained to her that she had other options—such as keeping the baby and raising it, or giving it up for adoption later. She said she had thought it over and was ready to go through with the procedure. She never once said the word *abortion*. She kept calling it 'the procedure.'"

"Did everything go all right?"

"Oh, yes. Julia Banks was discharged the following day. We normally don't keep patients overnight, but Mr. Bennett insisted. He was afraid there might be complications."

"Was Simon Bennett the baby's father?"

Calmer now, Nurse Parson ran a steady hand through her hair. "That subject never came up, but because of his interest and the secrecy that surrounded his visit, I assumed he was."

Dan watched the woman for a moment, knowing that the most difficult part of their conversation was yet to come. "What happened after that?"

Cynthia took a deep breath, then, "Three weeks ago a man came to see me. He said his name was Jack Smith and that he was checking up on his wife whom he suspected of having had an abortion on October 3.

I told him I couldn't give him the information he wanted, even if he was her husband.''

She met Dan's gaze. "But he, too, was persistent. He knew all about my little girl's illness and said he could make it possible for me to help her get well.''

"You mean he was willing to pay for the information.''

"Yes," she said in a whisper.

"Can you tell me what he looked like?''

"Medium height, stooped shoulders, gray hair, gray beard. He wore baggy clothes and a hat that covered the upper part of his face.''

Dan leaned back in his chair. "He wore a disguise.''

"I'm sure he did, though I didn't realize that until later." Bowing her head, she stared at her hands, which were tightly clasped. "He offered me fifty thousand dollars—in cash.''

Dan took a deep breath. Whoever the killer was, he had done an excellent job of finding the right person to bribe. Poor Cynthia. There she was, a widow, with a sick daughter and debts up to her ears. What mother wouldn't have done exactly what she did? Rather than press her to continue, Dan sat back and waited.

"I didn't want to do it," Cynthia continued. "I knew it was wrong, just as I knew that if Dr. Laken ever found out, he'd fire me on the spot." Her eyes took on a fervid intensity. "I didn't do it for me, Mr. Santini. I don't care about money. I did it for Molly. I wanted my little girl to be well again.''

Even with all the training and practice he'd had distancing himself from the people he interrogated, Dan was finding it hard to keep a dry eye. "The woman

Jack Smith was interested in," he asked gently, "was that Julia Banks?"

"Yes. He showed me a picture of her and Simon Bennett. He seemed to know Mr. Bennett because he called him by his name."

"So you identified them both?"

She wrapped her arms around her. "Yes. A few days later, Dr. Laken told me that his friend, Simon Bennett, had died in a car crash, but I didn't start adding it all together until Jack called me to say that an informal investigation was being conducted and it was important that I kept quiet.

"That's when I started to get suspicious—and scared. I remembered the way Jack had looked that first night, with his face in shadows and his shoulders stooped—too stooped, perhaps, as if he was trying to appear shorter than he was."

"What did you do when you realized he may have killed Simon Bennett?"

"What could I do? By that time, I was an accomplice, or an accessory, or whatever you want to call it. I was afraid to go to prison, afraid there'd be no one to take care of my little girl."

"What about Dr. Laken?" Dan asked. "Did he suspect foul play when he heard about his friend?"

"No, he had no reason to. Jack didn't go to him with that half-cocked story. He came to me."

"And you never saw this Jack Smith again?"

"No, but he called me again—the night before Jill Bennett came to the clinic."

Those words had the effect of a kick in the gut. "He knew Jill was coming to see you?"

"Yes, and he was afraid I'd give myself away, so

he called to give me a pep talk, to remind me of all I had to lose if I screwed up. As if I could forget.''

Her gaze drifted toward the window and Dan followed it. On the lawn next door, a mother and her toddler were building a snowman.

"You don't know what a nightmare this has been for me.'' Cynthia's eyes remained fixed on the peaceful scene outside. "If it weren't for Molly, I would have turned myself in long ago.'' She took a minute to collect herself before returning her attention to Dan. "What's going to happen to me now?''

"At the moment, nothing,'' Dan said truthfully. "Without a positive identification of this Jack Smith, your story has little value except that it confirms what I already suspected—that Simon Bennett was murdered.''

"Does that mean...'' Her eyes filled with hope. "You won't say anything? To Dr. Laken or the police?''

"There's no need for that.'' And even if there had been, Dan would have found a way to spare the young woman. She had gone through enough. "However, I'd like to find Julia Banks, provided her address checks out. Could you give it to me?''

"I'll have to get it from the clinic's records.'' She glanced at her watch. "I suppose I could make some sort of excuse to stop by.''

"I'd appreciate it.''

She stood up, smoothing down her uniform. "I'll need to call my baby-sitter. Do you want to meet me at the Golden Dawn Diner on Hazelton Avenue? You passed it on your way here. I shouldn't be more than half an hour.''

"That'll be fine, Cynthia. Thank you.''

Twenty-Three

"I can't believe you talked me into doing this."

Scowling, Ashley watched as Jill and Frankie pulled the dusty canvas cover off the two snowmobiles. "It's been years since I've driven one of those things," Ashley said. "I'm probably going to break my neck and be in traction until Easter."

Frankie, who had taken a liking to Ashley immediately, grinned at her over his shoulder. "No you won't, Ash. It's like riding a bicycle. You never forget."

"How do you know?"

"'Cause Jill told me."

Still looking skeptical, Ashley slowly walked around the shiny red sleds. "Those are not your old Arctic Cats, are they? They look bigger than I remember."

Jill stacked the folded covers in a corner of the three-car garage. "They're Ski-Doos. Daddy bought them a couple of years ago. They're much more stable than the old ones." She gave Frankie a conspiratorial wink. "They go up to ninety miles an hour. And they can jump moguls this high." She stretched her hand high above her head.

"You can forget the moguls," Ashley said. "In

fact, I'm not sure I want to ride at all. A cup of hot chocolate and a warm fire is excitement enough for me.''

"Chicken," Jill said.

Frankie was already sitting on one of the sleds, holding on to the handlebars and making revving sounds. "Can I have this one, Jill?"

"Nice try, squirt, but you're riding with me."

Jill smiled as he made a big deal of appearing disappointed. Now that they were here, she could feel herself relax. Frankie had behaved perfectly during the two-hour drive, gazing out the window, asking dozens of questions, joking with Ashley. Maybe taking care of children wasn't as big a deal as she made it out to be.

"Come on." She gave the boy's behind a little tap. "Help me check the gas gauge."

Topping off the tanks and starting the engines took only a few minutes. When they were finished, they both went in to change into their ski clothes while Ashley, true to her word, went in to start a fire.

"Are you sure you won't join us?" Jill asked as she and Frankie came down the stairs ten minutes later.

"I'm still thinking." Ashley walked out to the garage with them, a mug of hot chocolate in her hand. "Let me watch you guys for a while, okay? If I decide to go, I'll catch up with you."

"Okay, but be sure to follow my trail. With all that snow, it's hard to tell where you're going unless you're familiar with the terrain. And be careful of that edge up there." She pointed toward a steep hill. "Don't get too close or you'll end up in the river."

Ashley touched her forehead in a military salute. "Yes, boss."

Jill turned to Frankie, who was jumping up and down with excitement. "As for you, young man, you hold on to me and you don't do anything crazy or the ride is over. Is that clear?"

Frankie bobbed his head in agreement.

"Good. Put on your helmet."

Within moments, they were sliding downhill, slow at first, as Jill tested the deep powder, then faster as she felt the powerful machine respond. Soon they were in the open field, bypassing the two-to-three-foot moguls for smaller bumps that weren't as harsh.

Despite being one of the larger sleds in its class, the Ski-Doo handled beautifully, with both skis holding firmly on to the snow, even as Jill executed a series of sharp turns.

Cranking up the speed, she headed for the summit, that wide-open area that overlooked the Beaverkill River and offered a spectacular, endless view.

Behind her, Frankie tugged on her sleeve, shouting to be heard above the roar of the engine. "Faster, Jill."

Laughing, Jill gave another quick push on the throttle, experiencing a familiar thrill as the sled shot forward.

"Hey!" Frankie nudged her again. "Here comes Ashley!"

Surprised, because she hadn't thought Ashley would be changing her mind so soon, Jill stole a quick glance in one of the hood-mounted mirrors. Still well behind her, the other Ski-Doo was flying in their direction. But it couldn't be Ashley, Jill realized. She would never ride at such high speed. And her ski suit was light blue, not black.

Irritated, Jill threw another glance in the mirror. Though her father had installed No Trespassing signs throughout the property, he had been adamant about not fencing it in. As a result, a rider or two, attracted by all that wide-open space, occasionally ventured in until they were chased away.

But this sledder, Jill realized, had no intention of leaving. Instead, he kept barreling toward them in a straight path.

What the hell was that fool trying to do? Kill them?

Unaware of the danger, Frankie pounded her back. "Don't let her catch us, Jill!"

Trying to keep a grip on her mounting fear, Jill pulled away from the path of the incoming snowmobile, which, she now realized, looked exactly like the other Ski-Doo. What was going on here? Had he taken her sled for a joyride? Right under Ashley's nose?

Before she could answer her own question, the rider had changed course, just as she had, and was coming toward her again, at full speed.

She had to get away from this maniac, get back to the house, or to Joshua's cabin.

Opening the throttle, she drove the machine downward, swerving wildly to keep the other sled from colliding into her.

But because of Frankie, she didn't dare go as fast as she would have if she had been alone. One hard bump or too sharp a turn and he could fall off.

The other sled continued to gain until it was less than ten feet away from her.

As the machine suddenly roared past, missing hers

by a hair, Jill's blood went cold. He wasn't trying to hit her.

He was trying to force her over the cliff and into the icy river below.

Frankie's arms tightened around her waist. The poor kid. He, too, must have realized something was wrong and was scared. But she couldn't think about that now, and she had no time to reassure him. She had to concentrate on keeping them both alive.

Before she could move away from the dangerous edge, the rider was back, readying for another pass.

Adrenaline pumping wildly through her bloodstream, Jill cranked up the speed and sent the sled flying toward the woods. There, in the relative safety of the dense forest, she might be able to lose him.

The man in black followed her down, bounding over moguls with an expertise that exceeded that of any rider she knew. She would have to outsmart him by leading him where she hadn't planned on going—Deadman's Drop—then veer off into the woods and hope he'd overshoot them.

But there were risks. If she didn't turn off in time, she would send her own snowmobile flying over the edge. Years ago, before her father had bought the property, a sledder had met with such a fate and died, hence the name.

Praying she'd spot the old, faded caution sign in time, she sped forward. Then, as the forest began to thicken, she saw it, a weathered cedar plank nailed onto a tree.

Tightly gripping the handlebars, Jill gave a sharp twist to the left and tore into the forest, clamping on the brake handle. The maneuver sent their machine skidding for several feet before it finally hit a tree.

Jill and Frankie were propelled into the air just as the other snowmobile flew by. Jill hit the ground with a thud.

Dazed and a little disoriented, she lay still for a moment. When she was sure no limbs were broken, she pushed herself onto her elbows and looked around her. Frankie was nowhere near.

Nor was there any sign of the rider.

"Frankie!" Filled with cold panic, Jill pulled off her helmet and scrambled to her feet. The snowmobile was a short distance away, its left side smashed in. One ski was twisted into a figure eight, its tip pointing toward the sky. Beside it was Frankie. He lay motionless, his eyes closed.

"Frankie!" Jill plowed her way toward him and dropped to her knees. "Frankie, wake up." She shook him gently.

When there was no response, she clamped her teeth over one glove to free her hand and quickly felt for a pulse. She almost cried with relief when she felt its strong beat beneath her fingers.

She had to get help. Shaky but clearheaded, she glanced up toward the trail they had just left. If her sense of direction was correct, the house was straight up the hill, about a mile away. Not an easy walk in two feet of snow and with a boy in her arms, but she'd have to do it.

She *would* do it.

The morning sun had disappeared behind a dark snow cloud and flurries had already begun to fall.

Soon the temperature would be dropping. She had to keep Frankie moving, make sure he'd stay warm.

Just as she was about to scoop him up in her arms, she heard a soft groan.

"Frankie?"

The boy's eyes opened and a corner of his mouth pulled into a small smile.

"You're okay." Laughing and crying at the same time, Jill took his beautiful face between her hands, resisting the impulse to cover it with kisses. "You *are* okay, aren't you?"

He nodded. "I think so. 'Cept for my ankle. I think it's broke."

"Let me see." Her fingers moving quickly, she unlaced his boot and pushed his pant leg up a few inches. His ankle was red and swollen but it didn't seem to be broken. "It looks like a sprain." She left the boot untied and lowered the pant leg over it.

"Jill?" Solemn hazel eyes stared at her.

"Yes, Frankie?"

"That wasn't Ashley, was it?"

Jill didn't answer right away. The last thing she wanted was to scare him any more than he already was. On the other hand, he was too smart for an outright lie. "No, it wasn't."

"Then who was it?"

"Some show-off who wanted to play games—stupid games."

"But…it looked like he had your other sled."

Smart kid. "Oh, I don't know about that. All sleds look alike, you know."

He looked around him. "Is he gone?"

Jill detected a trace of worry in his voice. Casually,

she glanced past the old wooden sign and listened for the sound of an engine. There was none. Either the rider had gone over the edge, or he'd had enough fun for one day and gone home. With her sled.

"I'm pretty sure he is, Frankie." As she spoke, she looked upward again, worried about Ashley. She could be inside mindlessly watching TV or...

Not wanting to think of the alternative, she turned back to Frankie and tried to keep her voice cheerful. "We'll have to get moving, squirt. Think you can put any weight at all on that foot?"

"I don't know. I'll try."

She helped him to an upright position, but the moment his foot touched the ground, he grimaced. "I don't think so, Jill."

"Okay." She gave his small body a quick hug. "No big deal. I'll just have to carry you, that's all." Attempting to make light of the situation, she added, "And then when I get tired, *you* can carry *me*. You'll have to do it on one foot, though."

He smiled bravely. "How far are we from the house?"

"About a mile. Are you warm enough?"

"I'm kinda cold."

"Hold on to that tree. I'll be right back." She walked over to the useless snowmobile and opened the small back compartment, hoping to find a blanket or an extra sweater, anything that would keep Frankie warm. But because the Bennetts never took the sleds on long trips, her father had never bothered with such precautions. There weren't even any matches to make a fire.

Without a second's hesitation, she peeled off her jacket and slipped it on the boy.

"What about you?" Frankie protested.

"I'll be moving all the time, I don't need it."

When he was all bundled up, he climbed on her back. Jill's legs wobbled a little under the weight, then steadied. "Okay, squirt. Here we go."

They moved at a snail's pace, following the trail they'd made on the way down. Because the boy was heavier than she had realized, Jill had to stop every fifty feet or so to rest and allow Frankie to hop around a little so his blood would keep on circulating.

The snow was coming down harder now, making the climb and visibility more difficult. After another grueling ten minutes, there was still no sign of the house.

As she looked around her, wondering if she had been heading in the wrong direction, someone suddenly called out her name.

Jill looked up. "Ashley!"

Clutching two blankets in her arms, her friend was hurrying down the hill, falling every couple of steps and picking herself up again. There was a gash on her forehead and a red streak along her temple where blood had trickled down and dried out.

"Thank God!" Ashley cried as she fell into Jill's arms. "I thought he'd killed you."

Frankie's eyes were wide as he gaped at Ashley's wound. "Did that man do that to you?"

Jill gripped her friend's arm. "Did he?"

"Yes, but I'm okay now." She opened the blankets and handed one to Frankie and one to Jill. "Put these on. I called Wally as soon as I came to. He's sending a rescue team. But in the meantime, he said you have to keep warm.''

Frankie was in awe. "How did you find us?"

"I just followed the trail and prayed you were at the end of it."

Suddenly uneasy, Jill hugged the blanket around her. "Who was he, Ash?"

"I don't know. I never saw him. One minute I was watching you guys climb the hill, and the next, something, or rather someone, hit me from behind. I must have fallen forward and struck my head on the tractor because when I woke up I had this gash on my forehead." She rubbed the back of her head. "And a bump on my skull the size of a baseball."

With a feeling of foreboding, Jill looked around again. What if the man in black wasn't just an irresponsible rider, after all? What if someone had known she was coming here, and had been waiting for her?

Waiting to kill her.

The sudden roar of an engine made all three of them turn around. Two snowmobiles, operated by members of the Sullivan County Search and Rescue Squad, were heading their way.

Twenty-Four

Wally had personally driven all three of them to the nearby town of Rockland, where Dr. Keaton, a long-time friend of Wally's, had sewn up Ashley's gash and examined Jill to make sure there were no underlying injuries. While recounting his own experiences with a snowmobile, he had checked Frankie for a possible concussion, and x-rayed his ankle, which, as predicted, was only sprained.

"You'll have to keep it elevated for a few days, young man," he had told the boy. "Other than that, you're fine."

While Frankie was having his ankle bandaged, Wally drew Jill aside. "The rescue team found the other snowmobile. Not at the bottom of the cliff as we had expected, but halfway down. The heavy brush and a couple of trees stopped its fall and saved it from being totally wrecked."

"What about the rider?"

"All they found were footprints leading to a narrow side road, just off Johnston, and tire tracks from there to the main highway. He must have parked his car and made the uphill climb on foot until he reached your house." Wally's easygoing country ways had disappeared. His whole demeanor seemed to harden. "Determined bastard."

Jill glanced at Ashley, who had stayed with Frankie, then back at the constable. "This wasn't a joyride turned nasty, Wally. It was a deliberate attempt to push me over the cliff. That man wanted me dead, and he didn't care who else died with me."

Wally watched her for a few seconds, his expression somber. "What have you been up to, Jill? I thought you were letting Dan take care of the investigation."

"I was. Maybe the killer figured that with me out of the way, the investigation would end."

"Well, he figured wrong," Wally snapped. "And he made a bad move today, coming after you, because not only will I be conducting a full-scale investigation of this incident, but I'm reopening the case of your father's death." He gave her a long searching look. "Is there anything I should know, Jill? Anything that will help me catch this guy?"

She wasn't sure what he could do that Dan hadn't already done, but she told him everything, anyway, from the attack on her life two weeks ago to her father's affair with Vivian Mulligan and Dan's trip to Fairfax, the outcome of which she didn't yet know. The only detail she left out was her aunt's relationship with Yussef Abrahim and her father's blackmailing scheme. She and Dan had agreed that Lilly had nothing to do with the case, so why expose a scandal that could destroy her?

After Jill was finished, Wally was silent for a long time. He had never suspected Simon of being a cheater. During the twenty-some years he'd known the architect, Simon's behavior as a devoted husband and a loving father had been exemplary.

The thought that his old friend had, in some respect, duped him, left him feeling sad and a little disillusioned. But no less determined to find his killer. Especially now that the son of a bitch had come after Jill.

Wally closed the notebook he'd used to take notes. "Does your mother know about any of this?"

"She only knows about Daddy's mysterious trip to Washington. She doesn't know about the abortion clinic, or his involvement with Vivian Mulligan."

His mouth set in a tight, angry line, Wally turned to look at Frankie. One of Dr. Keaton's nurses had found a comic book and brought it back to Frankie, who was reading it avidly. Ashley, a gauze bandage taped to her forehead, was nursing a cup of coffee.

It was a scene Wally had witnessed hundreds of times. When one lived and worked in the mountains, snow-related accidents, some serious, others minor, were a common occurrence. But never in his thirty-two-year career as a law enforcement officer in Sullivan County had he had to deal with attempted murder on the slopes.

That Jill and a small innocent boy had been the target of such an attempt sent him into a rage he was trying hard to keep under control.

"I'll have Brad drive you home," he said, rising and slipping the notebook into his pocket. "I'll make arrangements for your uncle's Suburban to be returned later."

"There's no need to do that, Wally. I'm perfectly capable of driving back."

They argued for the better part of five minutes, then, knowing he was fighting a losing battle, Wally let her have her way and walked over to his deputy. "Follow them to Brooklyn, will you, Brad? Just to make sure nothing happens to them on the way. And don't let them see you."

"No problem, boss."

Once Jill and her little cargo had taken off, Wally went in to call Dan.

It was close to five o'clock when Jill, Ashley and Frankie arrived at Joe and Maria's house, where the entire Santini family had gathered to await their arrival.

In Maria's cozy living room, where a gigantic Christmas tree twinkled with multicolored lights, Frankie held court to a captive audience, recounting the incident in details that were as vivid as they were dramatic.

"Jill gave me her *jacket*," he said excitedly. "And then she carried me up that *huge* mountain, and every time we stopped, she made me jump around so I wouldn't get..." His handsome face puckered into a frown as he looked at Jill. "What's that word again?"

"Hypothermia."

"Yeah, hypothermia. The doctor said people die of it sometimes."

Standing between Jill and Ashley, Maria wrapped her arms around both women. "I don't know how I can ever repay you," she murmured in a choked voice. "You, Jill, for taking such good care of my son, and you, Ashley, for going after them in spite of your own injuries."

"You don't have to thank us, Maria," Jill replied. "If anything, I feel guilty that Frankie was hurt at all—"

As loud protests drowned Jill's words, Dan leaned over to whisper in her ear, "Might as well give it up, Red. Fighting the Santinis' gratitude is a little like trying to stop a running bull. The more you try, the faster he goes."

Naturally, she and Ashley had to stay for dinner, which once it was brought to the table looked more like the Last Supper than the simple family meal Maria claimed to have prepared.

When Dan was finally able to talk to Jill alone, his first question was straight to the point. "Who knew you were going to the mountains today, Jill?"

Jill stretched her back, which felt stiff from the long drive. "Nearly everybody at B&A—from my uncle, who told Philip and Olivia, to the secretaries. You know how that grapevine is."

"Anyone knew you were going without me?"

"Only my uncle." The sick feeling in her stomach worsened. "And Paul. He was in my father's office when I went there to borrow the Suburban."

Dan's jaw clenched. "I already talked to Wally. He's going to check every employee's alibi for this morning. Anybody who wasn't where he or she was supposed to be will be grilled."

"Surely you can't be including my uncle in that list."

He gave her a hard look. "I said everybody, Jill. No exception."

"What about Mulligan?"

"Oh, you can be sure he won't be overlooked. In

fact, I plan to check out his alibi myself, not just for this morning, but for November 28, as well.''

"Why? What happened on November 28?"

"That's the day a mysterious man by the name of Jack Smith offered Cynthia Parson fifty thousand dollars for information regarding a young woman and a man Nurse Parson identified as your father.''

Jill's eyes widened in bewilderment. "What are you saying? That my father *was* at Alternatives?''

Dan nodded. "The woman he brought there was pregnant, and Cynthia is fairly sure Simon was the father.''

Jill's stomach began churning. "Who was the woman?"

"She registered as Julia Banks and gave a Georgetown address. Both the name and the residence turned out to be phony.''

"You went to Georgetown?"

Dan nodded. "There was no reason not to since I was right there.''

"So this...Julia Banks, or whatever her name is, could be living anywhere, including New York.''

"She could, but it's not Vivian Mulligan. I called her. She was nowhere near Maryland that day and can prove it.''

Jill was suddenly bone tired. "I can't believe Cynthia Parson lied to me. And Dr. Laken.''

"Dr. Laken doesn't know anything about the murder. He lied to you out of ethics. And Cynthia lied to you out of necessity. She was scared.''

He told her what he knew about the fictitious Jack Smith and how he had put pressure on Cynthia. "I promised her I'd keep her out of this mess unless it became absolutely necessary for her to come forward."

Jill smiled. "You're a good man, Dan."

The old Santini sparkle was back in his eyes. "Haven't I been trying to tell you that all along?"

A burst of laughter returned Jill's attention to the dining room, where Nick was hopping around on one foot, pretending to have sprained his own ankle. "Oooh, it hurts so much," he cried, his face contorting with affected agony. "Quick, Nonna, another piece of pie."

The homey scene made Jill smile. After a while, she tore her gaze away and turned to Dan. "So what are we going to do now? We have a killer we can't identify because he wore a disguise, and a mysterious woman who could be anywhere between New York and Maryland. Not to mention that there probably won't be a single fingerprint on that snowmobile the rescue squad recovered."

"That's okay, Jill. I don't care how clever this killer is, he's going to make a mistake. Sooner or later they all do. He's also scared or he wouldn't have come after you today. That fear will make him careless."

Jill felt suddenly uneasy. "You mean...he could come after me again?"

"I won't give him a chance to, Red. From now on, you and I are glued at the hip."

Although the thought of having Dan near her twenty-four hours a day was not totally unpleasant, Jill shook her head. "I can't ask you to devote all your time to my safety, Dan. It would be both unpractical and unfair, to you and to your family."

When the look in his eyes told her she wasn't going

to win this debate, she added, "Maybe we could work out some sort of compromise. I call in at regular intervals, I do not work past five o'clock and I promise to let you know the moment I have to change my plans."

Dan was thoughtful for a moment, clearly mulling over her proposition. Then he said, "I'll agree on two conditions. One, you give me your word that you'll respect the rules you've just set, and two, I come home with you tonight and bunk on your sofa. Just for tonight. And just in case that jerk decides he wants to finish the job."

"Are you trying to scare me?"

"I'm trying to make you realize we're dealing with a desperate man who came damn near to killing you today."

"Wally said that once he announces he's reopening the investigation, the pressure would ease off."

"It will, but he hasn't done that yet. Chances are, news of your brush with death won't be out until tomorrow, so for the time being, we play it safe."

"All right." She had probably agreed much too quickly, but so what? Much as she hated to admit it, today's harrowing experience had left her terrified of spending the night alone. Knowing that Dan would be there with her lessened that fear.

For the first time since her father had died, she might finally be able to have a decent night's sleep.

Twenty-Five

"Is the tea strong enough?"

Sitting on her sofa, with her legs tucked under her, Jill cradled the mug Dan had just brought her and nodded. "It's perfect, and stop fussing, will you? I'm fine."

"Maybe so, but it's not every day that I get to make tea for a hero."

"Don't call me that. I didn't do anything you or anyone else wouldn't have done."

"Try telling that to my family."

Jill laughed softly. "I know. For a while there, I thought they were going to give Ashley and me a ticker-tape parade."

"They still might." He came to crouch in front of her and laid his hands on her knee. "Don't ever say you're helpless around children, Jill. What you did today was an act of courage and strength. You'll make a wonderful mother someday."

She stared at his hands, so big and strong, yet so gentle. Oddly enough, the thought of motherhood no longer frightened her as it once had. In fact, at this very moment, and as long as Dan was by her side, she felt as though she could do or be anything.

Too bad that realization came thirteen years too late.

She looked up to find him staring at her with an intensity that made her blush. Desire, quick and unexpected, stabbed through her. She tried to dismiss it, as she had once or twice before, but this time she couldn't. She was much too aware of the potent masculine appeal that radiated from him, of the way her own body responded to his touch, to his gaze as it moved from her eyes to her mouth.

A delicious shiver went through her and this time she knew she was in trouble. But she didn't care. Tonight she needed more than a warm hand covering hers, or gentle words of comfort. Tonight she needed him, *all* of him. She needed those strong arms around her, needed to hear those passionate words she hadn't wanted to hear before.

She took a sip of her tea, observing him as she drank, wondering, not without a certain excitement, if he had any idea of the wild thoughts that were going through her head.

Probably not. She had never been very good at the subtleties of lovemaking. Not to mention those damn rules she had set the other night when he'd kissed her.

She had made it quite clear that she didn't want to get involved—romantically *or* sexually. And Dan was too much of a gentleman not to respect a woman's wishes.

So why don't you let him know you've changed your mind and see what happens?

Jill held back a chuckle. Instigating sex was as foreign to her as walking on the moon. The only thing that *might* give her enough courage was the absolute knowledge that he wanted her as badly as she wanted him.

Unfortunately, at the moment, he gave no indication that he did.

"Would you care for some more tea?" She gave him her most beguiling smile. "I'll make it this time."

To her surprise, Dan shook his head. "I've had enough. Time to go to bed, Red." He stood up. "Your eyes are turning glassy, and I'm kind of bushed myself."

She gave him a startled look. "You are?"

"I guess I'm getting old. I can't keep up with those late hours anymore the way I used to."

She glanced at her watch. "It's only ten o'clock."

"Is it really?" He stifled a yawn. "Well, you know what they say, early to bed, early to rise. And I do have a full day ahead of me tomorrow."

Jill frowned. Was he being dense, or was he just playing with her? After the way she had rejected him the other night, she wouldn't blame him if he was.

"It's just that..." She cleared her throat, feeling like a teenager with a crush on the school hunk. "I'm rather...wound up tonight. I don't think I can sleep."

"Maybe a warm bath would help."

A warm bath? That was his remedy for a need that was dangerously nearing the boiling point? Maybe she hadn't made herself clear enough.

Uncoiling her legs from beneath her, she set her mug on the end table and stood up. Then, turning up the heat, she moved slowly toward him. "Dan, I'm not sure you understand what I'm trying to tell you."

"Oh." His mouth curved into a little smile. "*That's* what you're getting at." He looked down at her hand but didn't touch it. "You want to have sex."

"Well..." She hadn't expected him to put it quite

so bluntly, but since he had… "Yes." The boldness of her reply sent a rush of heat to her cheeks. What the hell was she doing?

"And sex is *all* you want?"

Why was he asking her that? Wasn't that what every man wanted from a woman? "I suppose so."

He shook his head. "Bad idea, Jill."

"Excuse me?"

"You said so yourself, remember? Only three nights ago."

"That was then—"

"And you were right," he said as if he hadn't heard her. "Neither one of us is ready for another stab at a relationship. As for sex for the sake of sex…" He shook his head. "It wouldn't work. Not for us, not after all we've meant to each other."

He was turning her down. She had practically thrown herself at him and he was turning her down. "You mean…you don't want to make love to me?"

"Oh, I didn't say that. But don't you see what's happening here? You had a very close call today, Jill. You could have died. And because of that experience, you feel vulnerable. Making love to you under those circumstances would be wrong."

That was the biggest crock she'd ever heard. Feeling like a fool, she waited for a burst of laughter, a wink, a mad embrace to tell her he'd been kidding her all along, that he couldn't wait to make love to her.

When he gave no indication that he was only teasing, she stepped back, totally mortified. "You know something?" she said in a scathing tone. "You're absolutely right."

Then, because an embarrassing flush was slowly

creeping up her neck again and onto her cheeks, she pushed him out of the way and marched out of the room and up the circular staircase that led to the loft. The hell with him. She didn't need him *that* badly.

Once in her bedroom, she went to the armoire, yanked out a blanket and a pillow then walked back to the railing overlooking the living room. "Santini!"

Dan looked up just in time to see a bundle of bed-clothes tumbling over the railing.

Lying in the dark, Dan chuckled. He had never seen Jill in such a state, and he'd had great fun getting her to that point. It had also taken an enormous amount of willpower on his part to resist that tempting invitation.

The title of a song—"What Kind of Fool Am I?"—sprung into his mind. How fitting.

Any other time, he would have responded to her not-so-subtle advances with lightning speed. But this was different. He knew that whatever needs she had tonight, they wouldn't extend beyond that.

This basic reaction of reaching for another human being after a brush with death was one he had experienced himself many times. And because he had experienced it, he knew that the feeling didn't last. And he knew Jill. By morning, she would regret it. She might even hate herself for initiating something she wasn't ready for. He couldn't have that. Not the way he felt about her.

Deep down, he suspected she felt the same way. He'd seen little indications here and there, puzzled glances, as if she was trying to figure out something she didn't quite understand.

But until she did, until she was willing to take a chance on them again, he wouldn't lay a finger on her.

Crossing his hands under his head, he stared up at the loft where he could hear Jill walking back and forth. So what now, Einstein? he asked in a silent question. The woman you love offered you a night of hot, unbridled passion and you turned her down on a principle. Does that make you feel noble? Or incredibly stupid?

Rather than answer the rhetorical question, Dan closed his eyes and tried not to think of Jill undressing.

Still fuming, Jill yanked off her clothes and sent them flying across the room. She had never been so humiliated in her entire life. Turning her down like some cheap floozy. If she wasn't so pissed off, she'd teach him a lesson, see how long he'd last once she decided to *really* heat things up.

In her pink Victoria's Secret satin bra and matching bikini panties, she stood in front of the mirror and studied her reflection with a critical eye. Okay, so she wasn't Raquel Welsh but she wasn't exactly Twiggy, either. There were curves there, curves some men might even call sensual.

Of course, with that heavy wool sweater and those baggy pants she had worn to the Catskills, those curves hadn't been all that apparent.

Maybe what she needed was a different approach, something she'd never done before, something that would take Dan totally by surprise, take the wind out of his sails, so to speak.

Something that would make that famous Santini control crack.

Her anger forgotten, she opened a dresser drawer and started going through her things. Not finding what she was looking for, she opened another drawer, then another.

Where *was* the damn thing?

When at last she found it, she allowed herself a wicked little laugh. Say no to *that,* Santini.

Her thoughts already zeroing in on her plan of attack, she walked into the bathroom, unhooking her bra as she went.

Bending over the tub, she turned on the shower, kicked off her panties and stepped under the steaming water.

Dan wasn't sure what woke him up. For a moment, he wasn't even sure if he *was* awake or if the vision before him was a figment of his imagination, the product of too many recent fantasies.

The vision stood at the bottom of the staircase, one hand on the wrought-iron railing, another on her slender hip.

Fully awake now, Dan felt his mouth open. She wore one of those lethal little nothings women, for reasons he couldn't fathom, called a teddy. This one was made of black lace. It skimmed her incredible body like a second skin and was cut low enough in the front to reveal a cleavage, so deep and luscious, he couldn't quite draw a full breath. Sheer black stockings, held in place at the thighs with a band of black lace, showed enough creamy skin to send his blood pumping. Completing the outfit were black stiletto heels that made her long legs seem even longer.

Remembering what those legs could do, how tightly

they could wrap around him, his heart began to beat like a bongo drum.

"Cat got your tongue, sailor?"

Not trusting his voice, Dan didn't answer.

With a low chuckle, Jill let go of the railing and began walking toward him, one slow, undulating step at a time. She had both fists on her hips now and was smiling seductively. As she came closer, that same scent she had worn years ago closed around him, prompting a thousand erotic memories.

His good intentions melting fast, he sat up on the sofa, unable to do anything but drink in the sight of her. This was not the Jill he knew. Yes, there had been passion in their lovemaking, and unexpected surprises, but she had always been shy about her body, unsure of herself as a woman, and, at times, almost inhibited.

There was nothing inhibited about her now. The young girl whose shyness had delighted him had turned into a siren, a seductress who could make a man forget his own name.

He didn't stand a chance.

"Well, well..." Kicking off one shoe, Jill propped her black-stockinged foot on the edge of the sofa. "For a man who was so eloquent a moment ago, you don't seem to have much to say now, do you?"

"You're beautiful." His voice sounded as hoarse as if he had just come back from a week-long pep rally.

"Am I really?"

Dan nodded.

"What is it that you find beautiful?"

He knew what she was doing. She was torturing him. And she would do so slowly, until he couldn't take it anymore and begged for mercy. "Everything.

Every inch of you is beautiful,'' he said, feasting his eyes.

She swung her knee back and forth, like a slow pendulum. ''You didn't seem to think so earlier.''

''Earlier I was a fool.''

Mesmerized, Dan watched that knee as it kept swinging, each time coming within a hair of his face. He wanted to grab and grope. His body, already aroused beyond its limit, was screaming for release.

Grinding his teeth, he held back the fierce lust that threatened to explode. This was her game, and it would be played under her rules or it wouldn't be played at all.

Placing a hand on her knee, he rubbed it gently, almost absently. ''Is that what you usually sleep in?''

''No, I usually sleep in the buff.''

''Oh.'' The vision sent his lust indicator up another notch.

''Ashley bought me this little number for my birthday last year. You like it?''

He swallowed. ''Love it.''

''She thought I'd want to wear it for Giancarlo.''

Dan sat up. ''Who the hell is Giancarlo?''

''An Italian count I met at a charity ball.''

''And…did you wear it for him?''

She looked at him coyly. He could even have sworn that her eyelids fluttered. ''Would you be jealous if I did?''

His hand moved slowly up her thigh. ''I'd kill him.''

''Oooh.'' She shivered with feigned delight. ''You won't have to do that, though. Giancarlo turned out to be a con artist. He was after my money, so I dumped him.''

Dan's hand climbed higher, his thumb gently stroking the inner part of her thigh where the skin was as soft as silk. "I hope you learned your lesson about fortune hunters.''

"Oh, I did. From now on, I will only be seduced by men who don't care about money.''

"I hate money.''

She laughed again, a sexy, confident laugh. "I know.''

With both hands on her thigh now, Dan gripped the lacy band and pulled the sheer nylon down, slowly, inch by inch. Bending his head, he kissed her skin as it was being exposed.

Jill's breath caught in her throat. She had planned to tease him mercilessly, to have him on his knees, begging. After all, it was a small price to pay for rejecting her earlier. She could have done it, too, if she hadn't been so hungry for him, if his mouth hadn't been so damn arousing as he kissed her naked thigh.

After all these years, and all the women he must have had, he still remembered what turned her on. That she could still respond with the same urgency as before didn't surprise her. Her body, as well as her heart and soul, had always belonged to just one man. This man.

When she was left with nothing but the teddy, Dan pulled her onto his lap. Sinking his hands into her hair, he brought her face to his and kissed her. His mouth was hot, his tongue eager as it claimed hers.

"Take me upstairs, Dan,'' she whispered against his mouth.

Still holding her, he slid one arm under her knees, stood up and carried her up the circular staircase, the way he had so many times before.

But that's where the similarity ended. Tonight would be different. Tonight there would be no desperation in their lovemaking, no hope that a few hours of mindless sex would solve tomorrow's problems. Tonight, they were just two people responding to a need they could no longer control.

As they climbed the stairs, she let her hand roam up and down his back. His body was just as she remembered it—lean and hard with muscles rippling in all the right places.

As Dan lowered her onto the big sleigh bed, the anticipation became almost unbearable. Reaching behind her back, his fingers found the small zipper and slid it down. As the upper part of the teddy fell off, her small breasts spilled free, their nipples already hard.

Her eyes locked with his and she slithered out of the black garment. Once naked, she threw the teddy at him.

Dan caught it in midair and pressed it against his mouth, inhaling her scent.

"You're overdressed," she whispered, glancing at his shorts.

Bracing herself on her elbows, she watched him as he took them off, then crooked a finger. "Come here."

Answering the command, he stretched beside her and took her in his arms. "Are you aware of what you're doing to me?"

Her laugh was husky as she felt his rock-hard erection against her. "Absolutely."

He cupped her buttocks and brought her even closer. "Tell me what you like, Jill."

"You already know."

"Hmm, let's see…" Bending over her, he drew on a taut nipple. "I think you used to like this."

She closed her eyes. "I still do."

Holding her hips still, he let his mouth move lower. With each kiss, she felt her skin heat up. When he reached her center, a violent shudder went through her entire body.

"How about that?" He pressed his mouth over her.

Feeling herself dangerously close to the edge, Jill gripped his shoulders and pulled him back to her. Later there would be time to explore each other's bodies, to reawaken old pleasures and discover new ones. Right now, she needed to be joined to him, needed to feel him inside her, needed to experience that slow, delicious, excruciating climb to the top.

He slid into her, filling her as gloriously as she remembered, pulling her into his rhythm, slow and measured at first, then more powerful as he quickened the pace.

Fingers entwined, their heart beating as one, they moved together, in perfect unison. She whispered his name, over and over, and dug her fingernails into the palm of his hands. Then, with one last cry, she gave in to the mounting heat and let him take her over the edge.

Twenty-Six

Curled up against Dan, her head on his shoulder, Jill began to wake up, making happy groaning sounds and slowly stretching her leg along his.

Gentle fingers pushed a curl from her forehead. "What are you grinning about?" Dan asked.

Jill laughed softly. "I just lost twenty bucks."

"How?"

She snuggled closer. "Ashley bet me twenty dollars that you and I were a better match now than we were thirteen years ago and that I'd soon realize that."

He kissed the top of her head. "So...what do you think? Was it money well spent?"

"Oh—" she ran her hand over his flat stomach "—I'd say I got one hell of a bargain."

"Then you don't have any regrets?"

She looked at him, rocked by the sudden serious expression on his face. Did he really think she'd regret making love to him, that last night had been nothing more for her than a satisfying romp?

She shook her head. "Of course not. But shouldn't *I* be the one asking that question?" she teased. "After all, *I* seduced *you*."

"Now that you mention it," he deadpanned. "I do have a few—"

Before he could stop her, she grabbed her pillow and was hitting him with it. Taking it from her, he tossed it aside and pinned her to the bed. "All I regret is that the night wasn't long enough."

"In that case, why don't we stretch it out a bit?"

They made love again, slowly this time and with a tenderness and an awareness of each other's bodies that brought tears to Jill's eyes.

Afterward, as she lay in his arms, spent and happier than she had been in years, she almost blurted out the words *I love you,* then stopped herself just in time. It wasn't what he wanted to hear. If it was, he would have said it first. So why spoil the moment?

Knowing that the news of Jill's snowmobiling accident would make the morning papers, Jill had called her mother and told her about both attacks.

Amanda had reacted predictably. "Isn't it enough that I've lost a husband?" she'd cried on the phone. "Must I now fear for my daughter's life, as well? Why didn't you tell me sooner about this?"

"Because I didn't want to worry you." It had taken a few more minutes to calm her down, to make her understand that, now that Wally was reopening the investigation, the killer no longer had a reason to come after her. "It's all in the open now, Mom. Wally knows everything I know, and the killer is aware of that."

Cyrus had been more understanding but no less worried. He had refused to hang up until Jill had promised him that from now on, she would leave the murder investigation to the authorities.

At B&A, where the news had spread quickly, sev-

eral of Jill's co-workers had been calling all morning
to express their relief that she hadn't been hurt.

If there was a murderer among them, as Dan seemed
to think, she was hard-pressed to guess who he was.

Even Olivia stopped by Jill's office on her way to
the board meeting Cyrus had called. "I heard you took
a tumble down a mountain," she said with her usual
flair for words.

"Thanks for your concern, Olivia." Jill stood up
and followed her cousin into the conference room.

"How are you, Jill?" Cyrus asked as the two
women entered the room.

Paul and Philip were equally concerned, especially
Paul, who apologized for having teased her the day
before.

Also sitting at the large conference table was Richard Sidel, the lead designer for the Falcon Department
Store in lower Manhattan.

Jill took a couple of minutes to tell everyone that
she was fine and another minute to suggest holding a
general meeting to brief the employees.

"They deserve an explanation," she said, looking
at each of her colleagues. "And the assurance that the
running of the company will not be affected."

Cyrus nodded. "I was planning to do just that, Jill—
shortly before the lunch break." He turned to Cecilia,
who sat behind him, taking notes. "Remind me, Cecilia, will you?"

Returning his attention to the five people around the
table, he added, "I must also warn all of you that
Constable Becker of the Livingston Manor police, will
be questioning everyone at B&A and checking alibis—"

Philip leaned forward. "You mean…we're under suspicion? He thinks one of us tried to kill Jill?"

Cyrus sighed. "Apparently so, Philip. But there's no need for alarm. It's just a routine questioning and I'm fairly confident that whoever is behind this ruthless attack on my niece does not work here."

"When does Constable Becker intend to start this…questioning?" Paul asked.

"Some time tomorrow. Now, if you don't mind, I'd like to move on to another matter." From the open briefcase on the table, he pulled out a stack of correspondence. "The bids for the Falcon Department Store."

Glancing at her watch, Jill realized that today was December 20, the day the bids were due in. "Who's the low bidder?"

"Mulligan & Son, which surprised me as much as it probably surprises you."

"Are you sure?" Philip asked. "Ever since Pete took over his father's business, he hasn't come even remotely close to a low bid in any of our projects."

"See for yourself." Cyrus passed them each a copy of all six bids. "He came considerably lower this time—two hundred thousand dollars lower."

Olivia made a note in her pad. "Then I guess he gets the job."

"That's for the developer to decide."

"But if he's the low bidder—"

"The developer still has the final word," Cyrus said. "Should he have any reservations at all about the contractor, he has the right to refuse the bid and go to the next one. However, I'm fairly sure Ted Falcon will not turn Mulligan down. His last two projects came in way over budget and he's watching his money.''

Cyrus glanced around the table. ''Now the question is, can we work with the man? Personally, I have no problem with him. I know there was bad blood between him and my brother, but he's always been civil to me. As for Simon's suspicions that Mulligan was using inferior material, I'll pass that information to Ted Falcon and let him decide if he wants to take a chance or not.''

He turned to the project's head designer. ''Richard, you'll be working with Mulligan more closely than any of us. What do you think?''

Richard shrugged. ''As long as the man does what he's paid to do, we'll get along fine.''

Cyrus's gaze rested on Jill. ''Jill? Any reservations?''

Plenty, Jill thought. After that outburst in her loft last week, she wished she never had to lay eyes on the man again, unless, of course, he turned out to be her father's killer, in which case she'd see the bastard behind bars. But until Dan or Wally could prove his guilt, she had no right to let her personal feelings interfere with a job.

''No,'' she said with a firm shake of her head. ''And even if I had, I wouldn't want to influence the developer and have Mulligan accuse us of manipulating the bids again the way he did with my father. That kind of publicity could be disastrous.''

''Then it's settled.'' Cyrus lay the palms of his hands on the table. ''I'll messenger the bids to Ted immediately.''

As Cyrus adjourned the meeting, no one noticed Olivia's huge sigh of relief.

This time, when Dan knocked at Joshua's door, the caretaker was tinkering with an old pocket watch.

"Hi, Joshua." Dan gave him a friendly grin and held up a small brown paper bag. "I have that heating coil for your toaster."

Joshua's eyes, suspicious at first when he didn't see Jill, lost some of their hostility. "You do?"

Dan handed him the bag. "See for yourself."

After a short hesitation, Joshua took the bag and let Dan in. "My friend put his card inside," Dan added. "So whenever you can't find something in Livingston Manor, give him a call and he'll get it for you."

"Thanks." Like a child with a present, Joshua looked inside the bag and pulled out the part, inspecting it carefully. Satisfied it was what he wanted, he took it to the kitchen counter and set it beside the dismantled toaster. "How much did it cost?"

Dan dismissed the question with a wave his hand. "There's no charge."

Joshua's face clouded. "I want to pay you." Digging inside a cookie jar in the shape of a pumpkin, he pulled out a few bills. "Mr. Simon says a man always pays his debts." He handed Dan three one-dollar bills. "I have more money in my sock drawer."

Dan realized Joshua would be deeply offended if he refused the caretaker's money, and took the three dollars. "That's just right, Joshua, thank you."

"You're welcome." The caretaker sat down at the dining table again and picked up the watch, looking at it closely.

"That's a very nice piece you've got here." Dan wished he knew something about pocket watches. It would have helped break the ice.

"Mr. Simon gave it to me. He said if I could fix it, I could keep it."

"Simon was nice to you, wasn't he?"

With a small jeweler's screwdriver, Joshua began to unscrew the back plate. "Yeah, he was. He let me buy the cabin." He looked up, his eyes suddenly bright with pride. "I have a receipt and everything."

"I'm sure you deserve it. Jill told me how hard you work."

"I like to work." With a precision Dan found remarkable for a man with such large hands, Joshua began to remove the other screw, his face so close to the watch that his long hair brushed against it.

"Did you ever see anybody get mad at Simon?" Dan asked after a while.

To his surprise, Joshua smiled. "Mr. Wally got mad at him sometimes, when they played cards." He chuckled. "One time he called Mr. Simon an old schmuck. But he was just pretending to be mad."

"You like Mr. Wally?"

"Yeah. He takes me shopping in his police car and sometimes he lets me turn on the siren. And he gets me work so I can earn my own money."

Dan would have expected nothing less from Wally. "What about the night Mr. Simon died, Joshua? Did somebody get mad at him? For real?"

Joshua's expression darkened. "I don't know nothin' about that."

"I think you do, Joshua." Dan was careful to keep his voice low and even. "But you don't want to tell me. Why is that? Are you afraid of something? Or someone?''

''I'm not afraid.'' He pulled himself straight. ''I can take care of myself. That's why Mr. Simon gave me this job, 'cause I can take care of myself.''

''I know you can, Joshua. But even people who can take care of themselves get scared sometimes. I do.''

The confession didn't bring the effect Dan had hoped for. Joshua remained bent over his work, his expression sullen.

''You want to know what I think happened that night, Joshua?''

Joshua didn't reply.

''I think someone came to see Mr. Simon and did something very bad to him. Maybe that person even killed him.''

Unexpectedly, Joshua sank the point of his screwdriver into the table, his face contorted as if he was about to cry. *''No!''* It was a heart-wrenching cry that sent a shiver down Dan's back.

''He didn't kill him! He didn't!''

Dan lay a hand on the big man's quivering shoulder to calm him. ''Take it easy, Joshua. It's okay.''

''He didn't mean to hurt him.'' Tears of anguish filled the caretaker's eyes and ran down his cheeks.

''Who didn't mean to hurt him?''

Joshua's answer was barely audible, but Dan heard it, and was rocked by it.

''Mr. Cyrus.''

Twenty-Seven

For a few seconds, Dan remained perfectly still. Cyrus? It couldn't be. Joshua was wrong. According to Wally, Cyrus was nowhere near Livingston Manor that night. Slowly, Dan withdrew his hand from Joshua's shoulder. "You saw Cyrus at Simon's house?"

Wiping his wet cheeks with his sleeve, Joshua nodded.

"Did you see him from your kitchen window?" Maybe the distance and the darkness had impaired his view.

Joshua shook his head. "The house was all lit up but I didn't see Mr. Simon's Jeep, so I was afraid I'd left the lights on." He cast Dan a quick, guilty look. "I do that sometimes, when I take things there."

"And you went to turn the lights off."

Joshua nodded again.

Remembering that Joshua was most comfortable when he was asked a direct question, Dan leaned across the table. "Did you go inside the house, Joshua?"

He shook his head once more. "I stayed outside, in front of the window."

"And what did you see?"

"Mr. Simon and Mr. Cyrus were mad at each other. They were yellin'."

"Did you hear what they were yelling about?"

He shook his head and covered his face with his hands.

"Were you scared, Joshua?"

"Yes. Mr. Simon…" He pulled his hands away and just sat there staring at them, huge, callused hands as big as bear paws.

"What did Mr. Simon do?"

"He hit Mr. Cyrus."

Once again, Dan was taken aback. "He did? Are you sure?"

Joshua nodded.

"Did Cyrus hit him back?"

Joshua nodded again.

Oh, Christ. This wasn't good. Not good at all. "Was Simon hurt?"

"I don't know. Maybe." Picking up the screwdriver again, he began stabbing the table with short, even strokes. "His head hit the fireplace."

"Joshua, this is very important. Do you remember what time it was when you saw all that?"

Joshua squinted as he tried to remember. "I think it was late, maybe eleven o'clock. I was watching a funny show on TV."

"What show was that?"

"I forgot what it's called. It's about a fat man who drives a bus. His friend works in the sewers."

It sounded like the old Jackie Gleason comedy show, Dan thought. But he'd have to check the listings to make sure. "Was the show called 'The Honeymooners'?"

Joshua lay the screwdriver down. "Yeah."

Dan was silent for a moment, trying to make sense out of what he'd just heard. Cyrus had lied, which explained why he hadn't wanted to discuss the case with him.

At the time, Dan had attributed this reluctance to the fact that Cyrus had never been overly fond of him, but he realized now that it was more than that.

"Did Simon get up after hitting the fireplace?" Dan asked gently.

"I don't know. I ran back home and went to bed." Joshua lowered his head as if in shame. "I hid under the covers."

Considering the man's distress, Dan wondered how he had managed to keep the secret all this time. "That's okay, Joshua. Lots of people hide under the covers when they're scared."

The caretaker gave an emphatic shake of his head, sending his long, unruly hair flying. "I should have helped him. He hurt his head and that's why he went off the road."

"No, Joshua, that's *not* why he went off the road." Dan didn't have the heart to tell him that Cyrus's blow might have killed Simon. "He went off the road because it was dark, and it was raining, and the roads were very slippery."

"Mr. Cyrus didn't mean to hurt him," Joshua whimpered. "He loved Mr. Simon. He was his brother."

"I know." Dan felt lousy. Of all the investigations he had conducted over the years, all the tricks and resources he'd had to rely on to get the information he needed to nail a murderer, none had ever left such a bad taste in his mouth as this one.

"You're not going to arrest Mr. Cyrus, are you?" Joshua's red-rimmed eyes watched him intently.

"I can't arrest people, Joshua. I'm not a policeman."

"Mr. Wally is a policeman." He looked worried again. "Is he going to put Mr. Cyrus in jail?"

"Wally is Cyrus's friend. I'm sure he'll try to help him."

The remark seemed to have a calming effect on Joshua but did little to relieve Dan's own turmoil.

How in the world was he going to tell Jill that Cyrus had just become his number-one suspect?

After thanking Joshua, Dan didn't stop at Wally's office as he had intended, but drove back to Manhattan.

When Jill's cab let her off in front of her apartment building a little after six o'clock, Dan was leaning against the wall, waiting for her.

"You're late," he said, kissing her.

"When did you become such a stickler for time?"

"Since some maniac tried to kill you."

In spite of his light tone, Jill picked up on his strange mood immediately. "Is something wrong?"

"I'll tell you upstairs."

Something inside Jill's stomach shifted. She wasn't sure she could take any more bad news. Once inside the loft, however, she dropped her purse on the foyer table, walked into the living room and turned to Dan. "Well?"

"I talked to Joshua again. And this time he told me the truth."

"Which is?"

"He saw someone at the house the night your father died."

Jill held her breath. Was that it? Was she finally going to find out the name of her father's killer? "Who?"

"Cyrus."

She flinched as if the word had struck her. "What?"

Taking her hands, Dan pulled her toward the sofa and forced her to sit down. "That's what Joshua couldn't bring himself to say the other day. He didn't want to get your uncle in trouble."

She yanked her hands away. "But that's ridiculous. My uncle wasn't even there that night. He was home. He was the first person Wally called about the accident."

"He may have been home when Wally called him, but that doesn't change the fact that Joshua saw him at the house two hours earlier."

Jill bit her lip, suppressing the need to scream. Had everyone gone stark raving mad? "Joshua is mistaken," she said, trying to keep her voice on an even keel. "He saw someone else."

"No, he didn't. He stood just outside the living-room window. He saw the two men argue. He saw them exchange blows."

"They *fought*?"

"Your father threw the first punch and Cyrus retaliated with one of his own. Apparently, the blow was powerful enough to knock your father against the fireplace."

Jill's face lost all color. Jumping to her feet, she started pacing the room. "What are you saying, Dan? That my uncle is a murderer? Are you out of your mind?"

"Until we hear Cyrus's side of the story, I'm afraid that's the only possible scenario."

She stopped in front of him. "I can't believe you. I knew you didn't like my uncle, but I never thought you'd turn on him by making up something so monstrous."

Dan ignored the outburst. "Maybe you should ask your uncle where he was that night."

"I know where he was that night! At home." She sank into a chair, waiting for the shock and anger to recede. When they had, she bowed her head. "I'm sorry."

Dan sat beside her and gathered her in his arms. "It's okay, baby. I could hardly believe it myself."

As a feeling of total exhaustion engulfed her, she leaned against him. "There has to be an explanation for this, Dan. He couldn't have..." She fought to keep her voice from shaking and couldn't quite manage it. "Because, you see, if he killed my father, then..." She raised stricken eyes toward him. "Then he's the one who tried to kill *me*."

"We need to talk to him, Jill. Do you know where he is?"

"Home. He left work early to get ready for a Christmas function at the Metropolitan Museum of Modern Art." Unable to stand still, she pulled away from him and stood up again. "You didn't tell Wally, did you?"

"No. I wanted to talk to you first."

"Good. It'll give me a chance to speak to my uncle and clear up this—"

The phone rang, cutting off the rest of her sentence. Filled with a sense of impending doom, she picked up the receiver. "Hello?"

"Jill!" her aunt Stephanie cried. "Thank God I found you."

A chill settled in the pit of Jill's stomach. "Aunt Stephanie, what is it? What's wrong?"

"It's Cyrus. He…" She was overcome by sobs. "He's just been arrested."

Twenty-Eight

Jill threw Dan a horrified look. "Aunt Stephanie, calm down. Who arrested him?"

"Two deputies from Livingston Manor. They said Wally needed to ask him a few questions in regard to Simon's death. They wouldn't tell me any more than that. They wouldn't even let me go with him." She started crying again.

"Are you sure he was arrested? They showed you a warrant?"

"They didn't say anything about a warrant. They asked Cyrus if he'd go willingly and he said yes."

"All right, listen to me. Call Philip Van Horn right away. Tell him what happened and ask him to recommend a criminal defense attorney. I'll call Wally and try to find out what's going on."

"Why is Wally doing this?" Stephanie asked in an anguished voice. "He's acting as if Cyrus is a criminal, as if he actually had something to do with Simon's death."

"I'm sure it's just a misunderstanding, Aunt Stephanie. We'll get it straightened out. Let me get off the phone, okay? I'll call you back as soon as I know something. In the meantime, call Philip."

Jill hung up and turned to Dan. "I thought you didn't say anything to Wally."

"I didn't. After I left Joshua's cabin, I came straight here."

"Well, he knows. Two deputies just took my uncle to Livingston Manor for questioning."

Dan was already dialing the phone.

"Who are you calling?"

"The only person with answers—Wally."

This time there were no pleasantries exchanged between the two men. Wally's tone was brisk. "You should have told me right away, Dan."

"Wally, come on. How could I do that without talking to Jill first?"

Wally grumbled something unintelligible that Dan took for an agreement. "How did you find out, anyway?"

"Joshua came to see me," Wally said. "Apparently right after you left him. He was terrified Cyrus would go to jail because of him. I couldn't make sense of what he was saying at first. Then, when he mentioned your name, and your visit, I started to put two and two together."

"Are you planning on arresting Cyrus?"

"Not until I hear his side of the story. Depending on what he says, I may have to turn him over to the sheriff's department in Monticello." He paused. "You'd better tell Jill to get him an attorney."

"She already has."

"Good. He's going to need one."

Dan glanced at Jill, whose color still hadn't returned. "Jill wants to see her uncle, Wally."

"Not until I've had a chance to talk to him. And that could be quite late."

"I don't care how late it is, please call me."

"Where will you be?"

"Right here, at Jill's loft."

There was a slight pause. "All night?"

The surprise in the policeman's voice didn't go unnoticed. "Yes," Dan said simply, offering no other explanation. Now was not the time to discuss his renewed relationship with Jill.

After he hung up, Dan repeated what Wally had told him.

Like a struck match, Jill's anger flared anew, as hot as before. "I can't believe Wally is talking about turning my uncle over to the sheriff. What does he think Cyrus is going to do? Confess to a murder he didn't commit?"

"Wally is just doing his job, Jill."

"His job is to protect the public, not to harass innocent people."

"He's also a fair man, and one of Cyrus's best friends. He'll do what's right."

"He didn't do what was right when he brought my uncle in. The whole thing could have been handled with one phone call."

"That's not how the police operate, Jill, even in a hamlet like Livingston Manor."

Jill let out a long breath and went to look out the dark living-room window. Of course, it wasn't. She knew that. She was just letting off some steam. If she could take a moment to calmly analyze the situation, she'd understand why Wally had little choice but to do exactly as he had.

"Feel better?" Dan had sneaked up behind her and wrapped his arms around her.

"A little." She leaned the back of her head against his broad chest. "Sorry. I'm being a bitch, aren't I?"

"No, you're being human."

She covered his arms with hers and held him tight. "I guess I'd better call Aunt Stephanie," she said after a while. "I told her I would."

Reluctantly, she moved out of his arms and walked over to pick up the phone.

Wally eased a hip over his desk and watched his deputy bring Cyrus in. His eyes on his old friend, he waited until Brad had left and closed the door before speaking. "Thanks for coming in, Cyrus."

"Did I have a choice?" Looking pale but composed, Cyrus removed his overcoat and tossed it on a chair. Underneath, he wore an impeccably cut tuxedo, no bow tie. His heavily starched shirt collar was open.

Wally ignored the question but observed him in silence for a few seconds. Though subdued, Cyrus showed no sign of nervousness and returned Wally's gaze without flinching. "You don't know how I hate doing this."

"I have a pretty good idea." Cyrus looked around the room. "I don't see a tape recorder. Is this an informal interrogation then?"

"It's not an interrogation at all. I just want to ask you a few questions. If you give me the answers I want to hear, I'll let you go."

Cyrus leaned back in the chair. "Fair enough. What do you want to know?"

"The same thing I wanted to know the day Simon died. Where were you that night?"

Cyrus's face remained impassive. "And I already told you. I was home."

"We have an eyewitness who puts you in Simon's house at about 11:00 p.m."

Cyrus gave Wally a long level look and said nothing.

Wally wanted to shake him. "So I'll ask you again," he said, keeping his eyes on Cyrus. "Where were you the night Simon died?"

"Who told you I was here?"

"Never mind that. Just answer the damn question."

For a moment, Cyrus seemed lost in the contemplation of his shoes, which were polished to a high gloss. "I was in Livingston Manor," he said at last. "At Simon's house."

Wally inhaled deeply. It wasn't what he wanted to hear. Despite his faith in Joshua, he had hung on to the slim chance that the caretaker had been mistaken. "Do you realize what you're saying?"

"You wanted the truth. Now you have it."

"Dammit, Cyrus, why didn't you tell me sooner? Why did you lie?"

"Because you would have come to the same conclusion you're coming to now—that I killed Simon."

"Are you saying you didn't?"

"You're damn right I didn't."

"And I suppose you weren't arguing with him, either? You were just having a cozy little chat by the fire."

Cyrus's eyes registered instant surprise. Surprise and something more. Fear. The look hit Wally in the gut. He had known Cyrus as long as he'd known Simon, and liked him equally, maybe more. Unlike Simon, who had thrived on attention and adulation, Cyrus was a simple, compassionate man with no ego and a deep sense of ethics. The thought that he may have killed his own brother was too ludicrous to imagine. And yet...

The next question had his stomach in knots, but he had to ask it. "Where were you on Tuesday morning, Cyrus?"

For a moment, Wally thought his old friend was going to rush him. Then the fury receded from Cyrus's eyes as if he understood why the question had to be asked. "I was at the office."

"Can you prove it?"

"If I have to."

"Then why won't you—"

"That's all I'm going to say until you tell me what *I* want to know. Who told you I was in Livingston Manor the night my brother died?"

There was no point in keeping Joshua's name a secret any longer. Cyrus was bound to find out, anyway. "Joshua saw you there. He came to the house thinking he had left the lights on. He saw you throw a punch. And he saw Simon hit his head on the fireplace."

Cyrus briefly closed his eyes. "Damn."

The single expletive, an admission in itself, drained Wally of any hope he had of clearing his friend. He waited for an explanation, but Cyrus didn't offer any. He kept studying his shoes.

"Want to tell me what happened?" Wally finally asked.

When Cyrus looked up, his eyes were flat. "Joshua

told you the truth. Simon and I did have an argument that night. He hit me, I hit him back and, yes, I knocked him against the fireplace. But I didn't kill him.'' His gaze remained steady. "He was very much alive and back on his feet when I left the house.''

"What were you two fighting about?''

Cyrus shook his head. "I've told you all I'm going to say.''

Wally jumped down from his desk. "What do you mean you've told me all you're going to say? Are you crazy? Don't you realize the mess you're in?''

"I think I do.''

"Then defend yourself, man. Give me something I can work with, so I won't have to slap a murder charge on you.''

"I can't.''

"Why? Are you protecting someone?''

"No.''

"Like hell you're not. Who is it?''

"I told you, no one.''

In a frustrated gesture, Wally ran his hand through his thick gray hair and tried another approach. "What time did you arrive at the house?''

Cyrus's mouth pursed for a second or two. "Between eleven and eleven-fifteen.''

"How long did you stay?''

"No more than fifteen minutes. I was back in New York by 2:00 a.m.''

"But you can't prove it.''

"You know I can't. Stephanie was in Massachusetts visiting her sister that weekend. She didn't get back home until Monday morning, after I called her to tell her about Simon.''

It was all true. Wally hadn't made anything of it at the time. He had gone through the routine questioning for Jill's sake, not really suspecting anyone, or even believing there was a killer on the loose.

"Did you see a car on your way down? Someone going in the opposite direction, perhaps, toward Simon's house?"

"No."

"Think carefully, Cyrus. It could be important."

"Don't you think I know that?" Cyrus snapped. "Don't you think if I'd seen someone, I'd tell you?"

"So why don't you tell me what you *do* know instead of playing games?"

"I'm not playing games. You want to arrest me, go ahead. You want to turn me over to County, do it. It won't change a damn thing. I won't tell them any more than I've already told you."

Wally leaned back against his desk and folded his arms. Cyrus had never been much on idle threats. "You realize I'm going to have to book you on suspicion of murder. Especially if we find evidence at the house."

Cyrus gave a curt nod. "In your shoes, I'd probably do the same thing."

"You're an infuriating jerk, you know that?"

The two men's eyes met and held. A sad smile pulled at the corner of Cyrus's mouth. "I've heard that before."

His nerves taut with frustration, Wally continued to look at his friend. He desperately wanted to help him but, without Cyrus's cooperation, there wasn't a damn thing he could do.

After a while, he gave a curt nod. "All right then,

if that's the way you want to play it, I have no choice but to hold you on suspicion of murder.''

"Are you going to transfer me tonight?"

"No. I'll do that in the morning. Our jail cell is no better than the one in Monticello, but at least you'll have it all to yourself. Unless they bring Marcus in for disturbing the peace."

"Thanks, Wally."

"I warn you, though. Sheriff Cutter is a consummate son of a bitch. And he wants to be re-elected in the worst way. A high-profile case like this is just what he needs to kick off his campaign. Believe me when I say he's going to milk this for all it's worth."

Cyrus made no comment.

"Stephanie and Jill have asked to see you," Wally continued. "I can call—"

"Don't bother," Cyrus said sharply. "I don't want to see either one of them."

Twenty-Nine

At ten-thirty, true to his word, Wally called back. "I'm afraid I don't have good news," he said grimly when Jill answered the phone.

She motioned for Dan to pick up the extension. "You talked to my uncle?"

"For over an hour. He admits coming to the summer house that night, having an argument with your father and even hitting him."

Jill pressed her hand to her mouth and sat down. Inside her chest, her heart was pounding erratically.

"What were they fighting about?" Dan asked.

"I don't know. Cyrus refuses to say anything more. The only point he's emphatic about is that he didn't kill Simon."

"You think he's telling the truth?"

Wally heaved a deep sigh. "I want to believe him, Dan, but the evidence is damning, even more so now."

"Why?" Jill gripped the phone with both hands.

"I just came back from your father's house. Brad and I found traces of blood on one of the fireplace stones. They're barely visible because of the reddish streaks throughout the stones, and I had to look damn close to see them, but they're there. The problem is, we don't have any of Simon's blood to compare it to, so we can't be sure it's his. But considering what Joshua told us and Cyrus's own admission, I'd bet my last dollar the blood is Simon's.''

Dan hoped the criminal attorney Philip Van Horn had recommended was a good one. ''What happens now?'' he asked, more for Jill's benefit than his.

''My office doesn't have jurisdiction over a murder case, which means I'll have to hand Cyrus over to the sheriff's department in Monticello first thing tomorrow morning. There he'll be arraigned and probably charged with second-degree murder—''

''Second-degree murder!'' Jill cried. ''Wally, that's ridiculous. Can't you do something?''

''I tried, Jill. But how can I help your uncle when he won't do anything to help himself?''

''I want to see him. I'll make him come to his senses.''

''I told him that, but he won't see anybody, not even Stephanie, who's been calling all evening. The only phone call he took was from your mother.''

Startled, Jill glanced at Dan. ''My mother? Are you sure?''

''Of course I'm sure. I'm the one who answered the phone.''

''What did she want?''

''I have no idea. I stepped out of the office while they talked. I suppose she wanted to give him support.''

His wife could have done that, Jill thought. Or his daughter.

Remembering the ordeal Joshua had gone through, Jill asked, ''How's Joshua?''

"Upset, as you'd expect him to be. I stopped at the cabin earlier and tried to explain what was happening. I didn't want him to hear the sordid details from anyone else. He's pretty much of a loner but you never know. This is a small village. News travels fast and not always with the best accuracy."

Jill smiled. Good old Wally, always thinking, always dependable. "Thanks, Wally. I'll call you tomorrow. Maybe my uncle will be ready to see me by then. Meanwhile, if you need me for anything, I'll be spending the night at my mother's."

"Good. And try to get some rest, will you? Dan, I'll talk to you later."

After hanging up, Jill dialed her mother's house. When Amanda answered, Jill said simply, "I'm coming over, Mom. We need to talk."

Henry had already gone to bed by the time Dan dropped Jill off at the town house. Amanda, however, was awake and pacing the floor, a bundle of raw nerves. She wore blue silk pajamas and a matching robe that rustled with every step.

"Thank God you're here." She rushed to her daughter and embraced her.

Jill, already on edge, was instantly alarmed. "Why? Did something happen?"

"No, I'm just relieved you're here, that's all."

"Did Aunt Stephanie call?" Jill asked innocently. "Or Uncle Cyrus?"

Amanda threw her a quizzical look. "Why would Cyrus call me? I'm told he won't talk to anyone."

Why was she lying? Jill wondered. What was she hiding now?

"I did hear from Stephanie, however," Amanda continued. "She's a total wreck. Thank God Olivia is with her. She'll be able to calm her down."

"I'm sure she will." For all her faults, Olivia adored her mother and had a remarkable stabilizing influence on her.

"Your aunt Lilly called, as well," Amanda stopped in front of the sofa to fluff up a small pink pillow. "She wanted to come by but I told her that wasn't necessary since you were staying over."

Looking concerned, she laid a hand on Jill's cheek. "Are *you* all right, darling? There's no aftereffect from that nasty fall you took, is there?"

"No, none."

"And the boy?"

What is *wrong* with her? Jill wondered, watching her mother with a mixture of worry and curiosity. Usually so reserved, she had suddenly turned into a chatterbox. "Frankie's fine, and so is Ashley. What about you, Mom? How are you holding up?"

Pressing her fingertips against her temples, Amanda shook her head. "I don't know, Jill. I can't believe what's happening to this family. A month ago, everything was so perfect, so…normal, and now, look at us. Your father is dead, your uncle is in jail and there's been two attempts on your life. What else can go wrong?"

"Maybe we can make everything right, Mom," Jill said gently. "By telling the truth."

Amanda lowered her hands. "What are you talking about? What truth?"

"Wally told me you called Uncle Cyrus tonight."

Amanda's back went rigid. "You talked to Wally?"

"I'd asked him to call me after he questioned Uncle Cyrus."

To Jill's surprise, her mother, who rarely drank at this time of day, walked over to the well-stocked liquor cart against the wall, opened a bottle of cognac and splashed a little in a Waterford snifter.

"Mom?" Jill looked at her intently. "Why did you call him?" She wanted to add, "And why did you lie?," but didn't.

Amanda made a vague gesture. "I was concerned about him. I wanted to…see how he was doing."

"He wouldn't take a call from his own wife, or from me, but he talked to you? That's odd, Mom."

"Why are you doing this? What are you driving at?"

"Did you tell Aunt Stephanie that you talked to her husband?"

"I can't remember." She took a quick sip of her cognac, then another. "I may not have. I was upset."

Jill shook her head. "I don't think that's the reason."

Amanda didn't reply.

"I think you know something," Jill said, talking to her mother as if *she* were the child. "And that something is connected to Daddy's death."

Her hands wrapped around her glass, Amanda stared into her drink. Her face had gone pale but other than that, it gave away nothing. "That's nonsense."

"Is it? Look at you, Mom. You're trembling. You're drinking at eleven o'clock at night and you can't even look at me."

"Stop this. For God's sake, stop it."

"Not this time, Mom. Whatever is happening here,

it's gone too far. There's too much at stake. I want to know the truth. For starters, how did Uncle Cyrus know where to find Daddy that night?''

''Why are you asking me?''

''Because you were the only person who could have told him.''

This time Amanda didn't protest, didn't make excuses, didn't evade the question. With a sigh that was as dramatic as one her sister might have heaved, she lowered her head. ''Oh, Jill, it's all so terribly complicated.''

''Lies usually are.''

With a gentle but firm hand, Jill pried the glass from Amanda's fingers and laid it back on the cart. ''Sit down,'' she said, pulling her onto the sofa.

This time Amanda didn't protest.

Jill sat beside her. ''Do you remember the time I decked Debbie Frisk in the school auditorium?''

Although startled by the sudden change of subject, Amanda smiled. ''Of course I remember. I had to come to the principal's office and listen to a stern lecture from Mrs. Montague.''

''And later that night, you came to my room and wanted to know what Debbie and I had been fighting about.''

''She had caught you kissing her boyfriend.''

''Actually, he was the one doing the kissing, but that's not important. What's important is that I let him do it. I might even have encouraged him, a little. That's the part I couldn't bring myself to tell you because I was so ashamed. But you sat with me, held my hand and told me that, no matter what I had done, nothing between us would ever change. You would always love me."

"I meant it with all my heart."

"I know. And so do I, Mom." Jill squeezed her mother's hands. "Nothing you've done in the past, or might do in the future, will ever change the love I have for you."

Jill paused, then asked the question that had to be asked. "Are you and Uncle Cyrus having an affair?"

The startled look in her mother's eyes made Jill heave a sigh of relief. "No, Jill." Amanda adamantly shook her head. "We're not having an affair. You must believe that."

"Then why were Daddy and Uncle Cy fighting? You might as well tell me. It's all going to come out—eventually."

"That's what I'm afraid of." Her eyes downcast, Amanda kept playing with her wedding band, a twin circle of diamonds Jill's father had given her for their twenty-fifth wedding anniversary.

"You're right," Amanda said with a small catchy sigh. "I have been less than honest with you."

Sensing that her mother needed to tell her story at her own pace, Jill waited.

Amanda looked up, her gaze brightly intense. "But before I do share this burden with you, you have to know that I loved your father with all my heart. When he died, I wanted to die with him."

Jill's grip on her mother's hands tightened. "Don't you think I know that? I was there. I saw what you went through. And I felt so helpless." Her voice broke. "For a while, I thought I was going to lose you, too."

"Oh, baby." Amanda's smile was strained. "I was trying to pull myself together. For you."

"I know."

Squaring her shoulders as if preparing for a difficult task, Amanda drew a breath and slowly released it. "As you know, your father and I had brunch at the Plaza Hotel with the Rumsons that Sunday. It's no secret that I've never been fond of Edith. She flirts shamelessly with every man she sees and, at times, her behavior is downright embarrassing. I don't know how Carl tolerates it."

Jill almost groaned. Her father and Edith Rumson? Please, God, she implored. Not that. "Why do you go out with them then?"

"Because Carl is a client and your father felt obligated to entertain him occasionally."

She refocused her gaze on Jill. "That Sunday, after too many mimosas, Edith began flirting with your father, right under my nose, as if I didn't even exist. Carl was amused but I wasn't. I was upset, with her, and with your father, who seemed to be having a grand old time."

"I'm sure it was harmless. She's hardly his type." And then again, maybe she was, Jill thought bitterly. After all she had learned about her father recently, nothing about him surprised her anymore.

"I know." Amanda's hands tightened into small fists. "But at the time, I wanted to strangle them both. Instead, I stormed out of the Plaza and took a cab home."

"And Daddy?"

"He came home shortly after I did. He was as furious with me as I was with him. He accused me of making a scene and that made me even angrier. He was scolding *me* for his childish behavior.''

''I take it you two had a big fight.''

''We had a *terrible* fight, the worst in all our thirty-six years of marriage. He told me things I'm sure he didn't mean and I...'' She bit her bottom lip. ''I fought back by saying something I should never have said. If I had kept my mouth shut that day, Simon would still be alive. I'm convinced of that.''

Jill felt her own eyes fill with tears. ''You can't blame yourself, Mom. Couples argue all the time—''

''Not like that.''

''What did you say to him that was so horrible?''

Amanda looked up, and the anguish Jill saw in her eyes was so real, so raw that she almost stopped her right there. Whatever her secret was, however badly Jill wanted to hear it, it wasn't worth seeing her mother like this.

''I told him you weren't his daughter.''

The words drove right through Jill's heart, numbing her. She took a moment to absorb them while at the same time fighting an absurd need to laugh. ''What did you say?''

''I told him you weren't his daughter,'' Amanda repeated.

Jill's eyes widened in horror. ''How could you even say such a blatant lie?''

''It's not a lie. It's the truth. Simon was not your father.''

Jill sat in stony silence. She tried to say something but somehow her mouth was unable to articulate even the simplest words. Rising from the sofa, she backed away, shaking her head. ''No...''

"I know how painful this must be, darling, and I'm so sorry. That's why I didn't want to tell you."

Jill's voice sounded as if it came through a thick fog. "If Simon was not my father...then who is?"

Amanda took a moment to answer, then in a voice that was barely above a whisper, she said, "Cyrus. Cyrus is your father."

Thirty

For a moment, everything around her went blank and very still. It was as if the world had suddenly stopped turning and she didn't know how to get it started again.

"Jill?"

At the concerned sound of her mother's voice, Jill's eyes flickered briefly. Her mouth parted but no words came out.

"Jill, darling, please say something."

When Jill was finally able to speak, her voice was hoarse, as unreal as the words she'd just heard. "I thought you said you and Uncle Cyrus weren't involved?"

"We're not. The affair happened a long time ago." Amanda twisted and untwisted her hands. "Everything was so different then, you see. B&A was a young company, only a couple of years old and your father was totally absorbed by it.

"I know it's no excuse," she continued as Jill shot her a quick, reproachful glance. "He was working hard, trying to make a success of himself, and the company. I tried to understand that, but I was a young bride, full of hopes and dreams. I didn't care about money and success and which architect would build

the world's tallest skyscraper. I wanted my husband,
I wanted long walks in the park, intimate little dinners,
togetherness. Instead, I was thrown into a world I
didn't know, made to befriend women who were as
superficial and brittle as old varnish. The days were
endless and the evenings lonely. You, of all people,
should understand that, Jill.''

Jill recoiled as if she had been slapped. "I didn't
run into the arms of my brother-in-law."

"That's not what happened."

"I'm here, aren't I?" Jill said sarcastically. "Something *must* have happened."

"Neither one of us saw it coming, and we certainly
didn't plan it. Cyrus was happily married, and I was
hopelessly in love with Simon. But after that first year,
I started to realize that, though Simon loved me, his
true passion was architecture. Cyrus was different. He
wasn't so obsessed with his career. And he was atten-
tive, funny, kind. And more and more he was there
when I needed someone to talk to."

"But you did more than talk, didn't you?" The
shock was gone, replaced by a resentment so deep, Jill
could feel it burning deep within her, poisoning her.
She wanted to run, anywhere, as far away as her legs
would take her. She would have done just that, had it
not been for a perverse desire to know the rest of this
sordid story.

"Yes, Cyrus and I became lovers, but what ulti-
mately drew us together was more a need for tenderness than true love. It didn't even last long enough to
qualify as an affair. After a month, we were both so
miserable about deceiving Simon and Stephanie that
we ended it."

"When did you find out you were pregnant?"

"A few weeks later. I suspected Cyrus was the father because Simon was usually so tired when he came home, we rarely made love. My suspicions weren't confirmed until after you were born and a blood test was done on you and Cyrus."

That explained so much, Jill thought—Cyrus's unconditional love, his presence at all her important events, his pride in her accomplishments, no matter how small, the way she caught him looking at her sometimes when he thought no one was watching. "And you never said anything."

"How could I? It would have destroyed so many lives—yours, Simon's, Stephanie's, Olivia's."

Had her father known about the affair? Jill wondered. And retaliated by having one of his own? "What did...Cyrus say when you told him you were pregnant?" All of a sudden she didn't know what to call him.

"He was thrilled. I'll never forget the look on his face. He was positively glowing. For a frightening moment, I even thought he was going to ask me to tell Simon the truth so we could get married, but he didn't. He loved Stephanie every bit as much as I loved Simon, but I could tell he was happy at the thought of having a child of his own, even if he couldn't claim the baby. He had Olivia, of course, and he loved her very much, but I don't think he ever felt about her the way he felt about you."

"And Olivia knew that," Jill said quietly. "I always blamed her for her nastiness, for reading more into my relationship with her father than there was, and all the time she was right."

She walked over to the window, surprised that her legs could support her. New Yorkers were just coming out of the theater, and on nearby Fifth Avenue the angry blare of horns could be heard, yet to Jill, everything was strangely muted and distant. "When you told Daddy I wasn't his daughter that Sunday, did he ask who the father was?"

"Yes. And I had to tell him. He was so angry that for a moment I thought he was going to strike me. After he left, I waited all day for him to come back from Livingston Manor so we could talk. When he didn't return and wouldn't answer my calls, I got scared and called Cyrus. I was hoping he'd be able to quiet him down, convince him to come home. But when Cyrus got there, Simon wouldn't listen. He was drinking heavily and spoiling for a fight."

Her anxious gaze searched her daughter's face. "I've blamed myself ever since that terrible night, Jill. I always will."

Jill tried desperately to sort out her feelings, to convince herself that nothing had changed. She'd had a wonderful life and, though Simon hadn't been the most devoted of fathers in the early years, he had more than made up for lost time later. They couldn't have been more alike if they *had* been father and daughter. Both were overachievers, both had the same quick temper, the same passion for their profession and the same love and respect for one another.

So why did she feel as though someone had punched a big hole in her heart? Why did she feel as though she was mourning her father all over again?

And what about Cyrus? Her beloved Uncle Cy. How was she supposed to act now that she knew the truth? She would never be able to look at him again and feel the way she had before. Or trust him again, knowing he had lied to her all these years.

Pressing her burning forehead against the cool glass, another ugly thought wove its way into her mind, filling her with dread.

What if Cyrus had killed her father?

She had escaped to the only place where she felt safe, the only place she could truly call home—her loft.

Huddled on the sofa in an old chenille robe that had faded to an almost unidentifiable shade of blue, she sipped chamomile tea. On the end table her phone kept ringing and she kept ignoring it, barely aware that the messages were accumulating.

Another moment passed and it rang again. It was her mother, leaving her third message. "Come on, Jill, pick up. I know you're there. We need to talk." There was a pause, a sigh, then a click as Amanda hung up.

She thought about turning the damn machine off, but didn't. Somehow, hearing the hurt and worry in her mother's voice brought her a strange kind of satisfaction.

She let out a dry chuckle that threatened to turn into a sob. Tit for tat. Is that what she was doing? How mature.

The phone rang again. This time it was Ashley. She had been awakened from a deep sleep by Jill's mother and she was pissed off.

"Jill? Are you there?" There was a short pause. "Dammit, Jill, what's going on? Your mother is worried sick about you. So if you're there, call her. Or call me and I'll come up. I don't know what happened, but whatever it is, you don't have to go through it alone, okay?'' There was a brief pause. ''I guess you're not there, so call me as soon as you come in.''

Click. The outside world was turned off again. Leaning against the cushions, Jill closed her eyes and tried to make her mind a blank.

The persistent ring of her doorbell woke Jill with a start. She had fallen asleep on the sofa with the empty mug wedged between her thighs.

Groaning, she stood up just as another burst of short angry rings pierced the silence.

''Jill, it's me. Open up.''

Dan. Her mother must have called him, too. ''All right, all right, I'm coming.''

He stood on the landing, one hand braced against the jamb. ''What's wrong with you? Why aren't you answering your phone?''

''Because I don't feel like it.''

As Dan took a second, closer look at her, his anger seemed to vanish instantly. ''Wait here,'' he said, giving her shoulders a quick, reassuring squeeze. ''I have to make a call.''

He walked over to the phone and dialed a number. The person at the other end must have answered at the first ring because Dan spoke immediately.

''She's fine, Amanda. Yes, she's home.'' He glanced back at Jill. ''I don't think that's a good idea right now. Maybe she could call you in the morning.''

He hung up, went to take Jill's hand and pulled her into the living room, forcing her to sit down. ''I thought you and I had agreed you wouldn't go wandering into the streets late at night.''

"Nothing happened, okay?" she said irritably. "I'm fine."

"You're not fine." He took her chin between two fingers and tilted her head up. "What happened between you and your mother?"

"Nothing." She chose a point above his head and stared at it. She had nothing left but her strength and dignity, and dammit she wasn't going to lose either by admitting she was a bastard child.

"Come on, Red, you can't fool me. Something's got you all torn up inside and it's not your uncle's arrest. So spit it out." When she remained stubbornly silent, he took her hands in his and brought them to his mouth. "That bad?"

His voice was soft enough, gentle enough to make her forget her vow of silence. "Worse." So much for strength and dignity.

"Tell me. Let me help you."

In a voice that shook at first, then grew steadier, she told him the whole tawdry affair, interrupting the flow of words with short comments and bursts of anger he didn't try to stop. She didn't realize until the words began pouring forth how much she'd needed to get all those feelings and emotions out. The task left her drained and exhausted, but strangely at peace with herself.

When she was finished, Dan was still holding her hands. "You have every right to be upset, even angry, but not wanting to talk to your mother ever again isn't right. She doesn't deserve that."

She jerked her hands away. ''I knew you wouldn't understand.''

''On the contrary, I understand perfectly. It just doesn't seem fair, to her or to you.''

''She hurt me.'' She sounded like a whiney little kid, but at the moment she didn't give a damn.

''People make mistakes, Jill.''

''She had thirty-four years to rectify that mistake.''

''How? By telling you Cyrus was your father? When was she supposed to do that, Jill? When do you think was a good time? On your fifth birthday? Your tenth? Your high-school graduation perhaps?''

''Don't make fun of me. I'm not in the mood.''

''I'm only trying to show you what an impossible situation she was in. No matter when she chose to do it, those young shoulders of yours would have never been able to carry such a burden.

''And what about the rest of your family?'' Dan continued when she remained silent. ''Your aunt, your cousin, Simon? They would have had to be told, too. Two families would have been shattered, perhaps even destroyed. That's what Cyrus and your mother were trying to avoid—the destruction of their respective families.''

''So they lied to me.''

''To protect you.'' He stroked her hair. ''That's what parenting is all about, Red. Someday, when you're a parent, you'll understand that.''

They didn't go to bed that night. Dan didn't think she was in the mood for sex or sleep, anyway. So, after making them both a pot of coffee, he turned the lights down low, wrapped a thick blue and white afghan around them and together they watched an old, soapy Joan Crawford movie on A&E.

It took Jill a while to fall asleep. Because her anger provided a shield against other emotions, she fiercely clung to it, but in the end exhaustion won out. Halfway through the movie, her head, which rested on his lap, became heavier, her breathing deeper.

He considered carrying her upstairs and putting her to bed, then thought better of it. If she woke up, she might not be able to go back to sleep.

Tucking the afghan around her, he watched her sleep and was filled with an emotion that left his mouth dry. When he'd first returned to New York, he had been certain that seeing her again would finally make him realize he no longer loved her. Unfortunately, the moment he had seen her standing there, every feeling he'd ever had for her had come rushing back like a torrent, stronger than before.

And tonight, watching her sleep in that thready old robe, the need to love and protect had been almost overwhelming.

But at thirty-four, Jill Bennett had learned to fight her own battles, and if he wanted to keep her, he would have to understand that.

If he wanted to keep her. He laughed. He wanted that so much, it hurt.

He continued to watch her sleep. In repose, she looked as young and innocent as the day he'd met her. But even then, there had been much more to Jill Bennett than met the eye. More perceptive than most, he had noticed the delicate nuances in her personality, the deeply rooted ambition, the almost childlike vulnerability, the pride that could be so easily bruised.

If he had put that insight to good use thirteen years ago, they might still be married.

Taking every precaution not to wake her, he stood up and went to shower.

Thirty-One

Jill woke to the tantalizing aroma of fresh brewed coffee. Remaining perfectly still, she opened her eyes and glanced around her. She lay on the sofa and was still wrapped in the warm afghan. Dan's comfortable lap was gone and someone had slipped a pillow under her head.

As she sat up, yesterday's events hit her with the force of a speeding train. Her uncle was in jail, accused of murdering her father.

Or rather the man she had always thought of as her father.

There was still pain and doubts, but the more she thought about what Dan had told her last night, the more his reasoning made sense. How could she walk away from the two people she loved most in the world because of one single mistake? If she could forgive her father all he had done, couldn't she forgive her mother and her uncle, as well?

Fully awake now and yearning for a cup of that wonderful coffee she was smelling, she gathered her robe around her, gave a tight pull of her belt and padded out of the room, barefoot and disheveled.

The kitchen was empty and silent. On the table, which was set for one, were two bagel halves spread

thinly with cream cheese, just the way she liked them,
a small pot of her favorite blackberry jam, and orange
juice, which, by the smell of it, was freshly squeezed.

On the counter, the coffeemaker had already done
its thing and a mug stood next to it, waiting to be
filled. Propped against the mug was a note.

Her mood vastly improved, Jill picked up the single
sheet of stationery and read:

Sorry I had to rush out so early. I wanted to check
Mulligan's whereabouts on Tuesday morning and
needed to start early. Will touch base with you
later.

                                        Love,
                                        Dan.

P.S. Rocco sends his love. Should I worry?

Jill laughed. Rocco's deli was the only store within
a ten-block radius that catered to early-morning com-
muters, a practice that had made him a very rich man.
Jill seldom had time for more than a cup of double
espresso, though he always chided her that she ought
to take time for a decent breakfast.

She had no idea how Dan had found him or why
he had gone out at such an ungodly hour and done all
this for her.

The first sip of the strong brew brought a smile to
her lips. No one made better coffee than Dan Santini.

The mug in one hand and a bagel half in the other,
she walked over to the window. Thoughts of last night
came back to her in bits and pieces, but this time the
memories were of Dan, of the way he had held her
through the night, of his soothing words as they'd

lulled her to sleep. Now, thanks to him, she felt rested and clearheaded, and maybe, just maybe, she'd be able to face the difficult day ahead.

Popping the last of the bagel into her mouth, she went to the door to retrieve the *New York Times* from the landing. To her relief, there was no mention of her uncle's arrest, which meant Wally had kept his promise. The delay would give her enough time to prepare another statement for the staff at B&A.

God, if this news didn't make them all jump ship at once, it'd be a miracle.

An hour later, dressed in a red wool suit, Jill was inspecting the contents of her briefcase when the angry ring of the doorbell made her jump.

"You bitch!" Olivia shouted as Jill opened the door. "You lousy, self-righteous, sanctimonious bitch."

Jill slammed the door shut and whirled around, her finger pointed at her cousin. "Don't you start with me, Olivia."

Olivia paid no attention to the warning. "Are you satisfied now? Are you? Is that what you had in mind when you said you'd see your father's killer behind bars?"

"Of course not! I had no idea Cyrus went to Livingston Manor that night. He never told me. If he had…" She let the sentence hang between them like a dark, ominous cloud. What would she have done if he had told her?

"You wouldn't have changed a damn thing. You figured since you couldn't get the presidency after your father died, you'd nail it by putting my father in jail."

The accusation made Jill see red. "Bull! I don't give a damn about the presidency. My goal was to find my father's murderer and I followed every clue regardless of where it led." Her voice dropped. "Unfortunately, one of them led to Cyrus."

"And now he'll go to prison." Like a punctured balloon, Olivia's body, which had been taut with self-sustaining anger, seemed to deflate. With a wrenching cry, she collapsed onto a chair, buried her head in her hands and sobbed helplessly.

Rocked by this sudden and unexpected show of grief, Jill ran to her cousin. Crouching in front of her, she laid a tentative hand on her knee, half expecting Olivia to slap it away. She didn't.

"I'm not going to let him go to prison." The words, spoken with more passion than she had expected, considering how she had felt last night, surprised her.

"And just what do you think you can do?" Her beautiful face smeared with black mascara, Olivia glared at her. "He's being transferred to the sheriff's department in Monticello as we speak. Even his attorney says proving his innocence is going to be a tough fight."

"But not an impossible one. First of all, second-degree murder is a bailable charge. With any luck, he'll be out of jail before noon. He'll be able to actively participate in his defense."

"He didn't do it, dammit! He shouldn't have to defend himself at all."

"Wally and Dan are working together. Between them, they'll find the real killer."

"Why isn't Dad saying what happened up there?"

Olivia groaned. "Why is he being so bullheaded about this? Doesn't he realize how guilty he looks?"

"I'm sure he does."

She looked at Jill through puffy red eyes. "Wally says he's protecting someone."

"I wouldn't know about that." Unable to look at Olivia, Jill averted her eyes. Her mother's secret was now her secret and that's the way it would stay.

Taking a tissue from a silver box on the end table, Jill handed it to Olivia. She was experiencing new feelings toward her temperamental cousin—a deeper attachment and a tolerance she hadn't had before.

Olivia wiped her face, took a look at the smeared mascara on it and rolled her eyes. "Great. Now I look like a raccoon."

Jill smiled. Even in the throes of despair, Olivia's concern for her looks were never very far. "Why don't you use my bathroom to clean yourself up?" she suggested. "You should find everything you need on the glass shelf above the sink." She paused. "And maybe we could share a cab to the office?"

Olivia gave Jill a startled glance, as if she couldn't quite understand why Jill was being so accommodating. "I can't," she said at last. "There's something I need to do first." As an afterthought, she added, "But I'll see you there, okay?"

"Okay."

As always at this early-morning hour, the Fulton Fish Market in Lower Manhattan was a noisy, messy, smelly bazaar whose sights and sounds were unequaled anywhere in New York.

Her face more or less presentable, Olivia paid her

cab and headed toward the low concrete building at the end of the pier, where Mulligan & Son was located.

Ignoring the whistles and catcalls from a group of rowdy longshoremen, Olivia kept walking while cursing Mulligan.

After more than a dozen phone calls, she had grown tired of the waiting game and had come to collect her money. And to make sure she wasn't leaving empty-handed, she had brought a little insurance with her—a tape recorder to take down every one of Mulligan's incriminating words.

As she waited for the receptionist to come back from Mulligan's office, Olivia unzipped her big leather purse and glanced quickly inside. The tiny but powerful recorder the clerk had sworn would record through a brick wall was in place, its little red light glowing.

"Go ahead, Miss Bennett," the receptionist said when she returned. "Mr. Mulligan is waiting for you."

Leaving her purse unzipped as an extra precaution, Olivia walked into Pete's office.

"Olivia!" Acting as if he was thrilled to see her, the contractor beamed as he came around his desk to meet her. "I was just about to call you."

"At seven o'clock in the morning?"

"Well...my day starts early, you know."

"Yeah, thanks to me."

"Oh, come on, Olivia." He walked back to his desk and sat down. "Don't be mad at me. You know I'm grateful for what you've done."

"You can shove the gratitude," she said, sitting

down and holding her bag on her lap. "Just give me my money."

"Yeah, well..." He scratched the back of his head. "I'm a little strapped at the moment."

"So am I, but a deal is a deal." She hitched her chair a little closer so the recorder wouldn't miss a single word.

"Give me a few more days, Olivia. Time to collect on a few accounts. You can't imagine how hard it is to get your money these days."

"Tell me about it."

"I'm good for it, I swear."

"Don't give me that crap. I took risks for you, Pete. My cousin almost caught me red-handed, for Christ's sake, but I didn't back down. I gave you what you wanted and you got the job. You were supposed to do a wire transfer for ninety thousand dollars that same day, and here we are, two days later and I still don't have my money."

Suddenly impatient, Mulligan glanced at his watch. "Look, Olivia, you don't understand. Ninety grand is a lot of money, and my cash flow is...well...it's been better, you know what I mean? But I'll be solvent soon. I promise."

"No more promises. I want a check, one that will clear, otherwise I'll tell my father how you came to be the low bidder on Ted Falcon's job."

He laughed, a short sarcastic laugh meant to show her he had the upper hand. "And I'll tell your daddy you're lying through those pretty teeth of yours. I'll tell him you have the hots for me and this is your way to get back at me for rejecting you. And since he knows your reputation with men, who do you think he'll believe?''

"Me, if I give him proof."

His eyes narrowed. "What kind of proof?"

"You'll just have to wait and find out, won't you?" she said flippantly.

"Why, you little shit…" Before Olivia could move, he had come around his desk and yanked her purse from her grip.

"Give me that," Olivia cried, jumping to her feet.

He swatted her hand away and opened the purse. "Well, well…what have we here?"

He pulled out the recorder and turned it around, taunting her with it. Then, after dropping her purse to the floor, he flipped the cassette lid open, removed the incriminating tape and crushed it under his foot. "That was a stupid move, Olivia."

Backing her against the wall, he pinned her there by jamming his arm under her chin. His face was within inches of hers. "Now listen to me, you no-good, double-crossing little shit. Our partnership is over, you hear? And this little trick you just pulled? It nullifies our agreement. And that means no more money. Now get out of here before I really lose my temper."

But instead of releasing her, he tightened his grip. "I don't think you'll be stupid enough to carry out your little threat, but in case you are, let me tell you what an impression you made on my friend Gino the other night. Why, the poor guy got hard just talking about you sleeping naked in that great big bed, with those sexy red sheets wrapped around you. Did he tell you red is his favorite color? Anyway, he's itching to pay you another visit, so if you give me reason to, I'll call him and tell him you're just as anxious to see him. You get my drift, Olivia?''

Olivia could almost feel the hair on the back of her neck stand up.

Gino? As in Gino ''the slicer'' Pugliese? Was that him? Oh, God, Uncle Simon had been right to worry, after all. Mulligan *did* have deadly connections.

She tried to swallow but couldn't gather enough saliva to do the job. ''Let me go, Pete.''

''Just as long as we understand each other.''

''We do.'' Without taking her eyes off him, she bent down to pick up her purse, and the recorder, which Mulligan had also dropped on the floor. As she started to close her hand over it, the contractor stepped on her fingers, pressing hard. The pain made her cry out.

''Uh-uh.'' He shook his head. ''This stays with me. Even without a tape, fingerprints would be hard to explain.'' He gave her a thin, nasty smile. ''Nice try, though.''

Humiliated and frightened, Olivia ran out of the office.

Thirty-Two

Still shaky from her confrontation with Mulligan, Olivia walked into the crowded Sixth Avenue coffee shop, made her way to the counter where a stool had just been vacated and ordered coffee.

It was still too early to go to work and she was too damn scared to go home. Mulligan was right. She was nothing but a stupid amateur who should never have tried to con a con.

One more thing she'd managed to screw up.

The waitress, a bored-looking woman with a triple-D chest and an attitude, banged Olivia's cup on the counter, spilling coffee onto the saucer. Annoyed, Olivia started to call her back, then shrugged. In the grand scheme of things, spilled coffee didn't rate very high on her list of concerns. Not anymore.

As her conversation with Mulligan reran in her head, she mentally kicked herself. What had possessed her to play her hand the way she had? To practically *tell* him she had a recorder in her purse.

Desperation, that's what. In her eagerness to collect her money, she had made a costly mistake.

Maybe even a deadly mistake.

So what happens now? She had compromised her

integrity, not to mention the integrity of B&A, and she didn't have a damn thing to show for it.

On the counter, her coffee had grown cold. Doubting the bitchy waitress would be back with a refill, she took two dollar bills from inside her purse, dropped them next to her cup and left.

Lifting her head from the stack of correspondence she had been trying to sort through for the past hour, Jill watched Olivia walk into her office. Although apparently recovered from her earlier emotional outburst, her cousin looked pale and weary.

"You got a minute?" Olivia said.

Jill put aside the letter she had been reading. It wasn't every day that Olivia dropped the boxing gloves and asked to talk. In fact, it almost worried her. "Sure. What's up?"

Olivia sat down and placed a single sheet of paper on Jill's desk. "I'm tendering my resignation," she said in a flat voice. "Effective immediately."

"Your resignation?" Jill's gaze shot from Olivia to the one-paragraph letter in front of her. "Why on earth would you want to do that?"

"Because after you hear what I have to tell you, you'll fire me anyway and I'll be damned if I'm going to give you the satisfaction."

Jill was tempted to smile. Whatever had got her cousin so riled up hadn't affected her old spunk. "Okay," she conceded. "Now that we've got that little detail out of the way, why don't you tell me what the problem is."

Olivia leaned back in her chair. "I rigged the bids for the Falcon project in exchange for money."

For a couple of seconds, Jill felt as though the ceiling had just crashed on her head. "What did you say?"

Olivia's gaze did not flinch. "Remember last Saturday when you found me in my father's office? I lied to you. I wasn't looking for a copy of your memo. I went there to look at the bids. Then I told Mulligan."

Jill lowered her head in her hands. Rigging bids was a common practice among some contractors and not exactly punishable by death, but in the thirty-eight-year history of B&A, the company had never been involved in the slightest scandal.

Jill shook her head. "Please, Olivia, tell me this is another of your warped ideas of a joke."

"Not this time, 'cuz. Sorry. I wasn't even going to tell you. I was going to just split and never come back." Mirthless laughter shook Olivia's shoulders. "I don't know what got into me, but suddenly, while I was sitting in the coffee shop down the street feeling sorry for myself, I knew I couldn't do that to Dad." Her voice dropped to a whisper. "Or to you."

Strangely, Jill believed her. And stranger still, she was suddenly driven by a desperate need to help her cousin. "How did you ever get involved with a man like Mulligan?"

"It's a long story."

"I've got time."

The look in Jill's eyes, a mixture of compassion and concern, took Olivia by surprise. She had come here expecting a shouting match and had met with nothing but calm and understanding.

Because she found it more difficult to accept Jill's kindness than her scorn, she spoke without looking at her. She told her everything, from her first visit to an Atlantic City casino a year ago, to the night she had run into Pete Mulligan.

"If that's any consolation," she continued, "I didn't want to do it. I was too scared."

"But you did do it."

"Only because he sent a friend of his to convince me." She told him about her nocturnal visitor and her suspicion the man was Gino Pugliese.

"My God, Olivia. That creep got into your apartment, drugged the security guard, threatened you at knifepoint, and you didn't call the police?"

"Don't you understand? He would have killed me. He still might now that I've tried to blackmail Mulligan."

"*What?*"

"Mulligan was taking his sweet time paying me, so I decided to go collect my money, and record our conversation."

Jill gaped at her. "Oh, my God. What happened?"

"I screwed up, that's what happened. I gave myself away. He found the tape recorder and destroyed the evidence. Then he threatened to send his knife-happy friend over if I breathed a word of our little deal to anyone."

"And that's why you're leaving? You're afraid he'll make good on his threats."

"I *know* he'll make good on his threats. The moment you tell Ted Falcon what Mulligan did, he'll fire him, and Mulligan will know why. I'd be a fool to stick around after that, don't you think?"

For a time Jill just sat there, thinking. She didn't want to lose Olivia. Not only was she a brilliant, innovative PR director, but she was a board member, and her departure would be another blow the company would have to deal with.

She was also family, and she was in trouble. For no matter how far she ran, Mulligan would find her. And kill her.

"I can't accept your resignation, Olivia."

Olivia looked bewildered. "Didn't you hear a word I said? I rigged the bids. For money. You could lose the commission because of me, maybe even the company."

"I doubt we'd lose the company, and even if we lose the commission, which I also doubt, I still won't accept your resignation."

"You're crazier than I thought."

"No, I'm not. In the first place, I couldn't replace you. And second…I want to help you."

"How?"

"By not telling the board or your father what you did, or Ted Falcon. Cyrus already talked to him, anyway, so he knows the rumors about Mulligan, and he's not the least bit concerned. He said it wouldn't be the first time he did business with a mob-connected contractor. As for Mulligan using inferior material in some of his projects, Ted plans to keep a close eye on him to make sure he doesn't foul up this job. So you see, Olivia, no one would be interested."

"Except Dad."

"Well…" Jill made a face. "I won't argue there. He probably wouldn't like it. But he's not going to find out, so why worry?"

"You could get yourself in trouble."

"I suppose I could."

"And you're still willing to help me?"

"That's right."

Olivia's eyes narrowed. "Why are you doing this? What's in it for you?"

Jill smiled. Some things never changed. "Not a damn thing, Olivia. I know you're going to find this difficult to believe, but I care about you. I always have."

Olivia suddenly looked uncomfortable. "Thanks. I guess I owe you one."

"Well, since you said that, there *is* something I'd like you to do for me."

The corners of Olivia's mouth turned down in a bitter smile. "I knew it."

"Relax, it's nothing you can't handle. And it's for your own good." Standing up, Jill walked around her desk and came to lean against it, facing Olivia. "I want you to kick this lousy gambling habit of yours, once and for all. By joining a program."

Olivia turned pale. "I can't do it, Jill. You might as well ask me to go bungee jumping without a cord."

"You're exaggerating."

"No, I'm not. I already tried therapy, and I failed."

"You won't fail this time. I'll be there to see you through every step."

"Look, Jill, if you're doing this out of pity, forget it, okay? I don't need it."

Jill studied her cousin for a while, wondering if Olivia had the strength to go through a difficult program and see it through to the end. She had more or less admitted that she didn't, but Jill was more inclined to believe Olivia hadn't really tried.

"Have you ever heard of Yvan Block?" Jill asked.

"He's the head of the Manhattan chapter for Gamblers Anonymous."

"I've heard of GA. They're nothing but a bunch of boring, sniveling misfits."

"They do good work, Olivia. A friend of mine took their program last year. He hasn't been near a gambling table since. If he can do it, so can you."

Olivia laughed. "Don't bet on it."

Jill let the pun pass. "I know Yvan personally. I could set up an appointment for you. Would ten o'clock tomorrow be okay?"

"No, ten o'clock would not be okay. Jesus, you're a pushy broad, you know that?"

"Sure I do, you've told me often enough." Jill smiled, remembering how close they had been once. With a little effort on both their parts, they could be again.

"What about it, Olivia? You want to give the program a try? Before you find yourself totally broke and in a lot more trouble than you are in now?"

"And if I say no, you'll take back your offer not to tell my father?"

"No. My promise to you stands, regardless of what you decide to do."

"Oh, what the hell," Olivia said at last. "What have I got to lose?" She waved her hand. "Go ahead, call your friend. Set it up."

Smiling, Jill picked up the phone.

Thirty-Three

No sooner had Olivia left Jill's office than Ben Maitland of the Maitland Group called.

"We've got a problem," he said in a voice tight with anxiety. "A woman by the name of Blanche Zimmer, who represents a historic-preservation group here in Richmond, has come forward, claiming the Church Hill Tower site is a former Civil War camp of cultural and historical significance and cannot be built upon. As a result, the city planner, the city engineer and their consultants want to meet with us without delay. And to make matters worse, the story got leaked to a local television station that's blowing it all out of proportion."

Jill held back a sigh of frustration. Groups such as these, especially in historic communities, were increasing with alarming frequency and had almost unlimited powers to stop a project.

"What does this Blanche Zimmer have to back up her claim?" Jill asked.

"An old map showing the camp's various locations."

"I want to take a look at that document before we meet with the planning commission." Leaning across her desk, Jill flipped the page of her daily calendar to the following day. It was full but she would have to clear it. This was too important.

"I'll fly down first thing in the morning, Ben, and I'll bring our company's attorney with me. In the meantime, contact the historic commission in Richmond and tell them we want to hire a historian to do a complete historical and cultural resource study on the area in question."

She heard Ben's sigh of relief. "I'll do that. And Jill? Call me back with your flight info, will you? I'll have a car waiting for you at the airport."

"Thanks, Ben."

After hanging up, Jill dialed Philip's extension.

"Hello, kiddo."

Startled, Jill looked up from the set of drawings she had been working on.

Her heart lurched. "Uncle Cy."

He closed the door and walked into the room, his hands in his pants pockets. Except for the dark circles under his eyes, he looked the same as he had the last time she'd seen him. There was even a faint smile pulling at the corners of his mouth.

"You're free." She had no idea how to act or what to say. Any other time, she would have rushed into his arms, but all she could do was stand rooted to the floor and try to keep her emotions from getting the best of her.

"Not quite." He smiled, but it wasn't the mischievous smile she had grown accustomed to over the years. "My attorney got me out on bail, but I'll still have to show up for a preliminary hearing on January

4, and depending on the outcome of that, I may have to stand trial.''

''Was he able to get the charges reduced?''

The smile faded. ''I'm afraid not. The D.A. wouldn't agree to anything lower unless I pleaded guilty. And I won't do that.''

''If the D.A. knew the whole story, knew why you went to Livingston Manor that night, he might be more inclined to—''

Cyrus shook his head. ''No, Jill. I won't hurt Stephanie more than I already have.''

''Don't you think that seeing you stand trial and possibly go to prison for twenty years is going to hurt her?''

''I'm sure it will.''

Jill knew that nothing, and no one, not even her, could make Cyrus change his mind once he'd made a decision. ''So…what happens in the meantime? Can you come back to work?''

''I can do anything I want.'' His eyes gleamed briefly. ''Except jump bail. They'd frown on that.'' He took a few more steps inside the room until he stood no more than three feet away from her. ''This is awkward for you, isn't it?''

She held his gaze. ''A little.''

''I thought about calling first, but I was afraid you wouldn't want to see me.''

''Look, Jill,'' he said when she didn't answer. ''I know you have questions, and maybe later, after this mess is over, we'll talk. Right now I want to know only one thing—do you think I killed your father?''

She looked into his eyes. ''Did you?''

''No. He was up and walking around when I left

the house. I know I shouldn't have hit him back. He was drunk and he was mad and I just should have gotten the hell out of there.'' His gaze was so intensely locked to hers that she couldn't look away. "But I didn't kill him.''

"Then I believe you.''

The relief in his eyes brought a lump to Jill's throat. "That's all I wanted to hear.''

The awkwardness she had felt a moment ago began to fade, but before either one could say anything more, the door burst open.

"Dad!''

Olivia, her cheeks flushed and her eyes bright with tears, ran in. "Cecilia told me you were here.''

"I just got in, Olivia. I stopped by your office first but you weren't there.''

"I was in the conference room with the editors of *Architecture Record*.'' Choking back a sob, she threw herself in her father's arms.

Discreetly, Jill left the room and closed the door behind her.

Jill, who hadn't heard from Dan all day, was on pins and needles when Cathie finally put his call through at three o'clock.

"I'm sorry it took me so long to get back to you,'' he said from the Land Rover. "But finding someone willing to discuss Mulligan wasn't easy. Apparently, his men are terrified of him.''

"Are you saying someone did talk?''

"Two men who have only been working for him for a week or so. Unfortunately, I'm getting conflicting reports. One worker tells me Mulligan was at the New

York site all that day, the other thinks he was in New Jersey and didn't get back to New York until noon, but he can't swear to it."

"Where does that leave us?"

"Nowhere for the moment, but I'll be going to the New Jersey job site tomorrow. Hopefully, I'll have something more positive to report then."

"Good." Jill glanced at the brightly wrapped packages on her desk. "Do we still have a date to see Frankie this evening?"

"You bet. Your visit is all the kid is talking about. And don't worry if you can't find that blue action hero you promised him. All the stores are sold out."

"I found it."

There was a stunned pause. "Impossible. I went to four stores and was told the next shipment wouldn't be in until *after* the holidays."

Jill chuckled. "You ain't got the right connections, Santini."

"I guess not. Pick you up at five?"

"I'll be ready."

"You're spoiling him," Maria said as she and Jill watched Frankie show off his new action hero to Dan.

"Actually, I'm enjoying this more than he is." Jill took the second package from her purse and handed it to Maria. "This is for Nick. I didn't want him to feel left out. I know how much he likes computer games. I hope he doesn't have this one."

"Jill, really, you shouldn't have." Maria gave her a fond look. "But I'm sure Nick will love it." She laid the package on the coffee table. "They both talk about you all the time, you know. You've made quite an impression on them.''

"The feeling is mutual."

Maria's face sobered. "I just heard about your uncle's arrest on the five o'clock news. I'm so sorry about all that's been happening with your family, Jill. I pray that it will get resolved soon."

"Thank you, Maria. With Dan's help, I'm confident it will be."

Maria glanced at her brother-in-law. "He's one heck of a guy, isn't he?"

"The best," Jill admitted. "And still a terrific investigator." Seeing an opportunity to learn a little more about the man she had fallen in love with all over again, Jill dived right in. "Do you think he would ever consider coming back to New York and returning to the force?"

Maria shook her head. "New York, maybe. The force, no. That incident with Eddy Delgado affected him deeper than any of us realized. And teaching is truly where his heart is right now. Do you know that he calls his students 'his kids'?"

"No, I didn't."

"Sometimes I wonder if that's not what he was really born to do. He loves young people so much, loves to help shape their minds, guide them through the rough times. He's always had a knack for that kind of thing, even when he was young."

Jill was silent as she continued to watch Dan and Frankie. Her hopes that Dan would want to move back to New York were fading quickly. He'd never leave Chicago. Or his kids. And she had no right to ask him to.

Unaware of Jill's turmoil, Maria touched Jill's arm. "Come. Help me get dinner on the table."

Though the historian Ben Maitland had hired from the historic commission hadn't had time to fully analyze Blanche Zimmer's map, he had expressed serious doubts as to its authenticity.

"The ink is much too dark," he had pointed out as he bent over the document and inspected it closely. "And while such thin paper wasn't totally unheard of in the nineteenth century, maps were usually drawn on thicker paper, paper that could withstand all sorts of weather. I'll have something more definite in about a week."

Philip, always clearheaded in critical situations, had suggested making a short statement to the press before returning to New York.

"It's an excellent idea, Philip," Jill had told him. "Would you mind taking care of it for me? You're so much better with a crowd than I am."

Outside the municipal building in Richmond, where more than two hundred concerned citizens had gathered, Philip had faced their anger with his usual poise.

"Ladies and gentlemen," he'd said in his resounding voice. "My name is Philip Van Horn. I'm an attorney for the architectural firm of Bennett & Associates and I would like to briefly explain our position on the matter of the Church Hill project. First of all, be assured that the Maitland Group has no intention of erecting a building on a site of such historical significance. To show his good faith, Mr. Maitland has agreed to stop all excavation until we can perform the necessary research to determine if the document that was brought to our attention is authentic.''

There had been a lot of heated questions, and even a few threats, all of which Philip and Ben Maitland had addressed calmly for nearly an hour. Eventually, the crowd had dispersed, just in time for Philip and Jill to rush back to the airport and make their flight.

Now, as their New York–bound plane sped down the runway, Jill turned to Philip. ''You were great, Philip. Those people started to turn hostile toward the end, but you and Ben handled them beautifully.''

''Let's just hope the experts rule in our favor.'' Philip sighed. ''This is one commission we can't afford to lose.''

As they became airborne, he picked up his briefcase and set it on his lap. ''How did you find Cyrus?''

''Not his usual self, but he was glad to be back. And so was I. I'm not cut out to be president of a company.''

''Are there any serious leads now that Wally has reopened the case?''

Unwilling to discuss the details of the investigation with anyone outside the immediate family, Jill remained vague. ''Not really.''

''I feel so helpless, Jill. I wish there was something I could do.''

Jill laid a hand on his arm. ''You're doing more than you realize, Philip, by simply being here for us, and by remaining cool and calm in the face of disaster.''

He gave her hand a fatherly pat and smiled, something he did rarely these days. ''That's what you pay me those big bucks for, Jill.''

* * *

"Jill, Jerry Kranski is here," Cathie announced on the intercom the following morning. "He says he wants to see you."

"Send him in, Cathie."

Elbows on her desk and a welcoming smile on her face, Jill watched the teenager as he stepped hesitantly into her office. She marveled at the change in him. If she hadn't seen the spiked purple hair and the nose ring with her own eyes, she wouldn't have believed he was the same young man. In his dark pants, white sweater and Ivy League haircut, he could have passed for an architect in training.

"How are you, Jerry?"

"Fine." He threw a nervous glance around him.

"Bill Taggart tells me you're doing a terrific job in the print room."

"It's a great place to work, Miss Bennett. And I'm learning a lot about the architectural business."

"That's great." She smiled, wishing he'd relax a little. "Who knows? We might even make an architect out of you someday."

"Yeah, maybe."

Then, because he was still clearly ill at ease, she decided to give him a nudge. "Is there anything I can do for you, Jerry?"

"Not really." As Jill pointed to a chair, he sat down. "I don't want you to think I'm some kind of snitch or anything, but...there's something you should know."

"About what?"

"A conversation I heard."

"A conversation? Here at B&A?"

"No. At that project B&A is doing on Thirty-fourth Street. The nightclub?"

Jill nodded. "Ah, yes. Bob Freeman's design."

"Right. Well, Mr. Freeman sent me there earlier to deliver a set of revised drawings to the building inspector."

"That would be Chuck Abernathy." Jill hated the man and shuddered every time he was assigned to one of their jobs. Abernathy was a nitpicker who enjoyed finding small discrepancies that slowed down the job.

"Yeah, that's him." Jerry was beginning to relax. "I couldn't find him at first, so I went looking for him. That's when I overheard him talking to someone— about B&A."

"What were they saying?"

"Mr. Abernathy was telling the other man that, from now on, he'd have to go by the book, and that included the department store B&A was designing. He said that because of the warehouse collapse on South Street the other day, the heat was on and he was scared."

"What warehouse collapse?"

"Didn't you hear about it? It happened on Tuesday. The second floor where they store all the heavy machinery collapsed and killed one man."

Tuesday. That was the day she had gone to the Catskills with Frankie and Ashley. With all that had happened since then, she hadn't kept up with the news.

"Now the city engineer wants to test the concrete on that building," Jerry continued. "That's why Abernathy is scared. I heard him tell the other man to try to get the city engineer to keep his mouth shut otherwise there'd be hell to pay. The other man said he'd take care of it, not to worry.''

That crooked rat, Jill fumed. He was taking kick-backs from an unscrupulous contractor. She should have known.

"Thanks for coming forward, Jerry," she told the teenager. "I'm going to have to report this immediately. The city engineer might want to question you himself."

Jerry shrugged. "That's cool."

"Who's the other man?"

"I've never seen him before, but the building inspector called him Pete."

Jill froze. Mulligan?

"What did he look like?" she asked.

"Average height, good-looking, thick black hair. He drove away in a black Mercedes."

Jill's hands clenched into fists. *Got you, Mulligan.*

Thirty-Four

Independent testing revealed that the concrete used in the construction of the South Street warehouse was well below grade, a fact Pete Mulligan hadn't been able to contest.

By four o'clock that afternoon, the contractor had been arrested and charged with negligent homicide.

Upon investigation, it was further discovered that the concrete company was owned by Gino Pugliese. A warrant had immediately been issued for his arrest, but so far the authorities had been unsuccessful in locating him.

Word around town was that Pugliese had heard he was in trouble and fled the country.

Chuck Abernathy, though he had emphatically denied any connection with either man, was suspended pending an investigation.

Olivia had come to watch the latest developments on Jill's TV in her office.

"I'd feel much better knowing that Gino was in police custody," Olivia said to her cousin, "but I suppose having him out of the country is not a bad compromise, provided he stays out."

Leaning forward, Jill turned the set off. "He would

have no reason to come after you now, Olivia. You're not the one who turned Mulligan in, Jerry is."

"The kid isn't going to get in trouble, is he?"

"I doubt it. Now that Pugliese is gone, Mulligan doesn't have anyone to do his dirty work for him. Not only that, but suddenly it seems as if the whole town is abuzz with information about Mulligan's unethical practices. I wouldn't worry about him. His powers have vanished into thin air."

"Why didn't all those people come forward sooner? They might have prevented a man's death."

"Fear is a great motivator, Olivia. Mulligan knew exactly how to instill it."

As Olivia stood up to leave, Jill added, "By the way, how did your first meeting with Gamblers Anonymous go last night?"

Olivia blushed, a reaction Jill wasn't accustomed to seeing. "Okay. And you were right. Yvan is really a nice guy." The color on her cheeks deepened.

Quick to grasp what was going on, Jill grinned. "And quite attractive, don't you think?"

"I suppose."

Jill was thrilled at the thought that her cousin might finally be falling for a nice guy. Until now, she had attracted nothing but jerks and gigolos.

Before she could ask Olivia more questions, however, her cousin, claiming to have a pressing engagement, waved goodbye and left.

Shortly before five o'clock, Jill was preparing to go home to get ready for a dinner date with Dan when her secretary walked into the office, looking agitated.

"Jill, Philip Van Horn forgot to sign that contract

for the lease of B&A's offices and I need to messenger it back to the landlord first thing tomorrow morning."

"Can't Philip sign it then?"

"He's attending a symposium in Boston and won't be in until after lunch."

Jill glanced at her watch. "Give me the contract, Cathie. I'll take it to Philip's house and make sure it's back on your desk at nine o'clock tomorrow morning. Staten Island isn't that much out of my way, and I have my car today."

"I was hoping you'd say that. Thanks, Jill."

Moments later, Jill was at the wheel of her BMW, heading for Staten Island.

"See you tomorrow, Vera." Cynthia Parson walked her nanny to the door.

"Bright and early," Vera replied cheerfully.

Always in a good mood herself when she had the eight-to-five shift, Cynthia closed the door and walked back toward the kitchen. As she passed the living room, she glanced at Molly, who sat quietly watching a Barney video.

Cynthia sighed. She had hoped those four days at Walt Disney World would have improved Molly's condition, but the vacation had turned out to be such an ordeal for her that Cynthia had cut the trip short.

Fearing she had done irreparable damage to her little girl, Cynthia had immediately taken her to Dr. Madeas. The therapist had been quick to reassure her, explaining that Molly's reaction was a normal one considering the severity of her case.

"Try not to look at the trip as a setback, Cynthia,

but as a learning experience. Molly needs to be rein-
troduced to a normal social life very slowly.''

In the kitchen, Cynthia turned on the small television set on the counter and slid a pan of brownies into
the hot oven. Molly loved brownies. Maybe the smell
as they baked would bring a smile to her face.

She reached for the timer and froze.

From the TV set came a voice she recognized instantly.

Turning around, she stared at the screen. A man was
addressing a crowd outside what looked like an official
building. In his late fifties, he stood about six feet tall,
was well-dressed and attractive.

Just behind him was Jill Bennett.

Her teeth clamped on her bottom lip, Cynthia listened to the rest of the broadcast.

''...agreed to stop all excavation until we can perform the necessary research to determine if the document that was brought to our attention is authentic.''

Cynthia's hand flew to her mouth. It *was* the same
man, the man Dan Santini was so desperately trying
to locate.

The man Cynthia knew as Jack Smith.

The Todt Hill section of Staten Island, where
Philip's house was located, was an exclusive neighborhood south of the Staten Island Expressway, with
beautiful, rambling houses and exquisitely manicured
lawns.

The elegant white colonial was the same one Philip
and Barbara had bought shortly after their wedding in
1965. Jill had been a frequent guest of the Van Horns

during the subsequent years, but hadn't been here in ages.

By the time she arrived at the house, Philip, whom she had called from her car, had already changed into comfortable tan chinos and a navy sweatshirt. "Come on in, Jill." He shook his head as he let her in. "I'm sorry you had to come all this way because of my forgetfulness."

"Don't worry about it. I hope you have your copy of the contract with you. Cathie couldn't find it anywhere."

"It's upstairs. I brought it home the other night to read, then promptly forgot it had to be hand-delivered first thing tomorrow morning." He motioned toward a room down the hall. "Why don't you wait for me in the study and make yourself comfortable? I'll be right back."

In the study, which was neat and rather severe, Jill didn't sit but walked around, admiring Philip's artwork prominently displayed throughout the room.

She was studying a Remington sculpture when her gaze fell on an open box under Philip's desk. She wouldn't have given it a second glance had it not been for the object that stuck out of it—a small, worn-out teddy bear.

Her heart gave an extra beat. It was the teddy bear she had given Blair shortly before her young friend had moved to Oklahoma.

Tears stinging her eyes, Jill crouched in front of the box and pulled out the stuffed animal, remembering the name Blair had given him—Gomez, after the main character on the "Addams Family," Blair's favorite TV show.

Looking farther into the box, she saw that it was filled with odds and ends Philip must have brought back from the University of Pennsylvania after Blair's death.

Jill lifted a swimming trophy and let her fingers run along the long brass figure. Like her father, who had excelled in every sport, Blair had been a superb swimmer and had won several local and state meets before she and her mother had moved to the Southwest.

Beneath the trophy was a poetry book by John Keats. Blair, a true romantic, had loved Keats.

Curious to see what poem Blair might have been reading last, Jill opened the book at the page marked with a thin blue ribbon. As the pages parted, a photograph fell out.

Jill picked it up.

And almost reeled from the shock.

The photograph showed Blair gazing adoringly at a man. Their arms were entwined around each other, leaving no doubt as to the intimacy of their relationship.

But it was the handsome man who was smiling at the camera that Jill's eyes were riveted to.

That man was her father.

Thirty-Five

Her head spinning from the shock, Jill kept looking at the photograph. Blair and her father? It couldn't be. It was too ridiculous, too unthinkable, too...obscene.

She turned the photograph over. There, in the young woman's flowery handwriting, was the irrefutable proof that Blair and Simon had been much more than casual friends. The inscription read: "July '96—an unforgettable day on the Delaware with my darling Simon."

Jill felt sick.

"What do you think you're doing?"

At the sound of Philip's sharp tone, Jill's head snapped around. "I..." At a loss for words, she rose to her feet.

"Give me that." With an angry gesture, the attorney snatched the photograph from Jill's hand. "What right do you have to pry into my things?"

Surprised at how quickly he had shed his usual courteous manner, Jill was immediately on the defensive. "I wasn't prying. I was just walking around when I saw the box..."

Her mouth suddenly fell open. *"You knew."*

Philip blinked. "Knew what?"

She pointed at the photograph in his hand. "About

Blair and my father. They were lovers, weren't they?'' She wasn't sure how she managed to get the words out. ''And you knew it. You had to.'' Her gaze flickered toward the box under the desk.

There was a long, heavy silence as Philip continued to glare at her. His face was even paler than before, his jaw clenching and unclenching. The only sound Jill was conscious of was the wild pounding of her heart.

''No, I didn't know.'' He spoke in a low voice, but Jill could feel the hatred in every word. ''I had no idea what that son of a bitch had done to my daughter. It wasn't until I went through Blair's things that I—'' He stopped and sucked in a long breath.

Jill gripped the desk behind her. ''Oh, my God!'' As the horrible truth finally dawned on her, her heart gave a wild lurch. ''It was you. *You* killed my father.''

Philip's eyes narrowed and his entire body seemed to stiffen. ''You couldn't give it up, could you, Jill? In spite of everything, all the advice people kept giving you, telling you to mind your own business, you still had to play little Miss Marple.''

Jill stared at him in horror. ''You did kill him. You murdered my father.''

''Don't you dare judge me,'' he spat. ''I'm not the one who took advantage of a young woman half my age, who made her pregnant, who took her to have an abortion she didn't want.''

''Blair? It was Blair he took to the abortion clinic?''

Philip uttered a harsh laugh. ''Hard to believe, isn't it? A man of such integrity, a man who inspired such respect and admiration. In the end, he was nothing but a coward, incapable of facing his responsibilities. He killed my little girl.''

''No...'' Jill shook her head. ''He couldn't have...''

''He didn't do the act, but he might as well have. She killed herself because of him, because of what he made her do.''

''How do you know?'' Slowly, she began to skirt around the desk. She had to get away from here, before he killed her, too.

Philip didn't seem to notice. ''Her roommate told me. She knew about the abortion, had witnessed Blair's growing despondency afterward, her lack of appetite, how she cried herself to sleep every night.''

''Did she know Blair and my father were lovers?''

''No. Blair didn't tell anyone. That's why after Blair died, I hired a private detective. I wanted to find the son of a bitch who had done that to her and kill him with my bare hands.''

Jill's hand felt the outer corner of the desk. ''And you found him.''

''Not right away.'' He started walking toward her, his pace unhurried, as if he knew she wouldn't be able to escape. ''The investigator came up empty-handed. Simon had covered his tracks well.''

He let out a short, self-deprecating laugh. ''And to think I actually tried to save him from Pete Mulligan's wrath, and kept his dirty little secret. What a good laugh he must have had that night.''

Jill continued to back away.

''Why did you need a detective when you had all the proof you needed right there?'' She nodded at the photograph in his hand.

''I didn't find this snapshot until later.'' His voice

turned flat, almost dreamlike. "After Blair died, I couldn't do much of anything. I couldn't even bring myself to go to the university and pack her things. Her roommate did that for me. I gave the clothes away and only kept this box. Amy had packed it separately, thinking I'd want to keep what was in there. Four weeks ago, I finally had the strength to go through it."

His eyes suddenly locked with Jill's. "That was Thanksgiving Day. While the Bennett family was happily celebrating the holiday, I was here, discovering the ugly truth about my daughter and your father."

"You found the photograph." She was trying to buy time, trying to gauge the distance between her and the front door. Right now, it seemed miles away.

"I not only found the photograph," Philip answered, "but I found a set of discharge papers from Alternatives, as well."

"So why didn't you confront my father then?"

"Because I'm an attorney, Jill. I believe in proof. I knew the clinic wouldn't volunteer the information, so I went back to my private investigator. It took him a while but he finally found someone on the staff I knew would help me." He raised an eyebrow. "You met her, I believe. Nurse Parson?"

As Jill kept inching away from him, she tried not to think of Blair, of all the anguish, disappointment and sadness she had experienced. Later, there would be time for sorrow. But right now, she had to get out of here. Alive.

"So you drove to Livingston Manor, and in cold blood killed my father."

"No, believe it or not, that was not my intention. Oh, I won't deny that initially I did want to kill him.

But after a while, I realized that spending the rest of my life in prison was no way to avenge my daughter's death. I had a much better plan in mind, you see. I was going to destroy him—professionally and personally. I wanted his colleagues, his clients, the whole country to know about his dirty little affair with my daughter, know what he had forced her to do. And above all, I wanted you and Amanda to know. I wanted your mother to leave him, and you, his most precious gift, I wanted you to feel sick every time you looked at him. I wanted him to end up like me, alone and bitter.''

He had become so engrossed in his monologue that he stopped walking. Jill, her back to a broad bookcase, didn't dare take another step for fear he'd notice and lunge at her. She had to keep him talking. It shouldn't be hard to do. He wanted to talk, needed to get everything off his chest. And maybe brag a little, show her how clever he'd been in eluding them all.

"If you didn't want to kill him, then why did you?''

"Because he pushed me too far.''

"How?''

"When I arrived at the house, Simon was drunk and in a mean mood. He told me to go to hell.'' A strange sound, halfway between a sob and a laugh, escaped from Philip's throat. "He wasn't even grieving for my daughter.''

"I don't believe that.'' Why was she defending him? A man she no longer knew.

"No.'' Philip's voice was strangely distant. "I don't suppose you would. You've always had him on such a high pedestal.''

Although she had little experience with reverse psychology, she decided to give it a try. "That's true, I did, but I was wrong to think of him as a perfect man."

His eyes narrowed. "A second ago, you were defending him."

"That's because he's my father. But I'm not blind, Philip. Or stupid. I know he's done despicable things and I know he hurt you."

"Blair is the one he hurt. She couldn't live with the thought that she had killed her baby, a baby she wanted." A dry sob caught in his throat. "If only she had told me. I would have brought her back home, helped her raise the child. Instead, she went to *him.*"

In spite of her total concentration on staying alive, Jill felt her eyes fill with tears. "I'm sorry, Philip. I wish there was something I—"

To her horror, he reached for the green silk cord that held the heavy drapes and yanked it free. Looking at her, he snapped the cord taut.

Jill went numb with fear.

Thirty-Six

"All right!" Dan exclaimed as he landed on Park Place. "Sell me that baby."

Frankie, his bandaged ankle stretched out on the sofa, hit the cushion with his small fist. "That's not fair, Uncle Dan. You always get Park Place."

"Yeah," Nick said as he sat on the other side of the Monopoly board. "And Boardwalk, too. And look how many utilities he's got."

Chuckling wickedly, Dan counted his play money. "Quit whining, you two, and hand over the property."

As Nick, who had appointed himself banker, took the bills, Maria ducked her head in the living room. "Phone call, Dan. A woman from Fairfax, Virginia."

At those words, Dan scrambled to his feet. "Sorry, guys. I'll try to make it quick."

Cynthia Parson barely gave him time to say hello. "I know who Jack is," she said in a shaky voice.

Dan glanced at Maria, who was putting a casserole in the oven. "I thought you couldn't identify him."

"I recognized his voice. He was in Richmond yesterday, with Jill Bennett."

"What?"

"He was talking to a group of people outside the municipal building. Something to do with a Civil War camp. I just caught a replay of his speech on my local television station."

A cold chill settled in the pit of Dan's stomach. Only one person had gone to Richmond with Jill—Van Horn. "What's the man's name?"

"Philip Van Horn. He's the company's attorney."

"Are you sure it's the same man?"

"Very sure. The height is about right, though I now realize he was trying to appear shorter by stooping, but the voice is unmistakably his. I recognized his accent, especially the way he said 'perform' as if there was no *r* in it, and 'our.'"

She was right. Although Philip had moved to New York many years ago, he had never lost his Boston accent.

"Thank you, Cynthia." Knowing it had taken great courage for her to make this call, he wanted to reassure her. "I'm going to keep your name out of this as much as I can, so try not to worry, okay?"

From the sound of her voice as she said goodbye, he wasn't sure she believed him.

After hanging up, he immediately dialed Jill's loft. She had told him she'd be leaving work early tonight so she could look special for their "hot date."

He waited out the four rings then hung up as the machine came on.

Holding the button down long enough to disconnect the call, he punched in B&A's number, already annoyed at Jill for working past five o'clock, which was not part of their deal. He was told by the security guard that everyone had gone home.

Fear gnawed at him. Something wasn't right here.

She was supposed to let him know of any change in plans.

Walking over to the kitchen chair, where he had tossed his jacket earlier, he took out a small address book. After locating Ashley's number, which he had jotted down along with several others, he dialed it.

Ashley hadn't seen Jill but she instantly picked up on Dan's anxiety. "What's wrong?" she asked. "I thought the two of you were going out."

"We're supposed to. Look, Ashley, if you hear from her, tell her to stay put and not open her door for anyone."

"Dan, you're scaring me."

"Just try to find her, Ashley."

His call to the Bennetts' town house was equally frustrating. Amanda was having dinner with an old friend, and Henry hadn't seen Jill since the previous day.

Cyrus was more insistent and demanded to know what was going on. Because he saw no need to frighten Jill's family just yet, or risk a manhunt that might put Jill in even greater danger, Dan managed to satisfy her uncle's curiosity without arousing his suspicion.

While Maria threw quick, worried glances in his direction, Dan considered his next option—to call Van Horn. He'd play dumb and ask the attorney if he had seen Jill. The ruse didn't guarantee Philip wouldn't hurt her, but it might give him enough reason not to.

When the operator told him the number was unlisted, Dan slammed the phone down and leaned his forehead against the wall, trying to think rationally.

"Something wrong?" Joe was beside him, a worried expression on his face.

Dan pulled away from the wall. "I know who the killer is." He gave his brother a dark look. "Philip Van Horn."

Joe looked astounded. "How do you know?"

"I can't go into that right now. I've got to find Jill."

Joe's features tightened as the cop in him took over. "You think she's with him?"

"I don't know. I hope not. I've already called everyplace I could think of and she's nowhere to be found."

"What about that secretary you like? Would she know something?"

Cecilia. Why hadn't he thought of that?

She answered in the same brisk business tone she used at the office, softening it only after Dan had identified himself. "Dan, what—"

"Cecilia, I'm in a terrible hurry," Dan said tersely. "Jill could be in danger. Do you know where she went?"

"Why, no." Cecilia's voice shook as she talked. "Cathie might. What kind of danger?"

"I don't have time to explain. What I need right now is Philip Van Horn's address and phone number. And Cathie's, too."

He half expected Cecilia to tell him she wasn't supposed to give out addresses and phone numbers, but she didn't. She did, however, ask him to call her back the moment he located Jill.

The only sound he heard when he dialed Van Horn's phone was a busy signal. In frustration, he slammed the phone down, waited a beat then called Cathie.

"Yes, I know where she is," the secretary said in reply to his question. "She went to Philip Van Horn's house. He forgot to sign—"

Dan had already hung up. "She's at Van Horn's house," he told his brother.

As Dan grabbed his jacket, Joe did the same. "I'm coming with you. Just let me tell Maria."

Within seconds, the two brothers were in the Land Rover, speeding toward the Shore Expressway.

Her eyes riveted to the green cord, Jill took a step backward, felt a table behind her and went around it.

"Too bad you didn't learn your lesson that night on MacDougal Street, Jill. You could have saved yourself a lot of trouble. But you wouldn't quit, would you?"

He held the braided cord fully extended. "Your father wouldn't quit, either. He kept insulting me, kept telling me his relationship with Blair was none of my business. He refused to take responsibility for her death, and he laughed when I told him I was going to destroy him. You know what he said to me? He said to forget the whole thing and move on with my life." He laughed. "As if my daughter's death was something I could just discard, like an old shoe.

"That's when I went crazy. I grabbed the nearest thing within my reach—a brass candelabra—and hit him with it."

Jill closed her eyes, shocked at the sudden and devastating pain she felt as she finally found out how her father had died. Yes, he had done something vile and unforgivable, but Dan was right, in spite of it all, she still loved him.

"Why did you fake the accident?" Mesmerized, she kept watching that rope.

"What choice did I have? If I had known Cyrus was there earlier, I would have left the body where it was and let your uncle take the rap. But Simon never said a word about that, so I had to take certain precautions, make sure there wouldn't be an investigation.

"I washed the candelabra, and made sure to wipe off everything I'd touched. Then I locked up the house, just as Simon would have, put his body in the back of the Jeep and drove it down to that nasty curve a half mile from the house."

"What about your car?"

"I went back for it, drove it down to the same spot, pushed the Jeep over the edge and returned home."

Jill tried to block the horrible images as they forced their way into her mind. "How did you know my father was in Livingston Manor that night?"

Philip laughed as if he'd heard a good joke. "He called me from the Catskill house to say he'd be late for our bank meeting on Monday morning, that I should start without him. When I told him I needed to talk to him before then, he brushed me off, said he wasn't in the mood for company and hung up. So, I got into my car and drove up there.

"Why are you looking so horrified?" he asked. "Are you that sorry he died? Have you no compassion for Blair? For what she went through because of him?"

"Of course I do—"

"She was an innocent child. He was evil, and he

never loved her. He seduced her because she was young and beautiful and she made him feel good. And when she got pregnant, he couldn't deal with that, so he forced her to have an abortion.''

Something inside of Jill snapped. ''I don't condone what he did, but dammit, Philip, Blair committed suicide. You, on the other hand, committed murder. And you talk about innocence? What about Dan's nephew? You would have killed him, too—an innocent seven-year-old.''

''That couldn't be helped. You were becoming too much of a nuisance, Jill. When I heard you tell your secretary that you and the boy were going to Livingston Manor alone, I had to act. I didn't realize you had brought a friend until I got there.''

''You could have killed her, too.''

''If I had wanted to kill her, I would have.''

Her hands behind her, Jill searched for something she could use as a weapon, a bookend, a heavy frame, or even a book. But the shelves were so tightly packed with law volumes that she couldn't pry any of them loose.

''So what now?'' she asked. ''Are you going to kill me, too?''

''I have no choice, Jill. You know too much.''

Jill moistened her lips. All that separated them now was that mahogany table she had bumped into a moment ago.

She eyed the lamp that topped it. It was large and shaped like a ginger jar. If she could somehow lift it and hit him with it...

Don't let him look at the lamp. Distract him.

She cleared her throat. ''Cathie knows I'm here. I

told her I'd call her as soon as the contract was in my hands. She'll be calling soon.''

Smiling, Philip pointed at the phone he had already taken off the hook. ''I'm one step ahead of you, Jill.''

He had been all along.

''She still knows I came here.''

''She only knows you *intended* to come here. But it's been a long time since you came to my house, hasn't it, Jill? It would have been easy for you to take a wrong turn, end up in the ferry area, which, as everyone knows, is ripe with gangs and young hoodlums. The police will assume you stepped out of your car to ask for directions and met with trouble. I could even drive your car to a deserted area, set it up so that's exactly what they'll think happened.''

It was now or never.

Grabbing the edge of the table with both hands, Jill flipped it over, sending everything on it crashing to the floor.

Thirty-Seven

As Joe stuck his red emergency light on the roof of the Land Rover, Dan shot onto the Shore Parkway at fifty miles an hour, and headed north toward the Verrazano-Narrows Bridge.

While he weaved expertly through the evening traffic, Joe was talking on the cellular phone to a colleague in Brooklyn. "I need the number of the police precinct closest to the Todt Hill section of Staten Island," he said. "Hurry up, Ron, it's an emergency."

Thirty seconds later, Joe was dialing again. After he had identified himself to the eighth precinct desk sergeant, he explained the situation briefly but thoroughly.

One look at the way Joe's mouth tightened told Dan his brother wasn't getting the cooperation they had expected.

"No, Sergeant Delaney," Joe said in a patient tone. "I don't have hard proof that Van Horn is a killer, and no, I'm not asking you to barge into his house, guns blazing. But a woman's life may be at stake here. All I'm asking is for you to send a car to that address and check out a potentially dangerous situation."

Joe let out a sigh of exasperation. "You sent *every*

squad car in your precinct to a highway crash?'' he asked incredulously.

Without warning, Dan snatched the phone from Joe's hand. "This is Dan Santini," he said in a voice that was marginally warmer than an arctic blast. "If you don't send a car to the address my brother just gave you, and something happens to Jill Bennett, I'll hold you personally responsible. Then I'll deal with your department for leaving such assholes in charge of protecting the public. Do I make myself clear?''

"Keep your shirt on, Santini," the sergeant replied gruffly. "We have one hell of a mess on Hyland Avenue. I don't even know if I *can* dispatch a car to Todt Hill." He paused. "But I'll try, okay? If I can't, I'll call another precinct."

"Thanks." Dan flicked the switch to off and handed the phone back to Joe. "Try Van Horn's house again."

Joe dialed and hung up soon afterward. "Still busy. He must have the phone off the hook."

"This isn't good," Dan muttered between clenched teeth.

The Staten Island Expressway was a sea of traffic when Dan merged onto it, and while the flashing red light helped, it didn't exactly create a clear path for the oncoming Land Rover.

Joe pointed at an exit. "Take Richmond Road. It'll get us there faster."

As Dan took the exit, his fingers tightened around the steering wheel. "I swear, Joe, if he so much as hurts one hair on her head, I'll kill him."

* * *

As the table came hurtling toward him, Philip jumped back, cursing under his breath.

Jill bolted but wasn't fast enough. As she started to make a run for the front door, Philip caught her. They fell together, both hitting the oak-wood floor hard.

Flipping her over as if she were a rag doll, he straddled her, the way he had that night on MacDougal Street.

The only difference was that tonight she could see his face.

Jill fought him with all the strength she could muster. Using her hands and legs, she clawed and kicked and made it impossible for him to get a good hold on her throat.

Some time during the shuffle, he had dropped the cord, but she knew that wouldn't stop him from doing what he had to do. Kill her.

As she continued to writhe under him, something sharp jabbed her in the arm. Quickly, her hand felt for the object and found it. It was a small fragment of the shattered lamp, one side of which was sharp as a blade.

As Philip's knee pressed against her chest, Jill's fingers closed around the makeshift weapon. Then, thinking of nothing but her own survival, she dragged the sharp edge into his cheek in a vicious slash.

A sound she barely recognized as human came out of Philip's throat. Reeling back, he touched his cheek and stared at his bloodied fingers.

Jill scrambled to her feet and sprinted to the front door.

Thank God, it was unlocked, she thought fleetingly.

Once outside, she broke into a dead run, praying she had hurt Philip bad enough to at least slow him down.

All she needed was enough time to reach the next house. Before she could decide which direction to go, the front yard was suddenly inundated with lights.

"Police! Stop!"

Blinded, Jill came to a dead halt, letting out a scream as Philip ran into her.

"Stay where you are, Van Horn."

"Dan!"

But before she could run to him, Philip gave her a hard shove and took off toward a heavily wooded area, south of the house.

Dan caught Jill before she fell. "Are you okay?" he asked, gripping her shoulders.

When she nodded, he handed her to Joe. "Take care of her." He took off after Philip.

Because Dan had spent a lot of time in Staten Island during his youth, he knew exactly where Philip was headed—High Rock Park. From there he'd probably try to reach the Greenbelt, a four-hundred-acre parcel of undeveloped woodlands that accessed several highways in Staten Island.

Dan wasn't going to give him the chance to get that far. Philip may have been in great shape, and desperation may have given him wings, but his physical endurance was no match for Dan's. He could already hear the older man pant and groan.

Closing in quickly, Dan waited until he was only a few feet from the fleeing attorney, then leaped.

He landed on Philip's back. The two men fell to the

ground, and rolled down a hill until Dan was able to pin Van Horn down.

"You son of a bitch." He rammed his fist into Philip's bloody face, heard something crack and hit him again. "You miserable, fucking coward. You like to go after women, do you? And little children?"

A third blow snapped Philip's head from one side to the other.

"Stop... Ple...please... Can't you see...I'm hurt."

Dan was deaf to his pleading. Blind with fury, he pulled him up to his feet, held him so he wouldn't crumple to the ground and hit him again. He would have reduced him to a pulp if Joe hadn't pulled him off.

"Enough, Dan. Dammit, man, cut it out."

Dan tried to disengage his brother's grip. "Let me go. I'm not finished yet."

But Joe's strength was as powerful as his brother's. "Yes, you are, Dan. Let the law do the rest."

Two uniformed cops were running in their direction. On the ground, Philip was rocking from side to side and moaning as he held his face.

Joe gripped Dan's shoulder. "It's all over, big brother. Let's go back to Jill."

She was already running toward him. Dan opened his arms and she fell into them.

"What's going to happen now?" Olivia asked.

In Amanda's living room where Dan, Cyrus, Stephanie, Olivia and Jill had gathered the following day, all eyes turned to Dan.

"I just finished talking to Wally," Dan said. "Philip will have to face several charges—murder in

Sullivan County, attempted murder in New York City and attempted murder in Staten Island. His attorney is trying to work out a plea bargain, but we won't know about that for another day or two.''

"Does that mean they're going to give that son of a bitch a break?'' Cyrus asked.

"I hardly think so. If they make a deal, there might not be a trial, but Philip will definitely go to prison for a long time.''

Amanda pressed her hand to her throat. "Philip. Dear God. I still can't believe it. I've known him for twenty-five years. I would have trusted him with my life.''

Coming to stand beside her mother, Jill wrapped an arm around the woman's slender waist. "If it's any consolation, I never suspected him, either.''

Turning to look at her daughter, Amanda touched her cheek. "My beautiful, stubborn daughter. You never gave up, did you?''

"Please, Amanda.'' Trying to sound stern, Cyrus raised a pleading hand. "Easy on the praise, okay? That stubborn streak of hers almost got her killed.''

Jill looked at him fondly, glad that she no longer felt so awkward. She wasn't sure if her life would ever be the same again. Probably not. But she was mending. And for now, that was enough.

"You don't have to worry about me, Uncle Cy,'' she said with a small laugh. "Dan is making me turn my badge in.''

"Smart man.''

Cyrus and Dan exchanged a glance, and Jill was glad to see that the animosity between the two men had lessened considerably. Maybe someday they would both sit down and talk, but for the time being, their effort to be civil toward each other was enough.

Amanda, her hands still held against her chest, looked at Dan. "It was Philip outside Jill's office that day, wasn't it? He was the one who was eavesdropping on our conversation."

Dan nodded. "Philip was spending a lot of time listening to conversations, hoping he'd stay one step ahead of Jill. And he found out she went to Fairfax by playing her message on Cathie's answering machine. Then he went into Jill's office, found the pad on which she had written the clinic's address and did an old trick, one we still use in police work."

"What's that?" Stephanie asked.

"He ran the tip of a pencil across the blank page where Jill's writing had left pressure marks."

"And that blank page was blank no more," Olivia mused.

"Exactly."

"What about that young nurse in Fairfax?" Amanda asked. "Will she be okay? I know you were concerned about her, Dan."

"Wally says she'll be all right. The Sullivan County D.A. already said he won't prosecute her and, anyway, if there's no trial—and he's fairly sure there won't be—she won't even have to testify.

"Professionally," Dan continued, "she could have been in a jam, but won't be, after all. She couldn't continue the charade any longer and told Dr. Laken the truth. He was upset, gave her a lecture, then told her he had no intention of firing her. She was much too valuable."

Amanda heaved a small sigh of relief. "I'm glad."

While Dan continued to answer questions, Jill drew her mother aside. "Mom, did you know about Daddy's affair with Blair?"

"Dear God, no. I think I would finally have drawn the line if I had known."

"But you suspected he was cheating on you."

Amanda looked at her fingernails, which were polished with that pale rosy color that suited her so well. "Yes. I even knew he was going to Washington that infamous day when Blair had her abortion. I heard him change his flight, but I didn't know the exact reason for his trip, or whom he was going to see."

"Why didn't you tell me that when I questioned you?"

Amanda shook her head. "I didn't want anyone to know Simon was deceiving me. I didn't want to tarnish his memory, to have you and the rest of the family think horrible things about him."

She caught Jill's perplexed look. "I know this is difficult for you to understand, but it's so simple, really. I loved him. And he loved me, too. He had this weakness and I...accepted it, because in the end he always came back to me. And because he was a wonderful husband, in his own way."

"Oh, Mom." Tears were running freely down Jill's cheeks as she embraced her mother. "I love you so much."

"So do I, baby. So do I."

An hour later, Jill and Dan were back at the loft.

"Coffee?" Jill asked as they walked into the kitchen. "We might as well. Neither of us will be getting much sleep tonight. We're too keyed up."

"I don't mind keyed up." He tossed her an irresistible grin. "The last time you felt that way, you made me a very happy man."

Jill smiled but said nothing. Tonight should have been a night of celebration and hopes for the future, but she didn't feel like celebrating and her future looked bleak without Dan. He'd be returning to Chicago soon and getting back into his academic routine.

Within a few days, Jill Bennett would be nothing but a distant memory to him.

Taking her arm, Dan turned her around. "What's the matter, Red? You haven't said three words since we left your mother's house."

"I guess I'm just tired."

"That's not it. Come on, out with it. What's wrong?"

Jill threw him a dark look. Didn't he know? Couldn't he see that the thought of losing him again was tearing her apart?

"Tell me what I can do to bring a smile back to those beautiful lips," he teased.

Stay. Say you love me.

No, dammit, she wasn't going to say it. If he could walk away from this relationship, and not be devastated, then so could she.

"How about a little magic?" Dan asked brightly. "You used to like my little tricks."

"I've outgrown magic."

"No one ever outgrows magic." From her hair, he plucked a small paper rose and handed it to her with a flourish.

Jill smiled.

"Ah, no big belly laugh, but it's a start." He turned

around, inspecting every corner of the kitchen. "Let's see." Facing a cabinet, he raised his arms, sliced the air with his hands in a quick, crisscross motion. "Abracadabra!"

He yanked open the cabinet door and reached inside. When his hand came out again, it held a dozen beautiful, very fragrant, very real red roses.

Bowing at the waist, he presented her with the bouquet.

This time, Jill laughed. "How did you do that?" She sank her face into the flowers and inhaled deeply.

"I cannot tell a lie. Ashley was in charge of the roses."

"She has great taste."

"I've managed to make you laugh, but have I restored your faith in magic yet?"

Sensing he had more in store for her, she shook her head.

"Ah, the lady still resists. Very well." Positioning his hands above the brilliant red bouquet, he did his abracadabra routine once more. Then, plucking one of the flowers, he handed it to her. "Maybe *this* rose will restore your faith."

Puzzled, Jill glanced at the rose, started to smell it, then gasped. Buried in the flower's center was a diamond.

Her eyes wide with wonder and disbelief, she looked up. "What...?"

When he shrugged, she took the diamond out and almost gasped again when she realized it was a ring— an engagement ring.

Tears had replaced the disbelief. "Is this...? Are you...asking me to marry you?"

Suddenly solemn, Dan took the ring from her hand and slid it on her finger. It was a perfect fit. "If you'll have me."

"But what about...your job?"

"Well, I've got that covered, more or less. I'd like to finish the semester in Glenwood, which means that until May we'll have to content ourselves with a long-distance relationship. After that, I've made arrangements to be transferred to NYU, where the professor who teaches applied criminal psychology will be retiring soon. That's why I was so busy these last couple of days." He laughed. "I was trying to solve a crime and hunt for a job at the same time."

"Oh, Dan."

"Is that a yes?"

Because she didn't trust her voice, she nodded and threw herself into Dan's arms.

Thirty-Eight

Dispelling early rumors that Lilly Grant's return to Broadway wouldn't be the success many had expected, the Aquarius Theater was packed with an elegant and eager crowd when Jill and Dan arrived on opening night.

Jill, looking stunning in a red beaded dress, glanced around her. "Whatever happened to dismal ticket sales and lukewarm interest?"

"The wonders of publicity," Dan said.

Not to mention that Lilly had played every morsel of it to the hilt, Dan thought.

Unlike Amanda and other members of the Bennett family, who had refused to be interviewed by the press, Lilly had welcomed reporters and television crews with open arms, skillfully avoiding their questions about the murder and directing their attention to what truly mattered—herself. And the play, which she had predicted would be a hit.

In the last forty-eight hours, her face, her voice and her quips had dominated the media. The producers, quick to capitalize on a good thing, had sunk every cent they had into a massive publicity campaign.

Almost overnight, her face was everywhere—on billboards, on city buses and in parking garages. The

New York public, unable to resist such hype, had rushed to the box office in droves.

Yesterday, a beaming Luke Mansfield had announced that the play was sold out for the next three weeks.

As the curtain lifted ten minutes later, Jill gripped Dan's arms. "I'm scared, Dan. Tonight means so much to her."

Dan patted her hand. "Relax, Red. She'll be fine."

Jill glanced at the crowd around her. "I wish we could have all been seated together."

Luke Mansfield had tried, but due to the sellout, he'd only been able to hold a few seats together. Amanda and the rest of the Bennett family were farther back and would be meeting them later in Lilly's dressing room.

As the lights dimmed and Lilly walked onto the stage, looking regal in a 1920s lacy gray gown and a foot-long cigarette holder in her hand, the audience greeted her warmly with a solid round of applause.

But when the final curtain came down an hour and a half later, thunderous applause broke out and shouts of "Bravo" could be heard from every row of the old theater.

And when Lilly came to take her bows, two thousand spectators rose to their feet and continued clapping, bringing her back for five curtain calls.

As Jill and Dan made their way backstage a few minutes later, Jill wiped away a tear. "She was magnificent, wasn't she?"

Dan wrapped his arm around his fiancée and held her tight as they walked. "She was. I predict a ten-year run, at least."

Just before they reached Lilly's dressing room, from which they could already hear the sound of popping champagne corks, Jill stopped and pulled Dan away from the crowd. "You know," she said with a mysterious smile on her lips. "I never did thank you properly for all you did for me and my family these past four weeks."

Facing her, Dan braced a hand on the wall behind her head. There was a gleam in his eyes. "Am I about to be properly thanked?"

"Well…" Jill chuckled. "I am in a rather… generous mood."

"In that case, maybe we should skip the backstage party and go home?"

"Or maybe…" Jill opened a small beaded purse the same vibrant color as her dress. "I should give you part of your present now."

Dan raised a brow. "It comes in parts?"

"Yes." She took out a small white card and handed it to him.

Dan took it, flipped it around a couple of times. Except for a plus sign drawn in blue ink, the card was blank.

Puzzled, he smiled and looked at her again. Her eyes were unusually bright, her cheeks flushed. He had never seen her looking so radiant, so utterly breathtaking. "What's the matter, Red? You want me to add something for you?"

"No, silly." The mysterious smile deepened. "I want you to think positive."

"I see," he said, not seeing at all.

Taking his hand, she guided it to her belly. "Positive," she murmured for him alone. "As in... pregnancy test?"

It took Dan only a moment for the words to fully register. When they did, his expression turned from bewilderment to pure, undiluted joy. "You mean...?"

Jill nodded emphatically. "I'm pregnant. I took two tests to make sure. Both came out identical."

With a yelp that brought Lilly and her entourage out from her dressing room, Dan Santini picked up his bride-to-be and kissed her passionately.

A random predator is terrorizing Southern California. After children start disappearing, it's up to the FBI's finest to stop a killer...

RANDOM ACTS

Criminal profiler **Laurel Madden** is at the top of her field. But Agent Madden has a dark side and even darker secrets—which is why she understands the criminal mind so well.

Claire Gillespie is a reporter assigned to cover the case. She has another more personal agenda: to rip away the veil of secrecy that surrounds and protects Madden. Claire has evidence that the FBI top agent committed murder—and got away with it...until now.

Dan Sprague is the veteran FBI agent who stands between the two determined women—torn by duty and loyalty to one woman and an intense attraction to the other....

From the bestselling author of
The Best of Enemies...

TAYLOR SMITH

Available mid-September 1998
where books are sold.

By the bestselling author of
Romancing the Stone* and *Elusive Love

CATHERINE
LANIGAN

On a cold December evening, a shot rang out in a wealthy Chicago suburb and the lives of three women were forever changed. Bud Pulaski, successful businessman, committed suicide, leaving behind a shattered wife, an estranged sister, a bitter mistress and many unanswered questions. Now these three women are left to find strength, compassion and a ray of hope in love's shadow.

IN LOVE'S SHADOW

"Lanigan knows her genre well."
—*Publishers Weekly*

On sale mid-October 1998
wherever paperbacks are sold!

MCL435

Available mid-September from
New York Times bestselling author

LINDA HOWARD

Had he given his heart to the enemy?

Robert Cannon feels there is little doubt that
Evangeline Shaw is the key to the conspiracy that
threatens his company. Classified software developed
by Cannon's group is being sold to a foreign
government, and it isn't just theft or a case of
corporate espionage—it's treason. And the
trail leads to Shaw—a woman who by all
accounts has the means and motives.

Even though the facts still seem pretty black-and-
white, Robert's heart tells him she's no Mata Hari—
her small-town innocence is the real thing.

LOVING EVANGELINE

MIRA
BOOKS

Available mid-September 1998
where books are sold.

Discover the real magic
of Christmas with

DEBBIE
MACOMBER

A group of travelers, stranded in a shabby train depot, spend Christmas Eve with strangers instead of their loved ones. Anticipated joy becomes disappointment; excitement becomes despair.

Then the depot's reservations clerk brings them a small, leftover tree. Local kids come caroling. It's beginning to feel like Christmas!

CAN THIS BE CHRISTMAS?

Sharing Christmas cookies, stories and presents, hanging makeshift decorations on the tree, these strangers open their hearts to each other and discover the real magic of Christmas.

**Christmas comes but once a year; a
Christmas like this comes once in a lifetime.**

MIRA